Safety in the HILLS

Kevin Walker

DALESMAN

1995

Dalesman Publishing Company

Stable Courtyard, Broughton Hall,
Skipton, North Yorkshire BD23 3AE

First Edition 1995

© Kevin Walker

Cover photos by Tom Parker

A British Library Cataloguing in Publication record
is available for this book

ISBN 185568 086 6

Printed by Hubbards

CONTENTS

INTRODUCTION 9

Acknowledgements 10
How to use this book 11
Some basic do's and don'ts 12

1 CLOTHING & FOOTWEAR 14

The human machine 14
Principles of the layer system 17
Inner Layer 18
Thermal layer 19
Traditional outer shells 21
Modern outer shells 24
Protection for the extremities 26
Cold-weather clothing 28
Hot-weather clothing 29
Footwear 30
Boot care 33

2 HILL WALKING EQUIPMENT 35

Essential items 35
Daysacks 36
Food and drink 38
Survival bags 40
Survival rations 40
First aid kits 41
Watches 41
Maps and compasses 41
Whistles 42
Flares 42
Pedometers 43
Torches 43
Altimeters 43
Walking sticks 44
Ice axes 44

Crampons 46
Snow goggles 50
Sleeping bags and bivi-bags 50
Helmets 50
Ropes and ancillaries 51
Other useful items 52

3 HILL WALKING SKILLS 53

Pace 53
Security on steep ground 54
Scrambling 57
Basic ropework 59
Moving on scree 73
Winter skills 75
Ice axe arrest 77
River crossings 81

4 CAMPING EQUIPMENT 84

Tents 84
Sleeping bags 88
Sleepmats 91
Stoves 91
Pans and utensils 95
Lighting 96
Rucksacks 96
Useful items 99

5 CAMPING SKILLS 100

Sites 100
Cooking 101
Load packing and carrying 103
Camp hygiene 104
Camp routine 106

6 MOUNTAIN NAVIGATION 108

Types of map 108
Types of compass 109
Map skills 111
Compass skills 166
Estimating time 119
Estimating distance 121
Poor visibility navigation 122
Night navigation 123
Relocation 125
Route Cards 126

7 MOUNTAIN WEATHER 128

Airstreams 128
Temperature 129
Wind 131
Precipitation 136
Frontal systems 139
Lightning 141
Forecast sources 143
Self forecasts 144

8 THE MOUNTAIN ENVIRONMENT 146

Mixed ground 146
Boulder fields and scree 147
Stonefall 148
Bog 149
Flood 150
Ice 150
Cornice 152
Avalanche 154
Whiteout 159

9 AILMENTS   160

Mountain hypothermia	160
Heat stroke	165
Frostbite	167
Snow blindness	170
Sunburn	170
Blisters	171
More serious injuries	172

10 EMERGENCY PROCEDURES   173

Rescue call-out procedures	173
Self-help	175
Improvised shelters	177
Improvised stretchers	182
Basic search techniques	184

11 FURTHER INFORMATION   186

Selective bibliography	186
Useful addresses	187

LIST OF DIAGRAMS

Fig 1	The Human Machine.
Fig 2	The Ice Axe.
Fig 3	Tying standard crampon straps.
Fig 4	Body position on steep ground.
Fig 5	Tying off a Mountaineers coil.
Fig 6	Tying off an Alpine Butterfly coil.
Fig 7	The Bowline.
Fig 8	The Thompson Knot.
Fig 9	The Italian Hitch.
Fig 10	Tying into an anchor using a Figure of Eight knot around the waistline.
Fig 11	The Body Belay.
Fig 12	Classic Abseil.
Fig 13	Sit Harness formed from a Tape Sling.
Fig 14	Basic Self Arrest position.
Fig 15	Group River Crossing Methods.
Fig 16	Solo River Crossing Method.
Fig 17	Comparison of Tent Types.
Fig 18	Baffle Designs in Sleeping Bags.
Fig 19	Example of a Packed Rucksack.
Fig 20	The Orienteering Compass.
Fig 21	Contour Lines & the Vertical Interval.
Fig 22	Contour Patterns & Landscape Shapes.
Fig 23	Calculating a Grid Bearing.
Fig 24	Magnetic variation.
Fig 25	Back Bearings.
Fig 26	Example of a Route Card.
Fig 27	Air Flows.
Fig 28	Lapse Rate & the Föhn Effect.
Fig 29	Temperature Inversion,
Fig 30	The Beaufort Wind Scale.
Fig 31	Effect of high ground on wind.
Fig 32	Wind speed increase over shoulders.
Fig 33	Topography causing change of wind direction.
Fig 34	Leeside Eddies & Null Points.
Fig 35	Rotor.
Fig 36	Wind Chill Chart.

Fig 37   The Melting Zone.
Fig 38   A Frontal System.
Fig 39   An Occluded Front.
Fig 40   Section through a frontal system.
Fig 41   Less-Unsafe Zone.
Fig 42   Cornice development and slope angle.
Fig 43   Cornice fracture line.
Fig 44   Cornice hazards.
Fig 45   Natural snow shelters.
Fig 46   Basic features of a snow-hole
Fig 47   Rucksack carry.
Fig 48   One man split rope carry.
Fig 49   Two man split rope carry.

INTRODUCTION

When I first started instructing mountain activities, almost 20 years ago as I write this, I used to tell my clients that keeping safe in the mountains was purely a matter of common sense — nothing more, nothing less. I used to reason that if one was sensible and took no unnecessary risks, all would be fine. I must now admit that I was wrong! With the benefit of hindsight, I have modified and developed my ideas to the extent that I now consider mountain safety to be something far more complex. The major problem is that it is impossible to use your common sense if you do not recognise the risk nor appreciate the dangers.

No-one but an idiot deliberately puts themselves into what is potentially a life threatening situation, yet year after year we read of people being killed and injured on our hills. I would hazard a guess that by far the vast majority of these mountain accidents are caused, not by stupidity, but by ignorance — the people involved neither understood nor appreciated the total risk involved in what they were doing. Going into the mountains for the first time is a little like a young child playing with a box of matches: the pieces of wood are great toys until one is struck accidentally. Even when the child puts his finger in the flame and realises that this hurts, he has still not experienced the complete risk — it is not until the flames start spreading to clothing or furnishings that the major risk becomes apparent, and by then it is probably too late.

Of course, an element of risk is an important part of the adventure and enjoyment of the mountains, and this holds equally true whether you visit the hills to climb, scramble or simply to walk. Without an element of risk, the adventure would be reduced to the commonplace and the experience made less worthwhile. So the risk is essential — but so is the assessment of that risk, and to my mind one of the most enjoyable aspects of the art of mountaincraft is solving the puzzle of how to stay safe, of striking a happy balance between danger and safety.

One of the most significant aspects of solving the puzzle is that every situation you meet will be unique. Despite a number of common threads (most of them to do with a lack of awareness of the potential hazards!), no two mountain accidents have ever been caused by exactly the same set of circumstances. Similarly, no two days on the hill can ever be exactly the same, simply because there is an almost infinite number of interrelated variables at work every time you go out. You could sit on precisely the same stone at precisely the same time of day facing in precisely the same direction, every day for a year, and you would see 365 different views.

If you have picked up this book in the hope that it encapsulates mountain safety you are going to be disappointed, for that would be an impossible task. In any case, this is not so much a book about how to avoid risks as a book concerned with the appreciation and assessment of risks , and there is a subtle but significant difference. What I have attempted to do is give mountaincraft a framework, some form of shape, giving you some hooks on which to hang your thoughts and a structure which you can clothe with your experiences. In doing so, I hope it will open up a greater understanding and awareness of the mountain environment, and of the myriad facets which make up the mountain experience.

If you are new to the pleasures of the mountains, you should not expect this book to tell you everything you need to know in order to keep safe! Mountaincraft is an art, so it is impossible to become proficient simply by reading a book. As with any art you can only learn the skills through practical experience in a range of geographical areas and weather conditions. Although the basic techniques themselves are fairly simple, a basic requirement is that of judging when to use which skills and techniques and in what combination. This means that even if you are a skilled navigator, a proficient climber, and a capable weather-forecaster, you will still need to exercise your judgement if you want to stay safe. Good judgement is absolutely essential, but even the most experienced mountaineers can get it wrong, so you should be aware that you can make mistakes, be ready to admit to them, and be open-minded enough to alter your plans accordingly and learn from the mistakes.

Most important of all, I hope this book gets you thinking! I hope it stimulates arguments and conversations! And if you disagree with some of the things I say (as I am sure you will), I take that as a positive sign and would encourage you to discuss it with your mountain-going companions. Moreover, if there's something you vehemently disagree with, please write and tell me! None of us is foolproof — in the mountains there is no such thing as an expert — and I am of the firm belief that the interchange of ideas between mountain enthusiasts is extremely valuable.

Acknowledgements

This book would not have been possible without the assistance of the countless people with whom I have shared time on the hill. In particular I would like to thank Geoff Arkless, Bob Barrington,

Chris Hurley, Steve Pedrazzoli and Ian Waddington for countless hours of fine mountain experience and discussion. I am also indebted to everyone at Crickhowell Adventure Gear for allowing me to play with bits of equipment and generally get in the way. Thanks, too, to Les for putting up with me as the deadline loomed closer, to Megan for persuading me that the book was not the most important thing in life, to Guy and Paul for showing me that my word processor had some in-built games, and to the gang at the George and the RAFA for providing diversion, understanding, great company and alcohol!

How to use this book

What with new materials, synthetic fibres and computer design, things change so very quickly nowadays. Whereas in the past you only had to choose between one or maybe two items when selecting new mountain gear of any sort, you are now faced with a plethora of items, some of which are next to useless but most of which are excellent. Perhaps because of this, it seems to me that many newcomers to mountain activities have only a passing understanding of the basic principles, and it was with this in mind that I decided to write this book. Because I am dealing with basics, I have deliberately steered away from mentioning specific models, trade names, etc.

Although modern equipment and clothing have done much to aid the safe enjoyment of the mountains, they have also created their own dangers. It is, for example, very easy to be lulled into a false sense of security when you cannot feel how bad the weather is; similarly , there is a danger that you may become over-confident because you are using the very latest in ice axe and crampon technology. Good equipment is not a substitute for good technique. Buying the latest piece of kit will not make up for a lack of basic experience, nor will it provide an excuse for unsound practice.

I have divided the book into eleven sections. Although such division may seem somewhat arbitrary, I believe that the topics covered within each section sit well together, and I hope this makes the book easier to consult. Key words appear in bold, and I have cross referenced information where I have felt this was appropriate. I have deliberately steered away from detailing certain skills which I felt could only be learned through practical experience.

Technical rock climbing and many of the winter skills (notable step cutting and crampon technique) fall into this category, as do the skills of outdoor first aid, and if you wish to pursue these activities I would encourage you to learn from a more experienced companion or attend a course run by a suitably qualified instructor. If you wish to get more information about any given topic, there are some suggestions for further reading at the back of the book, together with a few addresses which I believe might be of use.

Last but by no means least, this book is not a substitute for personal experience. Although there are topics covered within which may be useful if consulted when on the hill, the book should really live on a handy bookshelf where it can be consulted before you visit the mountains, rather than in the pocket of your rucksack.

Some basic do's and don'ts

ALWAYS TAKE THE BASIC MINIMUM KIT WITH YOU

In **summer** this should comprise sturdy boots, warm, windproof clothing, full set of waterproofs (including overtrousers), woollen hat, gloves or mittens, map (1:50,000 scale as a minimum; 1:25,000 in more complex areas), suitable compass, whistle, survival bag, emergency rations, first aid kit, food and drink for the day, and a small rucksack (not a plastic carrier bag!).

If you intend to do any **scrambling** you should also take a suitable rope and should think carefully about wearing a helmet.

If you intend to **camp** in the wild you will also need a tent (or some other form of shelter), stove and pans, sleeping bag and sleepmat, extra dry clothing, lighting, and suitable rations.

In **winter** (including late autumn and early spring) you need a few extra items including a headtorch and spare batteries, extra spare warm clothing, overmitts and gaiters. If there is snow and ice around you will also need an ice axe, possibly a pair of crampons, and some ski goggles or snow glasses. At least one person in the party should carry a sleeping bag.

LET SOMEONE KNOW WHERE YOU ARE GOING

Unless you are going alone or are in charge of a group, this need not be anything too detailed, but should give at least a rough outline of your proposed route. It is also a good idea to give some idea of when you expect to return.

LEARN TO USE A MAP AND COMPASS EFFECTIVELY

Many mountain accidents are precipitated by poor navigation.

GET A LOCAL WEATHER FORECAST

Mountains make their own weather and conditions can change at an alarming speed. Get a forecast for the local area and, if new to the area, **seek local advice**.

KNOW THE BASIC ABC OF FIRST AID

If something goes wrong you could be a long way from help in terms of both time and distance. It therefore makes sense to know at least a little about first aid.

BE HONEST ABOUT YOUR ABILITIES AND EXPERTISE

Plan your routes according to your abilities and the expected conditions, and never be afraid to turn back. The more challenging routes will be more enjoyable when you have the skills to accomplish them.

BE AWARE OF YOUR SURROUNDINGS

Keep your eyes on the weather, your companions, and other people. Be observant.

TAKE EXTRA CARE DURING DESCENT

The vast majority of mountain accidents happen during descent.

BE WINTER-WISE

Never venture onto snow clad hills without carrying an ice axe (and knowing how to use it)

HAVE SOME IDEA OF EMERGENCY PROCEDURES

At the very least you should know how to call out a mountain rescue team, and you should also know something of the causes, treatment and avoidance of mountain hypothermia. It will also be of benefit if you have given prior thought to what you would do in the event of an emergency.

RESPECT THE MOUNTAIN ENVIRONMENT

Be conservation minded not just to the physical environment but to the human environment as well. Take nothing but photographs; leave nothing but goodwill; disturb nothing but the air around you.

1 CLOTHING & FOOTWEAR

Going to your local gear shop and buying the most expensive pair of boots and the latest in breathable-fabric technology jackets is not going to keep you safe on the hills, per se. These items do not possess any magic properties of their own — it is the how, when and why of their use that is important.

In this section we are going to look at various items of clothing and footwear — not individual models so much as broad types. As with most other aspects of mountain safety, what is important is that you understand the basic concepts — the logic behind the arguments — so that you are in a position to make an educated choice when you come to buy and use garments. To put it more succinctly, it is not what you wear which is important so much as the understanding of why you wear it. Once you know the basics, you can visit your local friendly gear shop and ask all sorts of awkward questions. If the retailer cannot answer them (or cannot find the answer fairly quickly), then I suggest you are in the wrong shop!

One of the major problems is that there is no such thing as the ideal mountainwear. Not only will the most suitable clothing vary from person to person according to individual preference, but it will also vary from hour to hour as external conditions change. As you will see later in the book, not only do mountains make their own weather, they also tend to change it, often with surprising speed. Due to this the clothing that you wear or carry may have to protect you from a wide variety of weather conditions during the same trip. Obviously, this factor is even more pronounced if you are away from a valley base for two or more days whilst on an extended trip or expedition.

The Human Machine

It will be helpful if you think of the body as a machine — a modern, high-tech model that requires precise operating conditions if it is to perform at optimum levels. There are two basic parts to this machine: the **core** (containing all the controlling mechanisms such as the vital organs), and the shell (all the external bits like skin and flesh and muscles) (see figure 1). In order for this machine to operate efficiently, the temperature of the core must be maintained within very precise limits. If this core temperature falls (as is hypothermia) or rises (as in **heat stroke**), even by only a small amount (i.e. +/- 1° Celsius) the efficiency of the brain and all the other vital organs will begin to deteriorate. The greater the fall or rise of core temperature, the greater will be the impairment.

Even if the core temperature is maintained to within its limits, it is possible that extremes of temperature at the shell will cause a number of problems, the most obvious being that of frostbite.

The main function of clothing, therefore, it to maintain the core temperature and to protect the shell, and particularly the extremities, from extremes of temperature. Due to the mountain environment experienced by most people who will read this book, it is protection from cold and wet which is the most critical. A secondary, but no less significant function is to protect the shell from other aspects of the environment such as the danger from cuts, abrasions, etc.

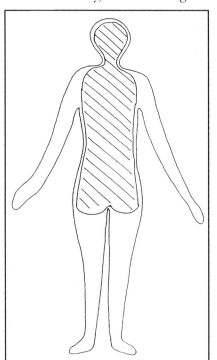

Figure 1: The Human Machine. The shaded area represents the core; the remainder, the shell.

In broad terms the human machine creates its own heat through stored energy — gained through food and fat reserves — and via muscular activity. It can also gain heat through external heat sources such as the sun. Heat loss can occur in any of five ways. In the mountain environment, these are often found in combination with one another.

Conduction is the mechanism whereby heat is transferred between two objects which are in contact with one another. For example, if you sit on a cold rock there will be a transfer of heat between your body and the rock. If the rock is hotter than you, it will warm you up, losing some of its heat as it does so. More commonly, the rock will be colder than you and you will therefore lose heat to the rock. In normal circumstances, your clothing will act as a barrier between you and the rock, thus preventing the heat loss from becoming uncomfortable. However, this is not the case if your clothing is wet as water is a good conductor of heat. Indeed, if you are soaked to the skin, your wet clothing will conduct heat away from your body at about 250 times the rate of similar dry clothing.

For our purposes, **convection** can be defined as the cooling effect of air passing over the body or through the clothing. Unless there is an effective barrier between the air and the skin (or between the wind and any insulating layers of clothing), there will be a noticeable heat loss. It is important to realise that the wind does not have to be strong for this to occur. Indeed, even a slight breeze can cause a marked heat loss.

Evaporation can be a major cause of heat loss in the mountain environment. To get an idea of the power of evaporation, wet a small section of the back of your hand and blow across it. Where you blow on dry skin, your breath will feel slightly warm; where you blow on wet skin, the area will feel suddenly colder. Of course, it is not just atmospheric moisture (i.e. mist, rain, snowmelt, etc) which can dampen the clothing — body moisture in the form of sweat can also have an effect. Indeed, many people underestimate the importance of effective ventilation, especially when on long ascents. Getting the ventilation right can take practice. You need to try and ventilate enough to prevent sweating without overdoing it so that you lose body heat through convection. You should also take into consideration that sweating is the bodyís natural response to overheating.

Radiation is the mechanism whereby heat is transferred from the source (i.e. the body) to the air, and it's importance as a mechanism of heat loss is often underestimated. For example, even on those rare, still days when there is not a breath of wind, you could be losing up to 50% of the body's heat production if you are not wearing a hat. Within certain limits, it is fair to say that the colder the temperature or the stronger the wind, the greater the effect.

Last but by no means least we come to **respiration.** The very act of breathing will have a cooling effect as the moisture in the breath evaporates. Although this heat loss is not normally marked, the effect can be significant during strenuous ascents in cold weather, especially at altitude, and in cases where the person concerned is bordering on the hypothermic.

Although an understanding of the mechanisms is vital, it is equally essential to keep things in perspective for, in practice, it is very difficult to separate the five different functions. Indeed, they all tend to work hand in hand, each one affecting the other. In an attempt to make this more clear, let's use as an example a poorly clothed, inexperienced walker who has left his car and toiled up a steep slope to reach a viewpoint on a ridge — a common enough scenario in popular tourist areas.

The weather is not particularly bad at the roadside but it is colder on the tops, there is a noticeable (although not strong) breeze blowing, and the odd low cloud is scraping across the ridge making conditions occasionally moist and misty. On reaching the viewpoint, the walker is hot and sticky. Muscular effort has produced heat, and the lack of ventilation had resulted in sweat which has soaked the clothing nearest his skin. Atmospheric moisture (the mist droplets) has also penetrated his outer clothing, and the stronger currents of the breeze pass through all his clothing to reach his skin. As it was not cold at the car, he did not see the necessity to take either hat or gloves. He also underestimated the distance due to the foreshortening effect of looking uphill, and the exertion has left him breathless and tired. He has sat on a convenient rock to admire the view (which can occasionally be seen through the mist!).

The level of heat loss in this scenario is not only awesome, it is also potentially lethal! There will be a considerable amount of radiation from the walker's uncovered head, and significant conduction into the rock on which he is sitting. Further heat will be escaping due to his high rate of respiration. The fact that his clothing is damp from the outer layers right through to his skin means that there is marked heat loss through conduction, convection, and evaporation.

Moreover, the strength of the breeze is such that the stronger blasts of air pass through his clothing, increasing evaporation and removing any pockets of warmed air which remain. And finally, because he is tired and resting, the lack of muscular effort means that he is producing very little heat, with few reserves of energy to redress the balance.

To put all this more succinctly, heat is being ripped out of his body at a rate far in excess of heat production. Unless this heat loss is checked, he will shortly become hypothermic (see page 160). The best way to check the heat loss — and to prevent it from occurring in the first place — is to wear the correct clothing.

Principles of the layer system

Undoubtedly the best way to protect yourself from the elements is by using the layer system. This works on the principle that air is an excellent insulator, therefore the more layers of air you trap, the greater will be the degree of insulation. Hence the advice read in all the old mountaineering books that two thin sweaters are far better than one thick one. There is, of course, an additional advantage that it is far easier to ventilate if you wear a number of thin layers than would be the case if you were to wear just one thick one.

Although in its most basic form the layer system simply involves wearing a number of garments, each of which traps one or more layers of air, the make-up of these layers bears closer scrutiny for there are three main components.

First comes the inner layer worn next to the skin. This is followed by one or more thermal layers, the number depending upon the insulation value of the garments worn (often quoted in terms of a **Tog Value**), and the time of year or ambient temperatures expected. All these layers are then enclosed with any one of a number of different types of outer shell. Finally, you should not forget some form of protection for the extremities — the hands, head and, of course, the feet.

Inner Layer

The innermost layer, which comes into contact with the skin, is perhaps the most misunderstood of all the layers. Its major role is that of wicking the moisture of perspiration away from the body to leave a dry layer next to the skin. In this way it plays a major role in helping to reduce the possibility of heat loss through conduction.

Of all the modern materials on the market, arguably the best for the inner layer is that made from 100% **polypropylene,** as will be the case with the vast majority of good quality thermal underwear. Of the more traditional materials, **wool** and **silk** are unbeatable, although many people find wool unbearable when worn against the skin.

When buying garments for your inner layer, no matter whether to clothe the upper or lower part of your body, it is worth giving the fit a little thought. Close-fitting, body-hugging garments work far better than loose fitting ones, but beware the dangers of chafing, especially around the tops of the inner thighs, under the arms, and around the pectorals. Make sure, also, that they restrict neither movement nor circulation.

Design, too, is worth considering. Depending upon the time of year when you are most likely to use the garment, it may be better to purchase a long-sleeved vest rather than a T-shirt design. Similarly, if you visit a well-stocked shop, you will probably be faced with a range of collar designs, the most common being polo-neck (with or without a short zip), crew-neck or V-neck. My personal preference for the colder months is a polo-neck with a short zip. This enables me to zip up the collar to give my neck some protection during draughty times, whilst still allowing me to open the front slightly in order to ventilate when necessary. However, what is right for me is not necessarily going to be best for you. So long as the garment does the job it is required to do (i.e. wicks moisture away from the skin) the next most important consideration has to be that of personal comfort.

Thermal layer

After the inner layer comes the thermal layer. The purpose of this layer is to trap air so as to form an insulating barrier between you and the outside elements. This barrier can be made up from one or more garments, the number obviously depending upon the time of year and/or the severity of the conditions. However, it is no good wearing several insulating layers if the first gust of wind passes through them and replaces warm air with cold, so although you will often be wearing a windproof outer shell, it is not a bad idea to include some fairly wind-resistant garments in this layer.

Looking at the natural materials, **wool** is again a good choice which has the added advantage of retaining much of its insulation value even when wet. Surprisingly, wet wool can actually emit a small amount of heat due to a complex chemical reaction. However, wool is heavy and bulky, and will absorb an alarming amount of water making it even heavier. It also takes a long time to dry out. Additionally, although some of the more closely woven materials have a high degree of wind resistance, your standard "woolly-pully" is not going to keep you warm on a windy day unless you wear a shell garment over the top!

Although wool has its devotees, it is probably fair to say that it has nowadays been largely replaced by modern **fleece** materials. These, too, retain their insulation properties when wet, but they are weight-for-weight warmer than wool, and are generally less bulky. Additionally, most fabrics absorb very little water (particularly those made from polyester and acrylic), which means they also dry remarkably quickly. Regarding wind-resistance, it is usual to find that the thicker, softer and more "snuggly" the fleece, the less it will be able to cut the wind. Thus although the thinner fleeces may not be as warm, weight-for-weight, as the thicker ones, they may be found more efficient on a breezy day in late spring or early autumn when the ambient temperature is not too cold. When out buying, the simplest way to compare the wind resistance of two fleece jackets is to blow through a layer of fabric on each.

Some manufacturers offer fleece garment with some form of inner or outer lining (such as **Pertex)** which will increase the wind resistance (and the price) quite significantly. Such garments fall into a grey area between that of thermal layer garments and outer shell garments. I do not mean this in any derogatory way — many of these designs are extremely useful and practical — but they should not be seen as an exclusive substitute for either of these other two layers.

Regarding thermal layers for the lower half of the body, exactly the same considerations apply although most people do not like to insulate their legs too much. This is almost certainly due to the fact that the legs do a lot of work in the mountains and the muscular effort therefore generates a fair amount of heat. Lightweight walking trousers made of polycotton or similar fabrics are extremely popular, as are the ubiquitous **Trackster** types. On colder days it is easy to add another layer either with thermal **long-johns** or a pair of tights, or you can test the theory of insulating by trapping air by wearing two pairs of Tracksters (it works!). For those really cold days, **fleece trousers** are superb; and if there is also a bitter wind blowing, try a pair of walking trousers lined with fleece.

As with the inner layer, the design of the garments can play an important part. All should be reasonably close fitting without there being any restriction of body movement, especially if you intend to do any scrambling or climbing. There must also be no restriction of blood circulation, and this is particularly important in cold, winter conditions where any restriction of circulation can lead to several problems including frostbite. More generally, there should be a good overlap between upper and lower garments in the area around the kidneys and the waist in order to prevent cold spots. Bearing this in mind, for severe winter use, or use when scrambling and climbing, **salopettes** (romper-suits for adults) are ideal, and these are available in a number of materials for use either as part of a thermal layer or part of an outer shell.

The ability to **ventilate** is important, and this is best done via full- or half-length front zips in at least some of the garments. Shirts can be useful here, too. It may be found useful if the design of the cuffs allows the sleeves to be pushed or rolled up slightly without cutting off the circulation, but this is very much a matter of personal preference along with such things as elasticated waists and pockets.

The shape of the neck-line, too, is really a matter of personal taste, although it is worth bearing in mind that it is possible to lose a considerable amount of heat from around an open neck if a garment is loose-fitting. Finally, it goes without saying that all this clothing should feel comfortable.

Traditional outer shells

It is of little use wearing efficient inner and thermal layers if the first draught of wind cuts through them and blows away all the warmed air, or if the first drop of rain soaks you to the skin. Therefore to finish off your protection from the elements you need an effective outer shell. When I first started visiting the mountains it was necessary to carry two different types of shell garment — a windproof **anorak** and a waterproof **cagoule.**

A traditional windproof anorak is made from one or more layers of closely-woven, cotton-based material, the best (and most expensive) being Ventile (see later). Whilst many of these garments are water-resistant, few are waterproof. This is an important difference.

Anoraks and more modern windproof walking jackets should be roomy enough to go over your inner and thermal layers without restricting movement or constricting circulation. They should be cut long enough to cover the buttocks, and should have a large hood which comfortably covers the head even when you are wearing a hat.

It should be able to accommodate a helmet if you intend to do any rock climbing, serious scrambling, or winter mountaineering. Some hoods are detachable, being held in place by press studs. If you choose this style of jacket, make sure that the press-studs offer a positive attachment and are positioned in such a way that there is no chance of getting draughts down the back of your neck. Other useful features include **storm cuffs** (elasticated inner cuffs) or some form of end-of-sleeve closure, plus at least one zipped or well-baffled pocket large enough to hold an Ordnance Survey map.

Two basic styles of garment are available. Those based on a jacket design should have full length zips, and it is well worth paying a little extra to get good-quality, large-toothed, two-way zips. These are far less prone to jamming or breaking, and the ability to unzip the jacket both from the top and the bottom can be extremely useful.

The zips should be covered with a strip of material (a **baffle**) in order to draught-proof them, and many jackets will have a zipped inner pocket which is accessible from behind the baffle. This is extremely useful as it allows you to access the pocket in bad weather without unzipping the jacket. Beware of jackets with unbaffled zips (very draughty), or with seams across the shoulders (a weak-point which can also be uncomfortable when carrying heavy rucksacks). Windproof garments based on the more traditional anorak design only have a half-length zip and are put on and taken off over the head — a manoeuvre which can have fairly obvious attendant risks if done when standing on a narrow ledge above a significant drop in windy weather! The better designs will have a well-baffled zip and a large front pouch pocket (also zipped and baffled). Storm cuffs and large hood should be as per the jacket styles, whilst many will have a drawstring at the waist and possibly a crutch-strap to stop the garment rising in strong winds.

Although you should aim to wear trousers or breeches which have a fair degree of wind resistance, it is possible to buy **windproof overtrousers.** Whilst many people will argue that these are essential in windy winter conditions, especially in the Scottish Highlands, the better ones are fairly expensive items and it is nowadays probably more cost effective (and equally effective) to buy a pair of overtrousers made from a breathable waterproof fabric (see later).

Because standard cotton-based windproof fabrics are rarely 100% waterproof, it is necessary for you to have a set of waterproof clothing as well. For serious mountain use this should include both jacket and overtrousers. There are two problems here. Firstly, it appears that different manufacturers have differing ideas about what constitutes a "100% waterproof" fabric! Secondly, any fabric that really is 100% waterproof will not allow body moisture to escape and you will therefore get wet simply by wearing it — even on a dry day!

Most newcomers to mountain activities are amazed at the amount of condensation which can occur in this way; if you are not sure yourself try running around your garden wearing a plastic bin-liner!

The traditional waterproof garment was the **cagoule** — basically a long nylon sack with arms and a hood. Unlike anoraks which are still to be seen gracing the backs of centrebound schoolchildren and yomping soldiers, the cagoule has largely been replaced by a more conventional waterproof jacket.

Modern **waterproof jackets** are usually made from nylon material which has been coated with a waterproofing agent, the most common being either neoprene or (better) polyurethane (pu). These coatings will not last indefinitely and, generally speaking, the lighter the material they proof, the quicker they will wear away. The lightest practical fabric is 2oz nylon, but I would advise you to choose something substantially heavier than this (at least 7oz) if you intend to walk in the mountains with any regularity. The jacket should be long enough to reach the base of the buttocks and, as with windproof jackets, the front opening should be closed with a well-baffled, large-toothed, two-way zip. Similarly, there should be no seams across the shoulders as these represent weak spots which will soon leak, no matter how well proofed they are initially.

All seams should be sealed in some way, the best method being **hot-taping.** The hood, which should be large enough to accommodate a woolly hat or, if necessary, a climbing helmet, should have a drawstring so that it can be pulled tight around the face, and it helps to have a wire reinforcement at the top (to enhance vision) and a front zip which extends well up towards the mouth. If, like me, you are bearded, make sure there is a **beard-guard** or some form of internal baffle. From painful experience I can assure you that getting large clumps of beard caught in the teeth of a zip is not an experience you would wish to go through twice!

In addition to a waterproof jacket, you will also need a pair of **waterproof overtrousers.** These should not be regarded as an optional extra but as an essential item of mountain clothing. A good pair of overtrousers will be fairly roomy, and will be cut in such a way that they cause no restriction of movement — especially when bending the legs at the knees. This is particularly important if you intend to do any scrambling, rock climbing or winter mountaineering. You should also be able to put on and take off the trousers without having to remove your boots, and this is usually accomplished either by having a baffled zip or (better) a large zipped gusset, extending from the bottom of the leg to just below the knees.

As was mentioned earlier, any material which is 100% waterproof will prevent body moisture from escaping. If, for example, you wear your waterproof shell on a mild but misty day, you will probably end up getting wetter from condensation than you would from the mist. However, it is still better to wear your waterproofs than not because they provide a barrier to evaporation and thus drastically reduce the potential heat loss. Additionally, because waterproof fabrics are almost invariably windproof, your waterproof garments can also serve as windproof garments, even though this may not be the most comfortable of experiences.

Modern outer shells

There can be little doubt that the advent of breathable water-proof fabrics has revolutionised outdoor clothing, and nowhere is this more apparent than in outer shell garments. Gone are the days when it was necessary to carry separate windproof and waterproof shells. Nowadays a single garment can comfortably perform both functions. However, breathable fabrics are not a wholly modern idea. **Ventile** — a closely woven cotton-based fabric — has been around for decades and possesses many of the features of modern breathable fabrics (including high cost). On the plus side, Ventile is extremely durable; on the minus side it is fairly heavy. The best garments are made from a double layer of the material.

Modern breathable fabrics fall into two categories: membrane

Windproof outer shells are extremely important

(or **laminated**) materials and **coated** materials. Of the two, the membrane materials are arguably the more effective, although this is not to say that the coated materials are no good. Probably the best known membrane material is Goretex, whilst Cyclone is one of the better known coated materials. Both types of fabric can work in one of two ways. **Microporous** fabrics contain a material which has microscopic holes, small enough to prevent water droplets from penetrating but large enough to allow water vapour to pass. **Hydrophilic** fabrics contain a solid waterproof material made up from chains of water-loving molecules which allow the passage of water vapour.

Whichever type of material you choose, you should be aware that it will not last for ever. Coatings will eventually wear away and membranes will deteriorate. Three layer laminates (in which the membrane is sandwiched between two layers of material) are generally more durable than two layer laminates (in which the membrane is bonded to an outer material, the inner lining hanging free).

Breathable fabrics all work on a similar principle. Preventing the passage of water droplets means they are waterproof; allowing the passage of water vapour means they reduce the amount of condensation of body moisture. I use the term reduce because I have yet to come across any breathable fabric which works with 100% efficiency under mountain conditions. Firstly, any dirt will cause the performance to deteriorate (effectively, the dirt will clog the pores), so you should keep your garments clean. With most fabrics, particularly the laminates, regular washing will enhance the performance, but you should follow the manufacturers washing instructions to the letter. Secondly, these fabrics will only work if the conditions inside them are warmer and more moist than the conditions outside.

Taking an extreme example, if you were to wear a breathable jacket in a hot, steamy jungle, water vapour could pass from the outside to the inside! Thirdly, if you are walking into a headwind during a rainstorm and the front of your jacket is saturated with water, it will be impossible for the water vapour to pass through. Occasionally, therefore, it is advisable to give the outer fabric a spray with a proprietary water repellent so that any water forms into droplets which are then shed before they saturate the fabric. As with washing, it is important that you follow the manufacturers reproofing instructions because some proofing agents will have an adverse effect on laminates and original coatings. Finally, mention should be made of some of the **microfibre** jackets now available. Commonly made from materials such as Pertex, these are incredibly light, will roll up into a remarkably small space, and are virtually 100% windproof. Whilst they are not waterproof, they are certainly water resistant and breathable, and can be highly effective in windy or moist, misty conditions. They are particularly suitable for use in late spring and early autumn when the ambient temperature is not too low but the wind has a definite bite to it. It goes without saying that all of these modern fabric garments should be well designed, comfortable and functional, possessing the same features as the more traditional garments.

Protection for the extremities

There is little point in covering your torso in warm, windproof, waterproof clothing if you neglect your hands, feet, and head. Protection for the head is particularly important as you can lose up to 50% of the body's heat production from here.

The traditional protection for the head is some form of **woolly hat** — either a simple bobble hat or a ski hat. Whatever style you favour, your hat should be large enough to cover the ears and the base of the neck. Many hill walkers like "Inca" style hats with ear flaps. For particularly harsh weather, a **balaclava** is extremely useful. Brushed wool is ideal, so too are polypropylene (thermal underwear material), silk, and fleece. The more wind-resistant the balaclava, the better, even though they will often be worn inside the hood of your jacket. Paramilitary masks with separate holes for each eye and the mouth are not the most suitable of hats for the mountains as restrict the vision and will probably get you strange, often unfriendly looks from people you meet along the way!

Also extremely useful are **headovers.** These are basically tubes of thermal material which can be used in a number of ways, the three most popular being round the neck as a scarf, twisted in the middle and doubled over the head as a hat, and over the head but under the jaws as a balaclava.

Protection for the hands is best obtained via **mittens.** These are generally far superior to gloves although they can be more cumbersome. Brushed wool mittens are excellent, as are those made from fibre-pile or fleece lined nylon. Whilst these are not waterproof they are windproof, and will retain much of their insulation value even when saturated. Waterproof thermal mittens are available (at a price), but it is probably more cost effective (and certainly more adaptable) to get a pair of thin thermal gloves (see below) or woollen mittens and a pair of **overmitts** which are both waterproof and windproof. Such a combination is essential in winter conditions, particularly if you intend to do any serious winter mountaineering in the Scottish Highlands.

If you prefer to wear **gloves,** avoid those made from leather as these have very little insulation value, especially if they get wet. Wool or fleece gloves are good, as are thin gloves made from thermal-underwear material, these latter having the advantage that they can be used as liners for mittens. They are also quite useful if you need to use your hand for dextrous work (tying knots, photography, etc). Also available for dextrous work are fingerless gloves and "shooters-mitts" or "flip-mitts" — mittens which can be opened across the knuckles to give access to the fingers.

Whatever you choose to wear, it is of vital importance that there is no restriction of circulation. Restriction of movement is one thing (your mittens, for example, may be cumbersome), but restriction of the blood flow is another matter altogether. Apart from the fact that a lack of blood flowing to the fingers will make them feel colder that much quicker, you also run the very real risk of frostbite or frostnip during winter conditions. If you intend to do any technical ice climbing, a pair of overmitts large enough to accommodate a piece of closed-cell foam across the top of the hand will help to reduce the risk of bruised knuckles!

Last but by no means least we come to the feet. Whatever the weather, these are best protected by wearing at least one pair of woollen **socks** or stockings. 100% wool socks are great, but tend to wear out fairly quickly; a 70% wool: 30% nylon mix is far more durable whilst still performing well. Foot care is obviously very important. What would be a minor blister around the garden can become a serious problem when you are several rough miles from civilisation and your only mode of transport is your feet

Socks have to fulfil a number of functions. They need to provide insulation from the elements and to offer a degree of protection from the hammering you give your feet as you walk. They should also reduce the friction between your foot and your boot and absorb any perspiration. The best socks are constructed either entirely of **loopstitch,** or have at least a loopstitch foot. This not only insulates the foot but also affords some cushioning. People with sensitive feet may not be able to cope with heavy wool next to the skin, in which case a liner of light thermal socks or everyday socks can be worn. It has to be said that an awful lot of rubbish has been written about how many pairs of socks you should wear. The standard seems to be two, but I know of people who wear three pairs and other who wear only one pair. The bottom line here is comfort. Once again, there should be no restriction of movement or circulation — you should be able to wiggle your toes with ease.

You should keep your socks clean, washing them regularly and using a good fabric conditioner. If you wear a hole in them, throw them away or use them for gardening! It is false economy to try and darn the socks you use on the mountains for, however well they are repaired, darned socks are far more likely to cause blisters than undarned socks.

In addition to socks, shock-absorbing **insoles** made from closed-cell foam, or sorbothane, are very effective if you are into long distance walking or if your boots are not a snug fit. Those shaped like a footbed can give extra support to the arches and many people find them particularly good.

In wet, cold, or windy conditions, **gaiters** can be a boon; in winter conditions they can be essential. Apart from the fact that they will afford a certain amount of protection from the wind and rain, they are virtually essential when wearing overtrousers as they prevent the water flowing down the trouser leg and straight into the boot. Make sure you wear your gaiters underneath your overtrousers otherwise they will have the opposite effect! You can also buy **waterproof socks** made from a breathable material which will keep your feet dry no matter what the weather throws at you.

Gaiters made from canvas are excellent, being durable and easily reproofed. Those made of nylon are lighter, but they tend to make your legs feel sticky, they lose their coating fairly quickly, and tend to make a surprising amount of noise! Gaiters made from breathable materials are very expensive and because they get so much punishment, they tend to loose their breathable/waterproof qualities within a remarkably short space of time. **Yeti gaiters** (which cover the whole boot) are excellent, although it is fair to say that their performance varies depending upon the type of boot. Certain types of boot have been designed to take certain types of Yeti gaiter, and these usually work together very well.

Cold-weather clothing

All things being equal, if you use the layer system you should be able to cope with most conditions you will meet in the British Mountains. However, there may be times, particularly north of the Scottish border in the winter months, when a little extra protection will be useful.

At one time **duvet jackets** were the trademark of the serious mountaineer. Nowadays they are commonplace in city streets, but many of the models available from the High Street stores are more fashionable than functional. Even those designed specifically for mountain use comes in various styles with different inner and outer fabrics and a range of fillings. For example, few of the cheaper duvet jackets are waterproof, and for this reason it may not be the best idea to buy a duvet jacket filled with **down** — for although this is a superb insulator, it loses its insulation properties when wet. Admittedly, it is possible to buy down duvet jackets with a waterproof (or breathable) outer fabric, but these cost a King's ransom and will probably be beyond the means of all but the most committed mountaineers. It is also possible to proof a down duvet jacket using a total-immersion waterproofing compound. For most people, duvet jackets with a totally **synthetic filling** (usually of spun polyester fibres) are generally more functional, although unless you spend a lot of money they will also heavier and more bulky. Having said this, bulk is quite important in a duvet jacket. Although it is possible to buy jackets lined with very effective thin insulation such as **Thinsulate,** they somehow do not feel so warm. Psychology plays a large part when it comes to feeling warm!

Whilst duvet jacket are obviously useful, especially when resting, particularly in an emergency or a survival situation, they are often too hot to wear whilst moving. An alternative is to buy a **body warmer** — a duvet jacket without arms.

As was mentioned earlier, it is possible to buy **lined fleece jackets,** the lining usually being of polycotton or (better), of a windproof, water-shedding material such as Pertex. Many of these are reversible. If you wear them with the lining on the outside they will be warmer than if you wear them with the lining on the inside, simply because the lining acts as a barrier to the breeze and prevents the escape of warm air.

Many manufacturers offer a range of **interactive jackets** which zip one inside the other. Thus you can buy a waterproof jacket and a fleece jacket and either wear them singly or zip them together to form a single garment.

Finally, **salopettes** (adult romper-suits) are ideal in really cold conditions or when you think you may be hanging around. These are available in a range of styles (long leg, breeches leg, bib top, sleeveless, etc.) and a variety of materials, including fibre-pile, fleece, and breathable waterproof fabric. It is even possible to buy quilted salopettes filled with down.

Hot-weather clothing

British weather being what it is, you are more likely to meet cold, wet and windy weather than a heat wave. However, there may be the occasional day when the sun beats down and all you want to do is keep cool. In these conditions there is no reason at all why you should not wear shorts and a T-shirt — so long as you carry clothing to cover your arms and legs with you in your rucksack. Although some people like to wear running vests, you should beware the possibility of sore shoulders caused by rubbing rucksack straps. Additionally, no matter how well you can soak up the sun in the valleys, when walking in the mountains in hot sunny weather you should carry a good quality sun-screen — and use it regularly.

Another essential item of clothing in hot, sunny weather is some form of **sunhat.** This should preferably be light both in colour and weight, with a wide brim to shade the eyes and give protection to the back of the neck. In the same way as hypothermia is a risk in cold, wet weather, heat-stroke is a very real risk in hot weather.

Footwear

It would be possible to devote a whole book to footwear suitable for the mountains. All I can hope to do here is give you a run-down of the basic types and the pros and cons of each. As with many other aspects of mountaincraft, what is important is that you understand the basics. You can then visit your local, friendly gear retailer to get the details and see the latest developments. A further problem is that there is no such thing as the ideal footwear for all occasions, so you either have to compromise and buy a general purpose boot or shell out and buy two or more pairs. For example, a pair of fully stiffened plastic boots, although ideal for winter mountaineering, are less than perfect for summer hillwalking.

First and foremost, you should be thinking in terms of **boots** — NOT shoes. Sturdy walking shoes may be okay for valley walks, but they do not give sufficient ankle support for walking across rough terrain. Recently some experienced mountaineers have been extolling the virtues of specialist **trekking sandals.** Whilst these may be all right for the experts in particular situations, (or for use when knocking about camp), in my opinion most of us lesser mortals do not have sufficient ankle strength to make sandals a particularly wise choice for wear in the mountains.

Your footwear probably represents the most significant mountain activities purchase you will ever make. So far as I am concerned, as long as the basic functions outlined below are fulfilled, the most important consideration is that of comfort; it is pointless buying a pair of expensive boots if they start to hurt your feet after a couple of miles. The **fit is absolutely vital,** so take your time when buying. You should also either take along the socks you normally wear when on the hill, buy some new socks to go with the new boots, or get the shop to loan you a pair of socks similar to your own. If the shop you are in is worth visiting, you should not feel hurried. Indeed, buying a pair of boots will probably take an hour or more

The correct footwear is of prime importance. Good, sturdy boots are essential

during which time you will have tried on a few different types and sizes and (if the shop is particularly good) will probably have been offered a mug of coffee! Furthermore, the best shops will allow you to exchange your boots within a week or so as long as you have only worn them around the house. Bearing all this in mind, I strongly recommend against buying boots by mail order.

In addition to general comfort there are a few things to note when choosing a **size.** If your heel moves up and down as you walk then the boot is slightly too large. This may lead to blisters on the back of the heel — a common complaint. If your toes feel at all cramped then the boot is too narrow a fit, and not only do you run the risk of blisters across the tops and sides of your toes, but walking could become excruciatingly painful after a few miles of rough terrain. If you can feel the end of the boot with your toes when you stamp your foot forward, then the boot is too small, and not only will descents prove painful, but you also run the very real risk of losing your toenails.

Regarding the method of construction and the style of boot, there are a number of aspects worth noting, one of the more important being the **stiffness of the sole**. Although personal preference will play a part, a good rule of thumb is that the rougher the terrain across which you intend to travel, the stiffer and more substantial should be the sole. Additionally, if you intend to do any winter mountaineering using crampons, you will need a boot robust enough to cope with step kicking with a fully stiffened sole.

There is little doubt in my mind that **fabric boots** of virtually any description are unsuitable for serious mountain use, the main reason being that they give insufficient ankle support. Additionally, all but a few are too flexible, and most are far from waterproof. Even if you spend a lot of money on boots made from a breathable waterproof fabric, in my experience the membrane cannot stand up to the constant hammering and breaks down remarkably quickly. Having said all this, I know of highly experienced mountaineers who extol the virtues of this type of boot.

A good, **general purpose boot** suitable for mountain walking, scrambling and simple rock climbing will be a medium-weight leather boot which, although difficult to bend by hand, flexes slightly across the ball of the foot. Such a boot is often described as having a three-quarters shank. In addition to stiffness along the foot, there should also be a high degree of stiffness across the foot, and the sole should be thick enough to cushion the feet from sharp stones and pebbles. If you hold the boot at the heel and the toe, it should resist any twisting motion.

The **sole** should be made of a rubber compound in preference to the cheaper PVC, and the tread pattern should be of the traditional "vibram" type or the more modern "monobloc". The **welt** (the projection of the sole around the boot) should be narrow. Beware those soles with cut-away heels — there is a growing evidence to suggest that the grip given by these soles is inferior to that of more traditional designs, especially in descent. Although a good pair of boots will grip well in most circumstances assuming you are placing your feet correctly (see page 54), both traditional and modern soles do have their limitations. In particular they have a notoriously bad grip on greasy rock, hard packed snow and ice, and (more surprisingly, perhaps) on grass which is either very wet or very dry.

The method by which the sole is attached to the boot is fairly important. Most soles are either sewn, glued, screwed or welded to the upper (usually via a mid-sole), and many manufacturers use a combination of two or more of these methods. If you choose a boot with welded soles you will find it difficult if not impossible to have it resoled. Additionally, boots with welded soles often lack tortional rigidity. The leather from which the uppers are made should be of good quality, and there should be as few seams as possible — the best (and most expensive) boots will be made from a single piece of leather, the only seams being at the heel and the tongue. The more seams there are, the weaker and potentially less waterproof the boot. A sewn-in or **bellows tongue** is essentially to prevent the ingress of water, and the most convenient form of lacing uses two forms of attachment: **D-rings** (which hold the laces in place at the forward part of the boot) and **speed-hooks** (which enable you to get in and out of the boot without too much difficulty).

If you intend to do any winter mountaineering your boot will need to be particularly robust, with a higher degree of longitudinal rigidity (full shank). Traditional winter mountaineering boots are very heavy — nowadays the lighter, warmer **plastic boots** have become the norm. Consisting essentially of two boots in one — a flat-soled, flexible inner boot made of leather, and a rigid plastic outer boot, usually with a Vibram-type sole — these boots bear all the hallmarks and features of a top quality leather boot. They have many advantages, not the least of which are ease of maintenance and the fact that the boot is about as waterproof as it can possibly be.

Boot care

Once you have chosen your footwear, you will obviously want it to last as long as possible. After each sojourn into the hills, remove any mud which may have clogged the treads by holding the boots at the ankle and banging the soles together. Check the condition of the laces, replacing them as necessary, and tease out any small stones from the treads using a blunt instrument (the handle of a teaspoon is ideal). Remove dirt from the uppers with a nail brush and damp cloth.

With plastic boots, there is very little else to do, but leather boots will need to be reproofed occasionally. First, allow the boots to dry out slowly. Stuff them with newspaper and leave them in an airy place. On no account try to accelerate the drying process by leaving wet boots in drying rooms, on top of radiators or near fires, for this will cause the leather to buckle and harden. In extreme cases it may even become brittle and crack. When dry, leather boots should be given a coating of good quality wax polish or a proprietary reproofing compound such as Nikwax, with particular attention being paid to the seams. **Water-based proofings** are particularly good as they seek out those places in most need of reproofing, giving them proportionally more protection. Avoid using **liquid conditioners** over prolonged periods as these will soften the leather causing excessive wear. Such liquid proofings can also become concentrated beneath the stitching with the inevitable result that the leather will soften sufficiently for the stitches to cut through. Finally, because leather contains natural oils which are lost through time, especially if it becomes saturated with water, your boots will benefit from an occasional dose of a specialist leather conditioner.

2 HILL WALKING EQUIPMENT

As with clothing and footwear, there are few hard and fast rules about what you should take with you when you go into the hills. Your choice of equipment will depend upon many factors including what you intend to attempt, prevailing weather, time of year, location, etc. Whilst there are a few essential items, striking the right balance between comfort and safety can be quite difficult, and it is fair to say that there are as many people who take too much with them as there are people who take too little.

In this section we are going to look at those items which most people consider to be the bare essentials for summer mountain walking, and describe a range of other items, some of which are essential in winter conditions, others of which may simply make life more comfortable.

It is worth bearing in mind that everything you take you have to carry. The more you carry, the slower you will be and the more energy you will use up. Because conservation of energy is an important consideration whenever you visit the mountains, there inevitably comes a time when carrying extra "safety" equipment becomes counter-productive.

A good way to put this all into perspective is to ask whether you could survive an unexpected night on the mountains. Not to put too fine a point on it, the chances of an ill-equipped, inexperienced party surviving a forced benightment in the Scottish hills in winter are negligible.

Essential items

There are few really essential items of equipment. In additional to the clothing and footwear you wear, you should always carry a **spare sweater** (or similar), a **full set of waterproofs,** a pair of **gloves or mittens,** and a hat (see section 1). These should be carried in a good-quality **rucksack** — not as is all too often seen, in a plastic carrier bag! Unless you are only going for a half day walk of a couple of miles or less, you should also take something to **eat** and something to **drink.** No matter what your plans, you should have the relevant **map(s)** and an orienteering or protractor **compass** as described on page 109, a **watch,** and a **whistle.** Additionally, lodged permanently in your rucksack and taken on every trip there should be a **survival bag,** some form of **emergency food,** and, at the very least, a **basic first aid kit.**

Please note that this is the basic kit for mountain walking in summer conditions. From autumn to spring you should add a **head-torch and batteries** to your list. In winter conditions you will need **additional spare clothing** including a pair of **gaiters,** and if there is any sign of snow an **ice axe** should be regarded as an absolute necessity (see below and on page 77). Additionally, during the winter months, at least one person in the party should carry a **sleeping bag.**

No matter what the time of year, if you intend to do any scrambling you should take a **rope** and possibly a **helmet,** as described on page 57.

Of course, the bottom line is that none of this equipment possesses any magical properties of its own, so it is pointless carrying any of it unless you know how to use it.

Daysacks

There is nothing to beat the convenience and practicality of having a small rucksack in which to carry your essential gear. Whilst **waist pouches** and **bum bags** may be perfectly adequate for low-level valley walks, they are not really suitable for more serious mountain walking. Many do not have sufficient capacity, and those that do tend to be cumbersome and unwieldy. However, a daysack which is too large is almost as much a problem as one which is too small because most people find there is an almost irresistible temptation to fill it to capacity.

Rucksack **capacity** is quoted in litres, daysacks typically ranging from about 20 to 50 litres. The further you intend to walk, the rougher the terrain or the more extreme the weather, the larger the capacity of daysack you will need. For summer mountain walking you will need a daysack of between 25 and 35 litres. If you intend to do any scrambling or rock work, a capacity of between 30 and 40 litres would be useful. If you intend to visit the mountains under winter conditions you should be thinking in terms of 40 to 50 litres. Many models are available with **compression straps.** These allow you to alter the capacity of the daysack according to your needs, this facility making the daysack extremely versatile.

Daysacks should be functional, and the simpler the **design,** the better. The main body of the daysack is best formed from a rectangular box-shaped bag of waterproof material, nylon-based fabrics being ideal. Some manufacturers have developed their own specialist rucksack fabrics and offer a lifetime guarantee. There should be few seams (seams represent weak-points in terms of both strength and water resistance), and those than there are should be strongly sewn. It is worth checking the quality of the stitching as this varies widely from manufacturer to manufacturer.

The top of the daysack should be fitted with an efficient draw-cord, the whole of this area then being covered by a large flap. This should have elasticated sides and should be shaped to fit snugly over the top of the daysack in order to keep out the majority of any precipitation. Although this may look effective, and despite the claims of many manufacturers, I have yet to come across any ruck-sack which is 100% waterproof in a mountain storm. Even if the material is waterproof, there are so many stress points (not to mention a large hole at the top!) that water is bound to seep in some-where. It is therefore prudent to pack any items you wish to keep dry (such as spare clothing) in a plastic bag before putting them into your sack. Alternatively, if you suspect the material may not be 100% waterproof you can use a **rucksack liner** — little more than a heavy-duty bin-liner. An empty (washed) fertiliser sack begged from a farmer does just as well, and doesn't cost!

The design of the **shoulder straps** and the method used to con-nect them to the main body of the daysack is obviously of critical importance. The straps themselves should be well-padded and at least 5cms wide. They will obviously need to be adjustable, and this is best done via non-slip friction buckles which are placed in such a position that they can be adjusted whilst on the move. You should aim to adjust the straps so that the load is carried as high as possi-ble on the back, the weight bearing directly downwards. A light **waist-strap** is useful when scrambling or crossing rough terrain, and some people find a **chest-strap** useful on the larger day-sacks.

The method of attachment should be sturdy and durable, the shoulder straps being firmly attached to the main body of the day-sack, preferably with some form of reinforcement. It is useful to have a **haul-strap** or webbing loop which can be used as a handle incorporated at this point. If the straps are set too close together there is the risk that they may cut into the back of your neck, and for this reason it is better to avoid those daysacks which are pear-shaped or triangular. In any case, such designs are to be avoided as they do not allow you to carry the load high on your back (see sec-tion 4). A low load results in a bad posture in which you are bent forward using your back and shoulder muscles. This can be extremely fatiguing. A high load results in an upright posture in which the weight bears directly downwards onto the pelvic girdle and thus onto the legs.

Long straps and large external **pockets** have an infuriating habit of becoming snagged at the most inconvenient times, and you would do well to avoid any daysack which is covered in pockets or has vast lengths of webbing all over it. However, one or two pockets can be extremely convenient for carrying any items which you might use regularly or need to hand, and some of the better daysacks have a shallow pouch pocket across the front, or two compact sides pockets. If you intend to go scrambling or rock climbing it would be better to avoid daysacks with side pockets as they are more unwieldy than those without. Many manufacturers incorporate a pouch pocket in the top flap, and this can be extremely useful. For obvious reasons, all pockets should be zipped and baffled. To save the apprehensive key-searching at the end of a long day, a few daysacks are available with small zipped **key-pockets** in which you can keep car keys, money, etc.

One problem with wearing a daysack for any length of time, especially on a warm day, is that condensation builds up across your back. This is particularly marked if the daysack is made from nylon fabric. Although most manufacturers have gone to some lengths in an attempt to reduce this problem in their backpacking rucksacks, few have done so with daysacks, although some use canvas or a similar material for the back panel. It has to be said that this is a less than perfect solution.

Food and drink

Due to the combination of fresh air and sometimes strenuous exercise, most people get ravenously hungry when visiting the mountains. Even if you do not feel hungry it is vital to maintain your energy reserves, so it is importantto take the right food with you. This is even more critical if you are camping (see section 5). You should aim to get a balanced diet which provides you with a minimum of 4000 kilocalories of energy per day.

By far the most important meal of the day is **breakfast.** A common misconception is that sugars are the best source of energy. Although sugars are rich in quickly available energy, in fact it is fats which are the richest source of energy, so a good old-fashioned fry-up is highly recommended. However, it takes time for the body to get to the energy locked in fats, so it is best to have a leisurely breakfast a good hour before taking to the hills.

Packed lunches for consumption on the hill should contain a high proportion of carbohydrates (i.e. sugars and starches). Although weight-for-weight these do not contain as much energy as fats, the energy they do contain is available to the body almost immediately. Sugars are the more effective of the two, so **trail snacks** (to be eaten whilst actively walking) should have a high sugar content. Choose something that you enjoy eating, not too heavy in weight and easily digestible.

Try to consume **little and often**. Stopping for an hour in the middle and consuming all your food may appear to be refreshing, but it is not the best way of keeping up your energy. Not only will your food lie heavy on your stomach, but long stops break your body's natural rhythm making you feel lethargic and stiff afterwards.

For most people, the **evening meal** will be the major meal of the day. If you are camping or visiting the mountains again the following day, this should be a substantial meal with at least one hot course which boosts energy reserves.

Many people seriously under-estimate the amount of liquid they should drink whilst active in the hills. Indeed, dehydration is a far more common complaint than most people realise. Although it is possible to go into water-debt for short periods without too many ill effects, it is not good practice. Liquid is required in order to metabolise energy, so you should aim to maintain a good water balance. During mountain walking in temperate conditions you should aim to consume about **4 litres of liquid per day.** Considerably more than this may be needed if you are undertaking particularly strenuous walks or if the weather is hot. As with eating, **little and often** is the best policy. Consuming large quantities of liquid whilst on the move will make you feel heavy and could lead to stomach cramp. Consuming large quantities of liquid in a local inn in order to "rehydrate" is an essential part of many people's day, but bear in mind that alcohol has diuretic properties and is therefore not the most efficient way of maintaining the correct balance!

In really hot weather, some form of **electrolyte replacement** drink is beneficial; in really cold weather a flask of **hot drink** can be a great morale booster and may even be a life safer in an emergency. Contrary to popular belief, most high mountain streams and **springs** are perfectly safe to drink from.

You will obviously need something in which to carry all this liquid, and there is little to beat a purpose made **water flask**. If choosing one made from high-density plastic, check that it has a well-threaded screw top with good seals. If choosing one made from aluminium, check that it is lacquered internally, especially if you intend to use it for fruit juices or cordials. **Vacuum flasks** are good not only for keeping hot drinks hot, but also for keeping cold drinks cold. Those with glass inners are fairly light in weight and relatively cheap, but they vary considerably in efficiency and are obviously fragile. Far more efficient, but also far heavier and far more expensive, are unbreakable **stainless-steel flasks**. Whatever type you choose, it will work better if you prime it with boiling or iced water (as appropriate) for at least 5 minutes before filling. If you are camping you will have with you a stove, in which case a vacuum flask is not strictly necessary. Nevertheless, it is still a convenient item of equipment which many will find indispensable.

Survival bags

A survival bag is an essential item of equipment which should reside permanently in your rucksack along with some survival rations (see below). This is basically a heavy-duty polythene sack about 1 metre wide and 2.5 metres long. Double versions (1.2 metres x 2.4 metres approx.) are also available. If travelling in a group, everyone should have one. In emergency situations, particularly with hypothermic casualties, they provide shelter from the wind and drastically reduce heat loss through evaporation (see page 16). It is worth noting that whilst bivouac sacks **(bivi-bags)** made from breathable waterproof materials can be extremely useful, they should not be carried as an alternative to a polythene survival bag simply because they allow water vapour to pass and will not, therefore, reduce heat loss through evaporation to anywhere near the same degree.

Hypothermic casualties have little body heat. Thus the popular silver **space blankets** which reduce heat loss by reflecting body heat and do not enclose the casualty (thus allowing draughts as well) are about as useful as a chocolate fireguard.

Survival rations

Speaking of chocolate brings us nicely to survival rations. These should take the form of high energy foodstuffs containing a high proportion of sugars. Chocolate bars (Mars bars seem almost universally popular), mintcake, dextrose tablets, dried fruit, glucose sweets and similar items are ideal. Although ready-made survival packs are available, it is far cheaper to make up your own, and it is a good idea to choose things you like.

Such items tend to have an almost irresistible attraction during a long day on the hill. The temptation to raid them can lead to occasional pilfering with the result that you find them gone when you really need them. The best way around this problem is to place them in a large plastic sandwich bag and seal them up with a whole roll of sticky tape.

First Aid kits

At least one member of any group visiting the hills should have a good first aid kit and should have had some basic first aid training. However, it is better if every member of the party carries their own first aid kit, however basic this may be. It is also useful if at least one person carries a waxed luggage label and a chinagraph pencil. This can easily be carried in the first aid kit and, in the event of an emergency requiring evacuation by a mountain rescue team, can be used to note down the details which will be required (see page 173).

Watches

At least one person in any party visiting the mountains should have a reliable watch. Not only is this an essential item for accurate poor-visibility navigation, but because it is easy to lose all track of time in the mountains it can also be useful as an aid to preventing accidental benightment.

Maps and compasses

No matter what the weather nor how well you think you know an area, you should always carry a suitable compass and the relevant maps when you visit the mountains. Full details are given in section 6. The time when efficient use of map and compass can become critical is during bad conditions, but it is of little use taking a map if it ends up as a soggy mass or is torn to shreds by the wind. Some form of **map protection** is therefore vital. Laminated maps are available, and some of the more modern of these are excellent being neither as bulky nor as unwieldy as their predecessors. Also available are "sticky" flexible plastic **map cases** sealed by rolling the plastic and then securing with a Velcro strip. Designed originally for canoe touring, these are weatherproof and durable, and far better than some of the cheaper versions which use a less flexible plastic which quickly becomes brittle and cracks. At the very minimum you should carry your map in a large plastic bag, preferably with some form of weathertight seal.

Wearing your map case on a lanyard around your neck is useful in that it keeps the map to hand, but you will soon become disillusioned with it in windy weather as it spins round and tries to strangle you. I find it far more convenient to keep mine underneath the shoulder strap of my rucksack.

Whistles

A whistle should be regarded as an essential item of emergency equipment for mountain and moorland walking. The sound of a whistle will carry a long way so it can be used for gaining the attention of others if you find yourself in difficulties. The **International Mountain Distress Signal** is six goods blasts on a whistle followed by a minutes silence, repeated ad nauseam. The answering call is three good blasts followed by a minutes silence, also repeated. Both signals can also be made using other media such as flashing a torch, shouting help, waving a bright object (such as a survival bag), etc. Over the past few years there has been occasional controversy in the letters pages of the specialist press regarding what is the correct distress signal. Suffice it to say that any whistling in the mountains is likely to provoke some form of investigation, so only use your whistle in emergency.

Flares

The standard mountain distress flare is the **2 star red**. These are not freely available, are quite bulky and very expensive. Because of the escape velocity of the flare when fired, you will also need a firearms certificate to own or buy one. If you are a casual walker and you think you ought to buy one — forget it!

More freely available are **mini-flares**. These usually come in mixed packs containing mainly red flares (emergency) with two or three white flares (signalling) and a pen-type launcher. The problem is that their elevation (the height they attain when fired) is not very great, and this is particularly true in windy conditions when they have all the qualities of a cheap squib. In any case, even if the weather and visibility is fine when you fire your flare, someone has to be looking in the right direction at the right time to see it, and has to have the wherewithal to note down the direction. Needless to say, I am not a great fan, and believe they have minimal use as a method of attracting attention.

Having said this, they may be useful after the alarm has been raised as a method of guiding a rescue team to a precise location.

Pedometers

Many walkers swear by pedometers, liking to know how far they have walked during the day. It is, of course, far cheaper to measure this on the map. Additionally, pedometers are nowhere near accurate enough to be used with any great advantage in navigation, especially when micro-navigating in poor visibility. If you find one useful, wear it, but it is certainly not an essential item of equipment.

Torches

If you are visiting the mountains in autumn, winter or spring you should carry a reliable torch with good quality alkaline batteries. Winter mountain days, in particular, are very short, and a small error in navigation or unexpected delay can lead to a dangerous descent in gathering twilight or, worse, to benightment.

The most practical torches for mountain use are **headtorches** which not only allow you to have both hands free, but also have the advantage that the light goes where you look. Best known are those made by Petzl, which have the battery case at the back of the headband (counterbalancing the weight of the lamp) and storage space for at least one **spare bulb** in the lamp housing. Three different types of bulb are available: standard, long-life (less light but more battery life), and halogen (more light but less battery life). Halogen bulbs are useful if you decide to walk out; long-life bulbs are useful if you decide to sit it out. If there is a storage facility for more than one spare bulb you can carry one of each.

There is no point in carrying a torch without **batteries.** When in transit, keep torch and batteries separate or insert the batteries in such a way that the torch cannot be switched on accidentally. Alkaline batteries give longer life than standard batteries but are considerably heavier. It is worth noting that alkaline batteries will leak or may even explode if they are short-circuited. It is also worth bearing in mind that batteries have a shelf life. If in doubt, take a spare.

Altimeters

Altimeters, on the other hand, can be extremely useful although, again, they are not essential. Altimeters work by sensing changes in barometric pressure and this has a number of consequences. Firstly, you must set your altimeter at the beginning of each walk (usually by setting start height not start pressure!). Secondly, during frontal conditions when the barometric pressure may be changing fairly rapidly, they can become inaccurate, so the weather must be taken into consideration. Finally, comparing a known height with the height indicated at that point by your altimeter can give you an idea of changes in barometric pressure, and this can be of help when judging likely changes in the prevailing weather (see also section 7).

Walking sticks

Walking sticks are rightly becoming increasingly popular. They can be of great help when crossing rough terrain such as boulders fields, and during ascent and descent. They take strain off the knees and spine, and generally aid balance.

Although an old fashioned wooden stick will do the job, far better are telescopic sticks based on ski-mountaineering poles. These can be adjusted to the most comfortable and supportive length no matter whether in ascent, descent, or traverse, and can be folded down and carried along the side of your daysack (especially easy if it has compression straps) when not in use.

Ice axes

No matter what conditions are like in the valley, an ice axe is an essential item of safety equipment if there is any sign of snow on the hill. It is not a tool purely for climbers, nor is it a luxury item. Moreover, if you meet lying snow unexpectedly when you are on the hill and have no ice axe, you may have to detour around it, even if this means retracing your steps.

The biggest cause of winter accidents is simple slips on easy ground. Let me illustrate this with a typical scenario. It is a cold, crisp winter day with perfect weather. A walker is traversing a gentle (10°) slope on which there is fairly hard-packed snow. There are no steep slopes or crags anywhere around. Because the slight breeze has a bite to it, the walker is wearing his jacket and overtrousers. Paying more attention to the view than to his foot placement, he stumbles over a slightly protruding boulder, falls over and starts to slide. The snow is too hard-packed for him to gain any purchase with his hands or feet, his clothing offers little friction, so he begins to pick up speed. By the time he has travelled 50 metres or so he is going at a considerable rate of knots (60kph+!). A short distance further his slide is suddenly terminated by a wooden fence post!

This accident could have been avoided if the walker had carried an ice axe and had learned some basic winter skills, the most important of which is **self-arrest,** commonly known as the **ice-axe brake.** This is described in more detail on page 77.

We are not concerned here with technical ice climbing which requires specialist equipment, but with more general winter walking and mountaineering which may include simple gully climbs. A typical example of the type of ice axe required for this type of activity is shown in figure 2. It should have a curved **pick** with a serrated underside and a sharp, chisel end, and a wide, straight-edged, flat-ended **adze** which mirrors the curve of the pick. The **head** (the pick and adze together) will generally be forged from a single piece of metal,. and it is useful if this has a **karabiner hole** drilled through it at the top end of the shaft.

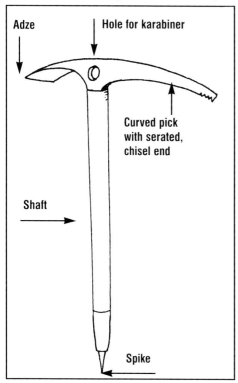

The curve of the head should approximate to the circumference of the swing of the axe when held towards the base of the shaft. The **shaft** itself should be straight with an oval rather than round cross-section, and traditional wooden shafts (usually of straight grained hickory) have now largely been replaced by stronger alloy or reinforced fibreglass, covered with a plastic or synthetic rubber material which affords good grip even when you are wearing gloves or mittens. The shaft should terminate in a sharp **spike.**

Whatever type of axe you buy, it should feel comfortable in your hand and should be of the right size. When held with the pick over your shoulder and the shaft

Figure 2: The ice axe

diagonally across your chest, the end of the shaft should protrude slightly below your hip. This is a good general length. If you intend to use it only for walking, the shaft can be slightly longer; if you intend to do a fair amount of easy gully work, the shaft can be slightly shorter.

Many axes come with some form of **wrist loop**. This often takes the form of a short sling attached to a ring which can slide along the length of the shaft, although longer slings attached through the hole in the head of the axe are almost as common. Whatever the type, the sling should be large enough for you to put a mittened hand through comfortably, but should also have some form of slider or tensioning device so that the sling can be tightened around the wrist. Although, at first glance, it may seem sensible to wear such a wrist loop (indeed, it is indispensable when climbing), it can lead to several complications when walking.

Firstly, as described on page 76, when traversing snow slopes the axe should always be held in the upslope hand. This means when zig-zagging up a slope you should be able to move your axe freely from hand to hand (there are similar considerations when step cutting). Many people dispense with the wrist loop in these situations. Secondly, if an attempted self arrest is unsuccessful (even in a practice situation), the ice axe which is attached to you via a wrist loop can do you more damage than the fall itself! When not in use the wrist loop should either be removed altogether (simple on some axes, impossible on others) or wrapped around the head and secured in place so that it does not flap around or drag along the ground where it may get caught in crampons.

Once you have bought your axe you need to look after it. Make sure you keep the pick, adze and spike sharp and free from rust, and buy **rubber protectors** for both the head and the spike (essential if taking it on public transport).

Information on how to carry, hold and use an ice axe are given in section 3.

Crampons

Modern crampons come in all sorts of shapes and sizes, some of which are hi-tech items of equipment designed for modern technical ice climbing and therefore totally unsuitable for more general winter walking and simple snow gully climbing. Crampon technique and the major pitfalls are mentioned in section 3. In this part we are concerned only with crampon types.

At the bottom end of the scale come lightweight **instep crampons** which can be quickly and easily fitted and removed from the boot. As their name implies, they sit between the front of the heel and the backmost tread of the front part of the sole, and should be a snug fit. Whilst they may be useful to give a modicum of added security across short sections of ice on low-level or valley walks, they are totally unsuitable for general purpose winter walking and climbing. Even if you intend to keep well away from steep ground and gullies, instep crampons should not be seen as a substitute for full crampons.

Next come **flexible crampons.** These come in a variety of designs, some of which have eight points, others of which have ten, but all are based on a central springy metal plate. In some designs the front two points point forward at an angle of about 45° The method of attachment to the boot (which, as we will see, is critical) often leaves much to be desired, being done via one long strap and four attachment points. As with instep crampons, these may be useful for short sections of ice on low level walks, but they are totally unsuitable for general use in the mountains.

At the opposite end of the scale come **technical ice-climbing crampons.** These are usually totally rigid and come with a wide variety of point shapes and sizes. They are not suitable for general

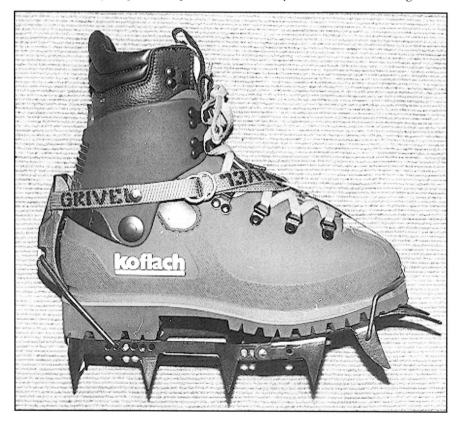

Plastic boots with step-in crampons

mountain use and fall way outside the scope of this book.

The most suitable **general purpose crampons** should have ten downward-facing points and two horizontal forward-facing points which should be angled slightly downwards, either flat or curved. The front two downward-facing points should also be inclined slightly forwards.

These crampons can be thought of as being divided into two sections, the four rear points making up one, and the eight front points making up the other. These sections are connected by a metal plate which effectively forms a hinge below the instep of the boot. This hinge is vital for without it the crampons would soon fail due to constant flexing. This is especially true if you wear boots which are either not fully stiffened or which do not have a totally flat sole. The **fit** of the crampon on the boot is especially important. Indeed, the crampons should fit so well that they remain on the boot without any form of binding. Few crampons are totally adjustable throughout a range of sizes, so it is important to take your boots with you when you go to buy. It is usually necessary to match crampons to boots. Things to watch for are the position of the inside post (which can be fouled by the instep of the boot), and the position of the front points relative to the toe of the boot. When a straight edge is placed across the front of the boot there should be about 2cms of front point sticking out. It may also be necessary to fit a **heel bar** to prevent the boot from slipping backwards. Once fitted, make sure any screws, bolts or nuts are fully tightened. It is prudent to use a proprietary locking agent to reduce the chance of them loosening accidentally.

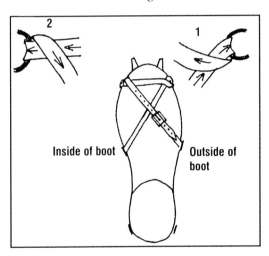

Figure 3: The standard crampon straps

When you come to wear your crampons, place them on the ground with all rings and **straps** outside the framework, clear any snow from the sole of your boot, then step into them from a standing position, making sure the boot sits firmly on the frame. There are two main methods of attachment, these being straps (either traditional or French-style) and **clip-on bindings**. As with fit, the method of attachment is crucial and I recommend you visit your local friendly retailer and ask advice. The best all-round method is **traditional straps.** These are flexible in use and easy to adjust and tension.

Make sure all straps are fastened neatly and without twists into the correct buckle. Fasten the back strap first, guiding it right around the ankle well below the ankle cuff of the boot before doing up the buckle. Now secure the front straps, threading them in the correct direction and order through the rings (see figure 3). **French-style straps** make use of a fixed strap with a ring at the front end of the boot. Although apparently more simple, they are not so flexible and a can be difficult to tension correctly. The back strap is secured first (as per traditional straps), then the front strap is passed through the toe ring (which must be in precisely the correct position) and secured.

No matter which strap method is chosen, the straps themselves should be made from neoprene-coated nylon with pin-type buckles, and should be checked on a regular basis. These should be pulled as tight as comfort allows with the proviso that there should be no restriction of circulation to the toes. Once secured, the strap protruding from the buckles should neither be too long nor too short — about 4-5cms is ideal. It is prudent to connect the straps to the crampons with two sets of rivets.

Clip-on bindings (crampons with this type of binding are sometimes called **step-in crampons**) are the quickest and easiest method of attaching crampons to boots, and have largely replaced straps. However, they are generally only suitable for use on good quality plastic boots because the attachment is via the welt. This is often narrower on leather boots, and prone to wear, so may not afford a positive grip.

In use, the toe of the boot is first placed under the front bail, then the tensioning lever is then placed on the rear welt and pulled up to the back of the boot. It is then secured in place by means of a strap. This strap is often of nylon webbing, in which case it should be done up via two D rings rather than a spring buckle. This method is far less likely to slip, but can be difficult to undo. The front bail, tensioning lever and cables, and restraining strap should be inspected on a regular basis for signs of wear.

Crampon points should be kept sharp on a regular basis using a hand-held file rather that a grinding tool as the heat may affect the temper of the metal. Front points should be sharpened from the top in a forwards direction; other points should be sharpened along their edges. Regular checks should also be made on all nuts, bolts and screws, and any areas of possible metal fatigue such as hinges and posts.

Snow goggles

In winter conditions when there is continuous snow cover, snow blindness is a hazard — even on a cloudy day. You should therefore have with you a pair of snow goggles, preferably with good ultra-violet and infra-red filter lenses. Ordinary sun glasses are not suitable, no matter how effective the lenses, because they do not give protection to the side of the eyes. If you find goggles too claustrophobic, glacier glasses, again with filtering lenses are a good alternative, so long as they have effective side shields.

Sleeping bags and bivi-bags

In winter conditions, especially in the Scottish Highlands or any remote site, at least one member of the party (if not everyone) should carry a good quality, 4-season sleeping bag. This may make the difference between life or death in an emergency. If this is combined with a breathable-fabric bivi-bag, so much the better.

Helmets

Many accidents in the mountains involve head injuries and you would be wise to consider carefully whether you need a helmet. Situations where it would be prudent for you to wear them include scrambling and general winter mountaineering in easy snow gullies. Should you intend to become involved in more serious rock, snow or ice climbing on mountain crags they should be regarded as an essential item of equipment.

Two main types of helmet are available, one type made from **fibreglass** (GRP), the other from **plastic.** Both give protection but in a slightly different way. Both should be discarded after suffering any severe impact.

Whatever the type chosen it should be reasonably light and fairly compact, and should not restrict the vision. It should also be comfortable. Those which give some protection to the temples are safer than those that do not, but are often less comfortable. The cradle should be adjustable to allow for the wearing of a hat, and the chin strap should be easily adjustable and connected via **Y straps** to give stability.

Ropes and ancillaries

Although technical rock climbing and snow/ice climbing are beyond the scope of this book, there are times when a rope should be regarded as an essential item of equipment. This is particularly the case in scrambling and winter walking where simple snow gullies are likely to be encountered.

The rope best suited to these situations is of **Kernmantle** construction, having a core of lightly twisted nylon strands held together with a plaited nylon sheath. It should have a **diameter** of between 9mm and 11mm, 9mm being the more popular for scrambling because it is lighter. The **length** of rope required will depend very much upon the situation in which it is to be used, but generally speaking a length of between 30m and 45m will be adequate.

It is essential that only rope designed for rock climbing and mountaineering is used, and that it should be **dynamic.** This means that it will stretch slightly under load, thus absorbing some of the shock of a fall. Static or prestretched ropes are totally unsuitable and should not be used. Make sure that your rope comes from a recognised manufacturer and has UIAA approval.

Ropes should be stored either loosely coiled or (better) laced in a cool, dry, airy environment, well away from sources of heat or contamination. If they get wet, they should be allowed to dry naturally. If they get dirty they should be washed in cold, clean, preferably running water. Battery acid, petrol and mineral oils, in particular, are seriously detrimental, so bear this in mind when slinging the rope in the boot of your car. Methods of coiling are discussed on page 60.

Ropes generally have a **lifespan** of not more that three years under normal usage, owing as much to the effects of ultraviolet light as to fair wear and tear. However, this can be seriously reduced under certain circumstances, and you should get into the habit of checking your rope for signs of wear or damage every time you handle it. Things to look for include excessive fluffing of the sheath, and any distortion of the core. Suspect ropes should be destroyed. Avoid treading on the rope as this can cause indirect damage by forcing grit particles into the core as well as direct damage if it is lying over a sharp stone. Beware securing the rope in such a way that it runs or rubs over sharp edges, or allowing a loaded rope to rub across rough rock.

Although you should be able to make use of the rope alone, there are a couple of other things which will make your life easier. Tape

slings made from nylon webbing can be useful in a variety of situations. Although it is possible to buy webbing off the reel and tie the loops yourself using a tape knot, the best and most convenient slings for our purposes are ready sewn slings made from full-weight 25mm wide webbing. These come in a variety of sizes, 240cms being the most versatile. Two or three slings should suffice for most situations. You should store and look after slings in exactly the same way as ropes.

To go with each of your slings you will need a **screwgate karabiner.** Like your rope, this should be UIAA approved. Offset D or HMS (pear shape) designs are the most practical as they allow the use of friction hitches (see page 65). Alloy karabiners are the norm as they are light in weight. However, they wear quickly if used with dirty ropes and should be discarded if dropped onto rock from heights of more than about 5m. Steel karabiners are much heavier but resist wear far better. Karabiners need very little maintenance apart from an occasional light spray with WD40 or (better) a silicon lubricant, paying particular attention to the hinge, screwgate and spring. Wipe away any excess.

Other Useful Items

There are several other bits and pieces which can go a long way towards making your mountain journeys more comfortable. Some are virtually essential in certain conditions, and in this category I would include **sun-screen, sun glasses,** and **insect repellent.**

No matter what the conditions or time of year, a short length of **paracord** can have many uses including emergency repairs to rucksack or gaiters, and spare bootlace. A plastic bag containing a few sheets of **toilet tissue** can also be useful.

Some form of **sit mat** may make breaks more comfortable and can easily be carried down the back of the daysack where it will provide extra padding. This is best formed from an offcut of closed-cell foam such as a sleepmat. Some experienced walkers never venture into the hills without their **binoculars** or **camera.** Others take books to help them identify birds, plants or rocks, or paper and pencil to draw or note down things they have seen

In the final anlysis, only you can decide what you wish to carry. So long as you have the basic essentials, it really is up to you. Indeed, some experienced mountaineers may be appalled that I have neglected to mention some piece of equipment which they feel is vital. If this is the case, write and tell me, make your case, and I may include it in any future edition!

3 HILL WALKING SKILLS

I have a pet theory. It is that most people have forgotten the correct way to walk. We spend so much of our time on level pavements, carpeted floors, ramps and stairs that our bodies are unused to moving along rough paths and across trackless terrain. The result is that not only do we place our feet incorrectly, we also hold our bodies in the wrong position relative to our feet and the ground.

In this section we are going to look at a range of hillwalking skills, both basic movement skills and somewhat more specialised safety techniques. From the outset I must emphasise that **these skills cannot be learned from a book.** Proficiency will only come with practice and experience. I encourage you to practice all the skills, but in particular you should gain practical experience of ropework techniques and winter skills (especially the ice axe arrest) in a safe environment **before you need them in an emergency.** When things go wrong in the mountains, they tend to do so with alarming speed and severity. It is of little use referring to a book at the time — the techniques should already be ingrained by practice and experience so that they have become almost second nature.

Pace

The basic mountain walking technique is a regular, rhythmic pace. This is a major factor in the safe enjoyment of mountain walking. Although there will be days when it feels good to stride out, and others when you gain pleasure from dawdling, you should generally aim to walk at a steady pace with a medium stride which uses the least amount of energy. Once you have found your rhythm and got into your stride, your body takes over leaving the mind to do other things — including enjoying the surroundings. This rhythm should be maintained up hill and down dale. If you wish to speed up or slow down, you do so by altering the length of stride, not the pace or the rhythm. Most experienced mountaineers finish the day at the same pace as they started; they have what could be termed a **24 hour pace** which can be kept up almost indefinitely. So avoid the temptation to go rushing off at the start, no matter how much energy you may have — you never know when you may need some reserves!

Deliberate, precise foot placement is paramount, especially over rough or loose terrain. Indeed, no matter what the surface, place each foot carefully, with as much of the sole of the boot on the ground as possible. Choose the easiest route, avoiding, where possible, high steps and long strides. When the terrain becomes rougher or more difficult, shorten your stride so you can maintain your rhythm. Whatever the conditions underfoot, try to keep the body-weight over the feet so that all the work of walking is done with the strong thigh and stomach muscles.

Good **route selection** should be on two levels. Not only should you look ahead so as to choose the easiest line through the landscape, but you should also look closer to hand in order to plan precisely where each foot is going to be placed.

Security on steep ground

As the ground becomes steeper, so route selection, foot placement and body position become increasingly important. When going **uphill,** shorten the stride, flex the ankles so that feet can be kept flat to the slope, and lock each leg at the knee as you step up. If the ground is loose or slippery, try to place your feet in such a way that there is something against them (such as a protruding stone) which will prevent them from slipping downslope, even if this means turning your feet sideways. Keep your body upright with your weight over your feet, and try to avoid springing up from your toes. Every upward step you take should be powered by your thigh and stomach muscles.

As the ground steepens still further you will probably find it easier to zig-zag in an ascending traverse, moving diagonally backwards and forwards across the slope. Indeed, many of the older mountain paths (such as those made by shepherds, drovers and miners) do this. If the terrain is trackless, the length and angle of each zig and zag should be determined by the nature of the terrain (and personal preference). Resist the temptation to **edge** your boots. Instead, flex your ankles and keep the soles of your feet flat to the slope. Few slopes other than rock slabs are perfectly smooth, and you should take advantage of the natural bulges and indentations. Plan your route in almost microscopic detail. Look first for flatter areas where you can safely place both feet prior to changing direction, then connect these with lines of weakness containing lumps, bumps and places where local projections create small platforms from which it is difficult for your foot to slip.

Although it seems the natural thing to do, try to guard against leaning in to the slope. If my experience on courses is anything to

On steep ground maintain an upright position with your weight over your feet

go by, some people find this incredibly difficult to do the first few times, so you may have to make a conscious effort. Remember, your body should remain upright with the weight over your feet. This is especially important if the ground is loose or wet. If you lean in, your alter your centre of gravity and place an outward pressure on your feet making them far more likely to slip (see figure 4). If there is a drop below you, the temptation is to pull yourself into the slope with your hands whereas, in reality, the safest thing to do is to push yourself away from the slope with your hands!

Many people find going **downhill** harder than going up. As with ascent, you should shorten your stride and flex your ankles to keep your feet flat to the slope, and make use of the local topography to help keep your feet from slipping. The smaller the step, the less of a shock load comes onto the foot, and the less likely you are to slip. Resist the temptation to lean back or dig in your heels, especially if your are wearing boots with cut-away soles (see page 32). Unlike ascent, however, where the knees should be locked, it is better to keep each leg very slightly bent so that the shock of the descent is taken and absorbed by the thigh muscles rather than the cartilage. No matter whether going up or down, the body weight should be kept as near vertical as possible so that it acts directly down on the legs and feet.

Few mountain slopes are at a constant angle, and you should be aware of two particular types of slope. **Convex slopes** are those which begin gradually and become steeper as they descent. Conversely, **concave slopes** start off steeply and become less steep as they descend.

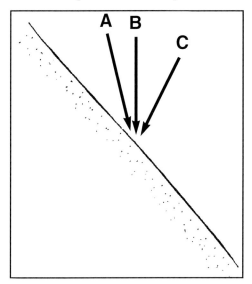

Figure 4: Body position on steep ground - A, WRONG - weight pushes away from holds; B, EXCELLENT - body weight lies directly over feet; C, GOOD - but take care not to lose your balance.

Particularly when you are on unfamiliar terrain (and especially in poor visibility), you should aim to descend concave slopes rather than convex ones. This is simply because you can always see what is ahead of you when descending a concave slope, whereas the future is hidden when descending a convex slope. Of course, in practice, many mountain slopes are **complex slopes**, with areas of concavity and areas of convexity. When descending this type of terrain, use your map interpretation skills to search out the concave areas and descend these, even if you have top weave your way backwards and forwards across the mountainside.

On slopes where there are loose boulders around, be aware of other walkers around you in case they dislodge a stone. If you, yourself, accidentally dislodge a stone which starts to roll or bounce downslope, bellow **"below"** at the top of your voice, even if you cannot see anyone (see also page 73).

Scrambling

A vast hazy area sandwiched between adventurous walking and technical rock climbing, scrambling is potentially the most dangerous activity in the mountains, yet it is arguably one of the most rewarding. This is probably more than just coincidence! A good maxim for anyone going scrambling is "discretion is the better part of valour". Indeed, I frequently tell clients on scrambling courses that I live my life by the rule: "Bottle out and run away; live to climb another day!", and there is more than a small degree of truth in this.

If I were to discuss fully the skills of scrambling, I would need to use the whole of this book. All I can do here is give you some pointers and mention a few basic skills. I consider the most important skill of scrambling to be the ability to **relax.** Indeed, when scrambling your moves should be made as much with your mind as with your body. My justification for this is simple. If I were to place a paving slab on the floor, virtually everyone could stand on it on one leg and hop. However, if I were to place the same paving slab on top of a pillar five metres high, most of those self same people would be unable to do it. Physically we can do it; mentally, we cannot.

In basic terms, the movement techniques in scrambling are simply an extension of the steep ground skills discussed earlier: body upright, weight over the feet, resist the temptation to lean in. Route finding and route selection become even more important. Indeed, finding and planning your route calls for good **judgement,** and that you can only learn through experience. In order to prevent yourself from scrambling into difficulty, not only do you need to work out your general line of ascent, you also need to work out each individual move as far in advance as you can. You need to learn to

Grade Three Scrambling - potentially the most dangerous activity

read the rock, and many newcomers to scrambling get themselves into difficulties simply because they look only at the rock in front of them instead of the rock all around them. Moreover, you should never climb up something you cannot climb down. I advise you to practice downclimbing because it does not come naturally and most people find it far harder than climbing up. If you are really keen to try scrambling, my advice is to go initially with a more experienced companion or book on a scrambling course at a reputable centre. If you want to get the most from such a course, the client:instructor ratio should not exceed 3:1. If you have already been scrambling a little and want to learn more, it would be useful to try some basic rock climbing, again either with an experienced companion or with a good centre.

In terms of equipment, you need very little apart from your basic hill kit. However, you should note that your boots need to be somewhat more sturdy than lightweight summer walking boots. Moreover, particularly on the more difficult scrambles (grade 2 and above), it would be prudent to wear a helmet and to carry a rope and perhaps a couple of tape slings with screwgate karabiners. Of course, it is of little use carrying this gear if you do not know how to use it correctly.

Basic ropework

The type of rope suitable for use in scrambling has already been discussed in section 2. In this part of the book we are going to look at a few simple ways in which it can be used. In order to use your rope safely and effectively in all situations, you need to be proficient in a number of skills, these being rope management, tying on, locating and using anchors, belaying, and abseiling. You should also be able to tie a number of specific knots quickly and effectively (no matter what the weather is doing nor how cold your hands), and should know which knot is appropriate to a given circumstance.

Again I must stress that these skills cannot be learned from a book. You should practise them in a safe environment before you need to use them for real.

When handled correctly, your rope can be a real friend. If mishandled, mistreated or used without circumspection, it can precipitate your downfall with potentially fatal results. Basic **rope management** skills are therefore essential.

Ropes can be coiled in one of three

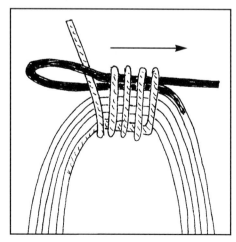

Figure 5: Tying off a mountaineers coil (pictured above)

ways, each of which have advantages and disadvantages. The **mountaineers coil** (figure 5 & photograph) used to be the standard way to coil and carry a rope and is still commonly seen. With practice it can be done quickly and neatly, and if you make each coil from a length of rope the width of your extended arms, the coil will sit comfortably around your neck and over one shoulder. However, in order to get each coil to sit flat against its neighbours, it is necessary to twist the rope with the result that there is a danger it can kink in use. This is particularly true if you store your rope coiled in this way. When uncoiling, undo the lashing then remove each coil in order, letting the rope fall to the ground in loose loops.

The **butterfly coil** (figure 6 & photograph) is quick and easy and has much to recommend it. It can be done with the rope doubled or single. If using it doubled, first find the middle of the rope and

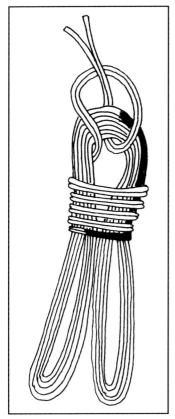

Figure 6 (and photograph): Tying off the Alpine Butterfly Coil

Lacing a rope

then put the two sides around your neck in such a way that you can place your thumb through the mid-point with your arm extended down your side. If using it with a single rope, place it around your neck so that one end touches the ground. Coils of equal length can quickly be made by passing the rope backwards and forwards across the back of the neck and running it around the thumb. The advantage of this method is that it is unnecessary to twist the rope to form the coils, so there is less chance of the rope kinking in use. When the coils are secured in the way shown, the rope can easily be carried like a rucksack, the ends being tied around your waits, thus securing the coils. Ropes coiled this way should be uncoiled as per the mountaineers coil.

Dutch lacing (see photograph) is a coiling technique borrowed from cavers. In this method the rope is first quartered by holding both ends together then, without letting go of the ends, running the rope through your hands until you find the middle. Now tie an overhand slip knot using all four strands, and pass a loop of the quartered rope through this to form another loop. Continue in this way until all the rope has been chained, passing the ends through the final loop to secure it. There is no need to pull the loops tight. This is the ideal method of coiling to use to store a rope. When uncoiling, pull the ends out of the final loop and the whole rope will unravel with ease. However, as the rope will still be quartered at this point, it will be necessary to run it through your hands twice before you can use it without risk of tangles.

No matter which method you use, make sure when uncoiling that you throw the first end away to one side so that the coils following it do not hide it. This first end becomes the **bottom end** of the rope (because it leads to the bottom of the pile of coils). The end which you finish with becomes the **top end** of the rope (because it leads to the top of the pile of coils). Whenever you use it, you should always take rope from the top end or else you run the danger of tangles.

In order to explain the other techniques in what is hopefully a

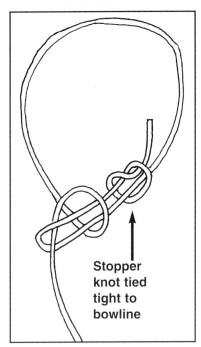

Stopper knot tied tight to bowline

Figure 7: Bowline

clear and concise way, I am going to use a scenario. Imagine that you are with a companion at the bottom of a short rock step. You have decided that you can scramble up it without too much difficulty, but your companion is not so sure of his own abilities and has asked you to protect him with the rope. You have uncoiled the rope into loose loops on the ground where it will not be trodden on. The next thing you need to do is tie on.

There are two methods of tying on to the rope — the waist line and the harness. The **waist line** is formed simply by passing the rope around your waist and securing it with a **bowline** (figure 7). Please note that the **stopper knot** is an essential part of the bowline; without it the knot can easily work loose or even invert, turning it into a slip-knot! The stopper knot should be tied tight up against the bowline. It is also essential that the rope around your waist is tight — when tied you should only just be able to get your hand underneath it. If you do not do this and you fall off, the rope can rise up around your chest and suffocate you.

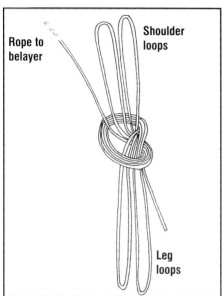

Figure 8: Thompson knot

Even if you are only tying on to belay someone (q.v.), the rope should still be tied tight to prevent the risk of excessive movement. Although this is a quick and simple way of tying on, please note that this method is **not recommended** for lowering nor for use in any situation where immediate recovery from a fall is unlikely, because of the risk of suffocation through compression of the diaphragm. Under these circumstances, or when dealing with children, very nervous or heavy adults, some form of **harness** is preferable. This is most easily tied using a **Thompson knot** (figure 8). Because this is being used to form a harness, it should be tied to the right size.

When forming the four loops, size them against the person who will wear the harness, the correct length being either "nose-to-toes" (from the end of the nose when looking down to the top of the boot) or "neck-to-deck" (from the top of the sternum to the ground), whichever you prefer. Tie the overhand knot in the middle of the loops initially, but make adjustments later to ensure that the harness fits as shown in the photograph.

In the scenario given, you now make your way carefully to the top of the rock step, your companion ensuring that the rope pays out freely. If there is any risk that you may fall, you should choose another route. If, for some reason, this is impossible, your companion should belay you using one of the methods described below. Obviously there will be no rope above you, so if you fall you are almost certain to hit the ground unless you can find a suitable flake of rock behind which you can pass the rope. In the event of a fall this acts as a **running belay** which may prevent you from hitting the ground. Running belays can also be formed by passing tape slings over projections or around chockstones then passing the climbing rope through a karabiner attached to it. Ideally your companion should be tied to anchors which will resist a pull in any direction (see below).

On reaching the top you must search for some form of **anchor.** Typical anchors include flakes of rock, large boulders, and chockstones jammed firmly in cracks, but choosing a suitable anchor or combination of anchors requires practice and careful thought. Whatever you use it should obviously be solid. Kick it, pull it, try to destroy it. If it moves, avoid it! Think about the direction in which any pull will come in the event

Correctly adjusted Thompson Knot

that your companion falls, and try to work out what will happen not only to the anchor, but to anything attached to it. If, for example, there is any danger that a rope tied around it could pull off under load, or could run over a sharp edge, look again. Try, also,

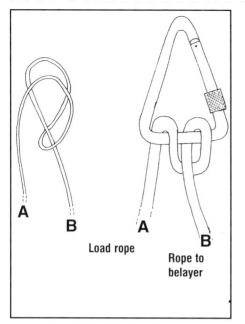

A
B
Load rope

A
B
Rope to belayer

Figure 9: Italian Hitch

to find an anchor which lies in such a position that, when in use, you can see your companion.

Anchors can be used in one of two ways: either directly as a means of securing the rope in order to hold a fall, or indirectly as a means of securing you so that you can hold a fall. The technique of holding the rope in order to prevent a slip from becoming a fall is known as **belaying.**

The quickest, simplest and most straightforward way of belaying is the **direct belay.** In this method the rope is passed directly around the anchor, the anchor providing sufficient friction to aid you in arresting the fall. As the climber ascends, so the rope is kept taught by being pulled around the anchor. In order to be effective, the anchor should be fairly broad, and should have no sharp edges which could cut the rope. Additionally, the rope between the anchor and the climber (the **live rope**) should run straight. If additional friction is required you can use a body belay as described below. The anchor must obviously be bombproof! If it is not and it fails, you have no hope at all of stopping the fall, and if you are using a body belay, you could be pulled over the edge as well.

If you are carrying a tape sling and karabiner, there is an alternative and arguably safer method of using the direct belay. In this method the sling is passed around the anchor and the rope is placed in the karabiner using an **Italian Hitch** (figure 9). It is important that the live rope is located on the back-bar side of the karabiner and not on the gate side. To use this method correctly, you must stand in front of the knot and guide the

Bowline with stopper knot tied to the knot

Figure of eight knot

Waistline

Good solid anchor

Figure 10: Tying in to an anchor using a figure of eight knot around the waistline

live rope into the karabiner whilst pulling the slack through with the other hand. In the event of a slip, pulling on the slack rope (the rope between the anchor and you) will cause the knot to bite thus arresting a fall, so although you can let go of the live rope, you should always have one hand firmly grasping the slack rope. Because the Italian Hitch is reversible (i.e. it provides friction both when taking in the rope and when paying it out), this method of belaying is particularly useful in an emergency when, for example, lowering an injured person down a short rock step.

There are times when a direct belay may be inappropriate, such as when the anchors are not quite as solid as could be wished for, when they are situated some way from the edge of the rock step, or when no single anchor lies in exactly the right position to allow

A direct belay using the rope alone

the rope to run in a straight line to the climber. Under such circumstances, an **indirect belay** may well be a better option. In this method, you secure yourself to the anchor then pass the rope around your body (a **body belay**) in such a way that you can arrest a fall. To connect yourself to the anchor take the rope issuing from the bowline around your waist and pass it either around the anchor or through a karabiner attached to a sling passing around the anchor. Stand at the point from which you will be belaying (see below) and thread a loop of the rope coming back from the anchor, through your waistline, pull it tight, and secure it using a **figure of eight knot** (figure 10 & photograph). If you feel it would be prudent to back up this single anchor with another, or if a line drawn between you, the anchor and the climber is not straight, tie into further anchors using the same method. When using two or more anchors your safe area lies anywhere within the angle formed by the outside anchors (see photograph), but note that their angle should never exceed 80°

There are a number of factors which must be considered regarding the relationship between the position of the anchors, the position in which you stand (the **stance)** and the route to be taken by the climber. Firstly, when standing at the stance, all the ropes between you and the anchors should be taut. Indeed, you should be leaning against them. You should be facing out with the anchors behind you, so the knots tied around your waistline should also be behind you — in line with the respective anchors. If this is not done you could be pulled over the edge of the rock step if your companion falls. Secondly, the direction of pull which will act on you in the event of any fall should pass directly to the anchors. If

A direct belay using a tape sling, karabiner and Italian hitch

using multiple anchors, you should be standing within the safe area; if using only one anchor, your stance should lie on a straight line drawn between the anchor and the climber. Thirdly, as the direction of pull on you in this scenario is going to be downwards, your anchors should ideally be above you. This is particularly important if the anchors are within 1 or 2 metres of the stance.

Once you have secured yourself to the anchors, get comfortable on the stance and pull in all the slack rope which lies between you and your companion. When it comes tight, pass it over your head and shoulders so you can run it around your waist. It should lie above the lines running from you to your anchors. Identify the two parts of the rope: the **live rope** (running from you to the climber), and the **slack rope**. Take a twist in the slack rope, passing it over and around your forearm before holding it. Brace yourself by leaning forward on your anchor lines, standing with your legs slightly apart and with the foot on the same side as the live rope slightly forward, knee braced. This is the basic position for the **body belay.**

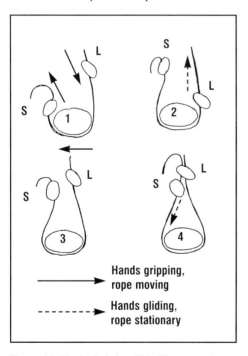

Hands gripping, rope moving

Hands gliding, rope stationary

Figure 11: The body belay. This illustrates the sequence of moves when taking in the rope. L=the live hand; S=the slack hand

To take the rope in, hold both live and slack ropes with your live hand, slide the slack hand back to your hips, grasp the rope firmly and pull it forward, feeding it into the live hand (figure 11). To give out slack rope, slide the slack hand forward then feed the rope around the waist with the live hand whilst moving the slack hand back towards your hips. To lock off in the event of a fall, bring your slack hand smartly across your chest. **All this takes practice!**

There may be times when, for one reason or another, you are unable to see or hear your companion clearly, and yet precise instructions and a knowledge of exactly what each other are doing at any given time are vital for safety. You therefore need to be able to communicate with clarity and without ambiguity. When climb-

Tying in to the belay with a figure of eight knot, sling and karabiner

ing up and being belayed, let your companion know if you are using a running belay by calling *"runner on"*. This will alert him to the fact that if you fall, the rope may now pull upwards instead of downwards. You should remain on belay until you have tied yourself in to your anchors at the top, at which point you call *"safe"*.

You now need to take in all the slack rope, so call *"taking in"* and continue pulling until your companion calls *"that's me"* to indicate that the rope is now tight on him. Once you have secured the rope in either a direct or indirect belay, and are in a position to arrest a fall, invite your companion to climb by calling *"climb when you're ready"*. He should acknowledge your call by shouting *"climbing"*, but should not start climbing until you have replied *"okay"*. If he starts to climb before this and you have not heard him, he will hit the ground if he falls off.

Whilst on the rock face only two calls should be used, although it is

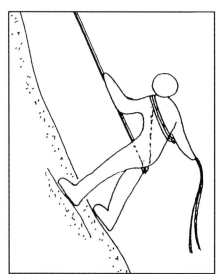

Figure 12: Classic abseil

common to hear several more if the climber gets into difficulties! If, for some reason, the climber wants to descend, he should call *"slack"*. When you hear this call, do not suddenly give him three metres of rope — simply allow the rope to run out as it is needed.

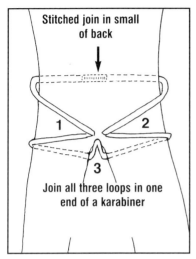

Figure 13: Sit harness formed from a tape sling (viewed from the front)

If, on the other hand, there seems to be too much slack rope and the climber wants it tightened, he should call *"take in"*. Never mix the two by shouting "take in the slack". This can lead to obvious confusion. The final ropework technique that needs to be mentioned is **abseiling** — a method of descending a rope in a controlled manner. It is fair to say that many accidents are caused by the misuse of this technique so it should not be approached lightly. The basic idea is to find the middle of the rope and loop this around a bombproof anchor, the two halves then being dropped down the rock step to be descended. If the anchor is chosen with care, the rope can then be retrieved once the descent has been made simply by pulling on one end.

A good stance, well braced, tight on the backline, and with the direction of force in a straight line between climber and anchor

A Y-hang, using two anchors. The safe position is anywhere between the anchors so long as (a) both back lines are tight, and (b) the angle at the waistline does not exceed 90°

There are two methods of abseiling which are applicable to a scrambling or hill-walking situation. In the **classic abseil** the double rope from the anchor is passed between your legs, around the back of one thigh, across your chest and over the shoulder opposite the thigh. It is then passed across your back and is held firmly in the hand on the same side as the thigh around which it passes (figure 12 & photograph). You will not want to go fast if you use this technique! In the **sling-assisted classic** a tape sling is formed into a sit harness. To do this, hold the sling so that the stitched join is against the small of your back and the karabiner hangs down between you legs. Bring the two sides around your sides then pull the karabiner between you legs and clip it into the two side loops (figure 13). There should be three loops in the karabiner, and the tape around your back should sit above your hips. Stand facing the anchor and pass the double rope over one shoulder. Pull it down and clip it into the karabiner and do up the screwgate. Now pass the rope from your shoulder across your back so you can hold it firmly in the opposite hand.

To descend, stand with your back to the cliff and walk backwards to the edge, allowing the rope to slide around your body and through your hand in a controlled manner. One hand will be holding the rope which goes across your back, the other should be holding the rope coming from the anchor. Resist the temptation to hold you weight with the anchormost hand — it is the backmost hand which controls the abseil and holds your weight. When you get to the edge, slowly lean backwards until you are at an angle of between 60° and 80° to the rock. Keep your legs fairly straight, pushing away from the rock, and your feet as flat to the rock as possible, with your heels well down. Turn slightly sideways with the controlling hand lowermost, and carefully walk backwards down the rockface. As with the belaying techniques, **this requires**

The Classic Abseil

When moving on scree beware of falling material

practice, and should preferably be done in a supervised, non-hazardous environment before it needs to be used in an emergency. If you feel you would like to know more about ropework or to learn how to use the techniques correctly, safely and effectively, I recommend you ask a more experienced companion to show you the ropes (sorry!) or join a suitable course at a reputable centre.

Moving on scree

Ascending scree can be a laborious task, and should be avoided wherever possible. However, there will be times when it is necessary. The same movement skills apply here as in other steep ground situations: move slowly and steadily, taking small paces and placing your feet carefully and with precision. If there are several in the party, it is advisable to ascend in a line abreast or an arrowhead formation. In this way the risk of someone being hit by dislodged material is minimised. If you do dislodge something and it gathers momentum, shout the warning "*Below!*".

If the scree is steep or long and you wish to zig-zag, keep the party fairly close together, and be aware of people who are zigging when you are zagging! Not only should you be conscious of people below you upon whom rocks may fall, you should also be conscious of people above you who could dislodge something onto you.

Descending scree is best done in a steady, controlled manner. Again, be aware of the danger of falling material and adopt an arrowhead formation if appropriate. **Scree running** can be exhilarating, but it can also be extremely dangerous. It will also damage both your boots and the environment. Indeed, several of the classic scree runs are now unrunnable because most of the loose material has gone. The basic technique involves taking large steps down the scree, digging the heels well back. As the stones begin to move, go with them, continuing to take large steps as if walking down an escalator. It is possible to gain considerable momentum, your speed being equal to that of your pace plus that of the falling stones! When you want to stop, take a little jump and dig both heels well back. As with all other movement on steep ground, try to keep upright. If you lean back you feet will fly out from under you and you will end up sitting down but still moving (not a pleasant experience). If you lean too far forward you run the risk of somersaulting headfirst down the slope (an even less pleasant experience!).

Before running down any scree there are a number of factors you should consider. Firstly, it is important that you are absolutely certain that you can see all of the slope. This will be impossible if the visibility is poor or if it is nearing dusk. Secondly, it is very easy for small drops to be camouflaged by the similarity in the stones above and below them, and it is therefore unwise to run down any scree slope which you have not previously viewed from below. Thirdly, the slope should be composed of boulders which are fairly small and uniform in size. Avoid slopes where there are large islands of rock or large boulders perched on the scree.

Scree often issues from **gullies.** These can be really nasty areas, damp and greasy, containing much loose material. When moving through gullies, either in ascent or descent, it is best to keep close together so any dislodged material can be palmed from person to person before it has a chance of gathering momentum. Obviously, if the gully is only short, it is safest and most convenient for people to ascend it one at a time, and it may be possible to divide longer gullies into sections between large rock steps which offer shelter from falling material. If this can be done, the party can move one at a time between these safer areas.

Winter skills

First and foremost we need to dispel a few misconceptions and put things into perspective. It is true to say that you can walk safely in the winter hills without crampons whereas you cannot do so without an ice axe. Although good crampon technique can, in most circumstances, reduce the need to cut steps, thus speeding things up (an important consideration), crampons themselves bring with them their own particular set of hazards. Indeed, crampons can be extremely dangerous pieces of equipment because they can lull the inexperienced wearer into a false sense of security, giving a feeling of invulnerability out of all proportion to the extra safety they can give.

Make no mistake about it, to venture into the mountains without an ice axe when there is snow on the ground is nothing short of madness. However, it is of little use taking an ice axe if you do not know how to use it correctly. Despite what you may have heard to the contrary, the most important use of your ice axe is not cutting steps, but self arrest (see below). It is a sad but demonstrable fact that the vast majority of winter accidents are caused by simple slips on easy ground.

Most people are familiar with the soft, white fluffy stuff which sometimes lies in the back garden in winter. However, this fun eliciting, snowball material is only one type of snow. During a day trip in the mountains you might start on soft, wet snow which compacts in the cleats of your boots forming blocks of ice, wander into an area of deepening powder through which you wade literally waist deep, then come to a slope where a thin crust of windslab supports your weight for a few steps before giving way and plunging you knee deep into the powder below. You can have snow the consistency of modelling clay in which you can kick solid steps, and snow which has consolidated to such an extent that a heavy kick will only make a slight indentation.

Step kicking is an art. Although hard work, it should appear virtually effortless, and good technique will result in less energy being used — an important consideration when on a strenuous outing. The basic technique is to hold the body upright and swing your leg from the knee letting momentum and weight do most of the work. Try to get into a slow but steady rhythm, and aim to create positive steps angled slightly downwards into the slope. As with all other steep ground work, resist the temptation to lean in.

When **ascending directly,** you should aim to create steps which will accommodate at least the front third of your boot — even if you have to kick several times to achieve this. Hold you ice axe in your preferred hand with the pick pointing backwards, and drive the shaft deeply into the snow so that it can be used for support and to assist balance. Only move the axe up once both feet are secure.

When **traversing,** ascending diagonally or **zig-zagging,** kick horizontal steps with the side of your boots using a sawing action. Take care when moving up, especially when moving the upslope leg. You are most secure when the leg closest to the slope is in front. Always hold your ice axe in the upslope hand, driving the shaft vertically into the slope above you. When zig-zagging, you should think carefully about where and how you are going to change direction. One method is to kick two good direct steps, change the ice axe to the other hand, then continue. Alternatively you could support yourself with both hands on a well-placed ice axe and turn on your upslope foot. The most simple and straightforward method is to kick a single large step which is big enough to accommodate both feet.

When **descending,** the best approach is the **plunge step.** Face away from the slope and use all your body weight to plunge the heel vertically into the snow below you. Keep your toes up and heels down to avoid the chance of rocking forward out of the step and make each move a positive one. Hold your ice axe in your preferred hand and, as in ascent, drive the shaft vertically into the snow to give support. On steeper slopes where you find the exposure intimidating, face into the slope and kick direct steps as described above. Make sure each step is a positive one before committing your weight to it, and resist the temptation to try and drop too far with each step. Every movement should be comfortable and controlled.

If the snow becomes too hard to kick positive steps, you are entering the realm of serious mountaineering and it will be necessary either to cut steps with your axe or to use crampons. Here we come to a problem, for neither step cutting nor crampon technique can be learned safely from a book. They need to be demonstrated practically rather than described theoretically, and then practised in a safe, controlled and preferably supervised environment before being put to use on the hill. Because of this, I do not intend to discuss these techniques in any detail.

With regard to **step cutting,** even the simple and extremely useful **slash step** requires a long apprenticeship if it is to be cut safely and effectively in any situation. If you want to learn how to cut steps safely I advise you either to ask an experienced climber to teach you or, better still, to go on a winter skills course run by an MIC or UIAGM qualified instructor.

With regard to **crampon technique,** it is fair to say that whilst crampons have largely replaced the need to cut steps, they should not be seen as having made step cutting totally redundant. In any case, crampons bring with them their own set of hazards. For example, many types of snow will **ball-up** under the crampons, compacting into ice and eventually reducing the depth of spike available to pierce the ground and give secure footing. There is obviously a significant difference between walking on metal spikes and blocks of ice! Additionally, they can slip unexpectedly on verglas or thin ice or when moving over rock steps concealed beneath a thin layer of snow, and unless you adopt a wide-footed gait, the front points have a nasty habit of catching in gaiters and tripping you up. Although the basic foot placement techniques are similar to those mentioned for summer conditions (i.e. feet kept flat to the slope so that all the crampon points bite into the surface), there are several other considerations, especially when changing direction on steep ground. As with step cutting, if you wish to learn how to use crampons safely and effectively, get an experienced climber to show you or enrol on a winter skills course run by an MIC or UIAGM qualified instructor.

Finally, if you are going to venture into the hills in winter conditions you should have a basic understanding of avalanche conditions (page 154) and cornices (page 152), and should know something about the effects of cold weather on the body (section 9). Because winter days are so short, it is also advisable to have some idea of winter survival techniques, particularly with regard to emergency shelters (section 10).

Ice axe arrest

The one ice axe technique which I must mention in a little more detail is that of **self arrest,** otherwise known as the **ice-axe brake.** This is a technique which, if used correctly, can prevent a simple slip from becoming something far more serious. It is not an easy technique to master, and **needs to be practised at the start of every winter season.** You should be able to apply it quickly and effectively from any position; indeed speed and effectiveness are critical factors for the longer you take to apply the brake, the faster you

Figure 14: Basic self arrest position (viewed from underneath

will be travelling, and the more difficult it will be for you to stop. Additionally, although many people practice by sliding feet first on their stomachs, this is the easiest position from which to use the technique and, in practice, you are more likely to be travelling headfirst.

In order to use the technique quickly in the event of a slip, you need to carry and hold your ice axe in the correct way. As soon as you reach the snowline, remove the ice axe from the carrying straps on your rucksack and, unless you intend to use it straight away, slide it diagonally down the back of your rucksack so that it is held in place by a shoulder strap. From this position it can easily be retrieved using one hand.

When **carrying the ice axe** in your hand, be aware of other people. If you must carry horizontally by the shaft, make sure the pick is pointing downwards and try not to gouge your companions with the spike. It is far better to hold it by the head with the shaft in a vertical position and the pick pointing backwards. Curve your

Always hold the ice axe in the upslope hand

thumb around and under the back of the adze, and point your index finger down the shaft. Although this may not be as comfortable as some other methods, it is the optimum position from which to apply the self-arrest technique. On sloping ground, always hold your axe in the **upslope hand** where it can be used to aid balance and give support.

In simple terms, the principle of the ice axe arrest is to use the

In icy conditions as here, crampons will make walking far quicker and more secure. Learn how to use them from an experienced friend or suitably qualified instructor

pick as a friction brake, digging it progressively harder into the snow with your body weight. In order to do this effectively, you need to be in a feet first, face down position with one hand firmly grasping the head of the axe, and with the adze tucked firmly into the hollow just below your collarbone. The shaft should be brought across your chest so that the other hand can hold the end of the shaft and cover the spike to prevent it sticking into either the snow or you. Your legs should be kept apart to give some stability, with your feet lifted well clear of the snow (figure 14). Keeping the feet up is especially important if you are wearing crampons for otherwise the front points can catch and flip you into a backward somersault. Having said this, the feet can be used as an aid to braking just before you come to rest.

The best way to apply the brake is to pull down on the head of the ice axe, at the same time pulling the spike away from the slope. This will have the effect of rolling you over the adze so that the maximum amount of body weight can be applied. Tucking your elbows into your sides and arching your back will enhance the effect still further. Do not lift your head as this will lift your shoulders — indeed, the brim of your helmet (recommended when practising even if you decide not to wear one when winter walking) should be so close to the slope that there should be snow inside your helmet when you stop! It is vitally important that weight is applied to the pick gradually or else it will catch suddenly and could be ripped out of your grasp. If you are a little too enthusiastic and the adze is pulled from its correct position in the hollow below your collarbone you may have difficulty in relocating it simply by pulling up on it. If this happens, lift your head so as to release the weight, relocate the adze in the correct position and then, and only then, try again.

What I have described so far is the **basic position** for the ice axe arrest — the simplest of all the scenarios. You may have to remember all this whilst plummeting down an icy slope with increasing velocity towards an awesome drop (or simply a pile of boulders)! In all probability you will be scared out of your wits. You will, no doubt, therefore appreciate that this most basic of winter skills requires practice, more practice, and yet more practice. Moreover, in all probability you will not be sliding feet first on your front; you may well be travelling head first, possibly on your back, or even rolling or somersaulting, so what I have described becomes the final stage in a sequence of manoeuvres. No matter which way you are falling, you must get yourself into this basic position and grip the ice axe correctly (one hand over the head with the pick away from you and the adze located under your collarbone, shaft across your body, and the other hand holding the base of the shaft and covering the spike). If you are rolling or somersaulting you must also try to stabilise yourself by spreading your arms and legs as wide as possible — not easy and possibly very painful.

If you are sliding head first, face down, gently push the pick into the snow as far to one side of you as possible so you swing round into a feet first position. If you are sliding on your back, get onto your front by rolling towards the hand holding the head of the ice axe. Never roll towards the hand holding the spike or else the pick will bite suddenly and the axe could be torn from your grasp. If you are falling headfirst on your back you have serious problems. The best manoeuvre involves holding the ice axe across your body and pushing the pick into the snow by your side. As you begin to spin around, roll your body around the shaft to end up in the right position. This all sounds complicated because is it complicated.

When practising these manoeuvres, do so from all positions and with the axe held in both hands. Always wear a helmet and use a high concave slope with a good, obstacle-free run-out at the bottom.

River crossings

The last skill I wish to mention is that of crossing rivers. I would hazard a guess that most people seriously underestimate the force of even shallow moving water and, whilst fording rivers is not a common cause of mountain fatalities, people do drown every year. The best advice on fording a swollen river is don't; the best method of crossing a river is via a bridge!

If crossing is imperative and there is no bridge, consult your map in case there is an area within striking distance where the stream splits into several channels. If not, head upstream looking for a suitable crossing point. Sites to avoid are those near bends or rapids, and the water at a wide crossing is generally shallower and slower (and thus safer) than at a narrow crossing. Wherever you cross, beware of underwater hazards such as submerged rocks, and flood debris. Walk along the bank in both up- and downstream directions so that you can view the crossing point from as many angles as possible. If you can also get a high vantage point, so much the better.

Before attempting a crossing, remove your socks and either roll up your trouser legs or remove them completely. Not only will this prevent you from having to continue with saturated clothing, but it will also reduce the potential drag as any material will increase the resistance and therefore make you more likely to be swept off your feet. You should, however, wear your boots. You should also close your rucksack tightly so as to trap air inside it. Although the buoyancy in a rucksack can be a lifesaver in an emergency, it can also cause grave problems, for if it is strapped to your back and you slip, it will tend to force you face down in the water. You should therefore undo any waist or chest straps and loosen the shoulder

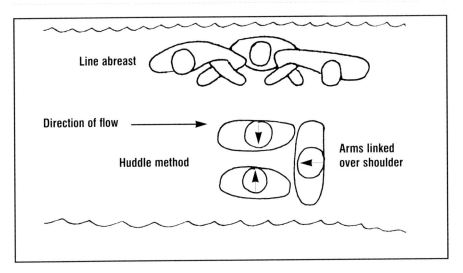

Figure 15: Group river crossing

straps so you can remove it quickly if necessary.

When crossing, keep your feet well apart and take short, shuffling steps, always ensuring that one foot is firmly placed before moving the other. Do not cross your legs as this could throw you off balance. Face upstream so you get warning of any flood debris coming towards you and so there is no danger of the current buckling your knees. The safest crossing techniques involve teamwork, either using the **linked-arms method** or the **huddle method** (figure 15). **Solo crossing** is not recommended, but if it is necessary try to present a diagonal profile to the river and, if possible, support yourself on the upstream side with whatever is available (walking

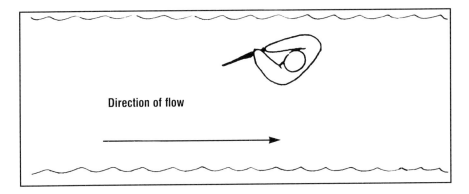

Figure 16: Solo river crossing method

stick, ice axe, tent pole, etc.) (figure 16). The use of ropes is not recommended because if you are taken downstream when held on a rope, the force of water will drag you under.

If you are unlucky enough to be swept off your feet, try to hold your rucksack across your chest and manoeuvre yourself into a position whereby you are heading downstream feet first. This will not be easy, but it is extremely important as the most common causes of drowning in this situation are hitting boulders headfirst and getting trapped by a **heel hook**. This is where a person floating headfirst downstream on their back gets an ankle trapped between two rocks. If this happens the pressure of water flowing against the body pushes it under and makes it virtually impossible to escape. Do not fight the current (it will always win!). Go with it taking the occasional stroke in an attempt to reach slower or shallower water near a bank or along the inside of any bend.

4 CAMPING EQUIPMENT

There is something elegantly primitive and totally captivating about camping beside a clear mountain tarn surrounded by gaunt crags, miles away from the nearest civilisation. If the weather is pleasant it can be a source of endless delight, but if the weather is malevolent it can turn into an unmitigated disaster with potentially serious consequences. Having said this, with the right equipment and skills, even bad-weather camping can be comfortable and satisfying.

In this section we are going to look at a range of basic camping equipment. As elsewhere in this book I have deliberately steered away from mentioning specific models, concentrating instead on basic design considerations. The outdoor market is so big nowadays that new models and innovations come and go with a speed which is nothing short of confusing. I work on the basis that as long as you know what you want from your equipment and what it needs to do then you should be able to visit your local friendly gear shop and make an educated choice when confronted with four or five things which all purport to do the same thing better than each other. Forget about the marketing hype and look at the basic design and quality of the materials and workmanship.

Space precludes the inclusion of detailed information. If you want to do any serious wild camping, you should know a little more about the equipment than I am able to give here. Suitable reference sources are to be found in the list of further reading at the back of this book.

Tents

Personal preference and budgetary considerations aside, a tent suitable for use in the mountains needs to fulfil a number of functions. It should, for example, be light in weight and low in bulk, weatherproof and stable, and simple to pitch, strike and pack. Unfortunately, in practice many of these are mutually exclusive, so in essence there is no such thing as the ideal mountain tent.

Since the advent of flexible tent poles, there has been something of a revolution in tent design. In addition to the standard ridge tent, there are now several variations on the theme plus wedge tents, tunnel tents, single hoop tents, crossover dome tents, and geodesic dome tents. Luckily, there is a simple way through this maze of shape as, in essence, there are still only three basic designs: ridge tents, tunnel tents, and dome tents. There are also a few hybrid designs in which manufacturers have tried to make use of the best features of each basic shape. The main features, advantages and disadvantages of each are illustrated in figure 17.

The main function of a mountain tent is to give shelter from the elements. To do this effectively it should be of a **double skin construction**. This means there should be an inner compartment which is totally enclosed by an outer layer (the **flysheet**) which reaches to the ground on all sides thus protecting both the walls and doors of the inner tent. The inner tent should have a **sewn-in groundsheet** made from a durable and totally waterproof material, and this should extend up the walls for at least 10cms and form a lip at the doors. The gap between the inner compartment and the flysheet is extremely important. Not only does it provide a degree of insulation but, more important, it plays an essential role in weatherproofing. It goes without saying that the quality of both materials and workmanship should be of the highest standard. All seams should be **lap-felled** (where the two layers of fabric are brought together then wrapped around each other before being sewn), and secured by a **lock stitch** rather than a chain stitch which can run if a fault develops. The quality of the stitching is crucial, especially at stress areas such as pegging points, pole sleeves, apexes, ends of zips, and seam junctions. Major stress areas should be reinforced in some way such as by **bar tacking.**

The flysheet should preferably be made from a totally waterproof fabric, although this is not absolutely essential, and should be big enough to give sufficient space in which to store gear and, ideally, to cook during inclement weather. In theory, if water does

TYPE	STABILITY	SPACE-WEIGHT RATIO	COOKING + STORAGE
Standard Ridge	Excellent	Poor	Fair
Sloping Ridge	Fair	Fair	Poor
Transverse Ridge	Fair	Good	Good
Wedge	Poor	Fair	Fair
Single Hoop	Good	Good	Poor
Tunnel	Poor	Fair	Poor
Crossover Dome	Good	Good	Good
Geodesic Dome	Good	Good	Good

Figure 17: Generalised comparison of tent design advantages and disadvantages

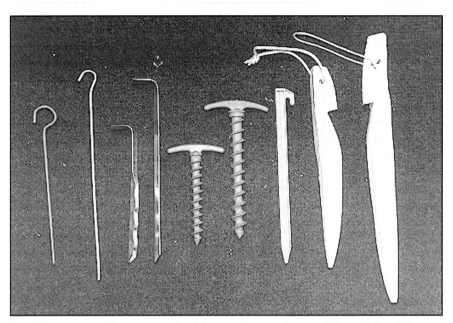

The right pegs are as important as the right tent. A range of pegs will be useful as different pegs hold better in different types of ground

penetrate the flysheet fabric it will run down the inside surface and will therefore not reach the inner compartment. This is fine so long as the separation between the inner and outer layers is maintained. If the two layers touch then inevitably water will penetrate the inner. Although at first glance it appears that the simplest way around this problem is to use a totally waterproof material for both the inner compartment and flysheet, in practice this causes more problems than it solves. In the same way that condensation can be a problem with totally waterproof shell garments, it can also be a problem in totally waterproof tents. What is needed, therefore, is an inner compartment made from a permeable fabric which will allow water vapour to pass through and condense on the inside surface of the flysheet. Here again, maintaining the separation between the inner and outer layers is critical. This important gap between the two layers is easier to maintain in some designs than in others.

Even in the best designed tents, condensation can occur within the inner tent in certain weather conditions, especially if you are forced to cook inside the tent. **Mesh panels** can help to alleviate this problem as can **two way zips** which allow you to open the door from the top to create ventilation.

The way in which the tent is pitched will obviously vary from model to model. There are certain things worth bearing in mind. For example, if you find it difficult to pitch the tent on a calm day in a perfect valley site, think what it will be like trying to do the same thing in a howling gale at a less than perfect high camp. To a degree, the simpler the design, the better, and ease of pitching and striking is an important factor. Moreover, during camping trips of two or more nights, it is a distinct advantage to have a tent which pitches **outer first**. If the weather is inclement, a tent of this design will allow you to do the vast majority of your packing and unpacking under cover of the flysheet.

The only **single-skin tents** suitable for use in the mountains are those made of a breathable waterproof material such as Goretex. Although these are obviously light and compact, in practice these do not work too well in temperate climates unless you are very large and they are very small. This is simply because it is difficult to maintain a climate inside the tent which is warmer and more moist than the climate outside the tent. Having said this, it would be remiss of me not to mention **bivibags**. These breathable-fabric sacks work extremely well and, whilst less comfortable and convenient than a tent, may be of interest to those who enjoy a Spartan existence. Some are available with flexible hoops which make them similar to a very small tunnel tent. There is, of course, no room to store gear, and no space in which to cook in inclement weather. You simply put your sleeping bag inside the bivibag, get in, and zip everything up!

The **poles** and pegs supplied with your tent can vary tremendously in quality. Generally speaking, hollow alloy poles are better than glassfibre poles although both have disadvantages. Alloy poles are prone to kinking whilst the cheaper glassfibre poles can shatter and get split ends. Poles of composite materials (including carbon fibre) are also available and these are generally very good.

Few tent manufacturers supply a really good selection of **pegs**. Indeed, many seem to supply only a handful of steel skewers. Some pegs stick better in different terrain than others, so it is worth taking a selection of pegs including alloy skewers as general purpose pegs, plus a handful of angles, maybe one or two screw-in types, and a couple of storm anchors. A good mountaineering retailer will be able to show you a wide range and explain the pros and cons of each type.

Finally, a good mountain tent is not going to be cheap, so it pays to see a range of models before you choose. When making the choice, ask yourself a number of questions such as how much room will you need, will you be using the tent for brief, overnight stops or as a base for longer stays, at what time of year will it be used, etc. Beware of models labelled "mountain tent" — although there are some excellent tents labelled thus they are often designed for use at high altitude in dry, cold conditions and are therefore totally unsuitable for our wet and windy mountains.

Sleeping bags

As with your tent, your sleeping bag should be light, compact and of good quality. Its main purpose is to keep you warm by preventing heat loss, the efficiency with which it can do this being quoted in terms of a **season rating**, this going from two season to five season! A two season bag is suitable for valley use in summer conditions; a three season bag for use in all but winter conditions except in valley sites; a four season bag for year round use except in extreme conditions such as those often encountered during high level camps in winter; a five season bag for high level camps in all conditions.

Both the construction of the sleeping bag and the type and quality of the insulation have a bearing on the season rating. There are two main types of insulation, these being natural materials and synthetic materials.

Most of the **synthetic fillings** suitable for use in the mountains will be based on some form of hollow polyester fibres, the best of these being only slightly inferior to the better natural fillings. In some sleeping bags, these fibres will have been formed into layers (known as **batts**) held together with resin. In other the fibres remain loose in which case the sleeping bag will be described as being **blown filled**. The use of terylene fibres in sleeping bags which are to be used in the mountains is not recommend-

Simple quilting   (potential cold spots along all the seams)

Double quilting

Box wall construction

Overlapping tube construction

Slant wall construction

Figure 18: Baffle designs in sleeping bags

There is a vast range of sleeping bags available nowadays

ed as it is too heavy and bulky. There are two main advantages to be gained by using synthetic fillings. Firstly, unlike natural fillings, they retain much of their insulation qualities when wet. Secondly, they are cheaper! On the negative side, sleeping bags with a synthetic fillings are generally heavier and more bulky than similarly rated bags with natural fillings, even though this difference may be minimal in the more expensive models. Additionally, they do not transmit water vapour as well as natural fillings (particularly those using batts), and this tends to make them feel sticky.

Natural fillings suitable for use in the mountains include down and down-feather mixes. Kapok is totally unsuitable. Pure eiderdown is extremely rare; most modern bags use either goose down, duck down, or down and down/feather mixes. The biggest advantages of using natural fillings is that they result in a sleeping bag which is lighter and more compact than a similarly rated bag filled with a synthetic material. They also have a warm, luxurious feel which tends to be lacking in bags using synthetic fillings. Apart from the price, the biggest disadvantage is that they loose most if not all of their insulation qualities if they get wet. For this reason it is **imperative that these sleeping bags are kept dry.** Using waterproof fabrics in the construction of the bag is not the answer due to the problems of condensation (see pages 22 and 86), and although bags using breathable waterproof fabrics are available, you will probably need a very friendly bank manager if you wish to buy one.

Perhaps the simplest way to put the differences between synthetic and natural fillings into perspective is to say that, warmth for warmth, the best quality synthetic filled bags are slightly heavier, fractionally more bulky, but less expensive than their natural-filled counterparts.

The **construction** of the sleeping bag is also of the utmost importance, particularly with natural fillings and blown filled synthetics. A sleeping bag is basically two sacks of material with insulation between them, and if the gap between the outer and inner sacks is not compartmentalised in some way, the fillings move about causing cold spots. Although simple quilting will stop this movement, there will be **cold spots** along all the seams. What is needed, therefore, is some form of **baffle** between the inner and outer sack, the most common designs being shown in figure 18. Heat loss can also occur from the foot of the bag, and the baffling should continue in this area in the form of a **box-foot**.

The **shape** of the bag is really a matter of personal preference, although some form of hood can of great benefit on cold nights. The most important consideration is that of comfort. Whatever the shape, there should be either some form of shoulder baffle or some method by which the bag can be tightened above the shoulders to prevent heat loss. **Zips** are, again, very much a matter of personal preference although they can make a high season rating bag more adaptable as they can be used for ventilation during warmer weather. If you choose a sleeping bag with zips, make sure they are well baffled.

The **material** from which the inner and outer sacks are made has a vital role. With natural and blown-filled synthetic materials in particular, it should be of a tight weave **(down-proof)** so that it does not allow any of the filling to escape. It should also be durable, rot-proof, light in weight and low in bulk. Additionally, because the human body loses a considerable amount of water during sleep, it needs to be permeable. Nylon fabrics are commonly used, although many people prefer a sleeping bag with a slightly heavier and bulkier polycotton inner as this tends to be more comfortable.

Choosing a sleeping bag suitable for all seasons can be difficult — those bags suitable for early autumn are not good enough for winter use, whilst those suitable for winter use are too hot for late spring. One answer lies in the use of **sleeping bag liners** made from polypropylene (i.e. thermal underwear fabric) or fibre-pile. These often have a season rating of one, and can therefore transform a three season bag into a four season bag, and so on. These liners are useful in their own right as items of emergency equipment. Being reasonably light in weight and low in bulk they can easily be carried in your rucksack during spring and autumn where they may be extremely useful in the event of benightment or an emergency. However, they should not be seen as a substitute for a conventional sleeping bag during serious trips in winter conditions.

Sleepmats

Like the thermal layers of clothing, the insulation in sleeping bags works by trapping air. When you lie down, you compress the filling reducing the amount of air which can be trapped and thus reducing the efficiency of the insulation. No matter how good your sleeping bag, you will therefore need a sleepmat to insulate you from the cold ground.

A standard sleepmat consists of a rectangle of **closed cell foam** which is placed between the sleeping bag and the groundsheet providing a cushioning effect in addition to extra insulation. Although these are widely available, their price varies considerably so it is worth shopping around. Make sure the foam is closed-cell not open cell — the latter works like a sponge and will absorb and trap water. Sleepmats are available in a range of different thickness and are sometimes given a season rating similar to sleeping bags. Also available are **inflatable sleepmats** which, although heavier and slightly more bulky (and a lot more expensive), give far more comfort and insulation.

Finally, if your tent has a thin groundsheet, or if you camp on a regular basis, you might like to consider buying a **groundsheet liner**. This is basically like thin (3mm) sleepmat, again of closed cell foam, and is usually sold off the roll. Unlike sleepmats, however, it is placed beneath the groundsheet where it gives protection in addition to extra cushioning and insulation. In all but the warmest conditions, however, it should not be used as a substitute for a sleepmat but as an enhancement.

Stoves

An efficient lightweight stove is an essential item of kit when you are camping maybe several long and difficult miles from the nearest habitation. As with most other types of modern equipment, at first glance there is a bewildering range of stoves available using a variety of different fuels. However, all these can be divided into three broad categories, these being gas stoves, methylated spirits stoves and pressure stoves. It is also possible to by light and compact stoves using **solid fuel** tablets or a form of **jelly fuel**. Whilst these may have a use as items of emergency equipment (see section 10), they are unsuitable for use as main source of cooking heat when camping and should not be regarded as alternatives to the types of stove described below.

Gas stoves are available in an ever-growing range of shapes and sizes including models which come complete with their own pan in which they can be stored when being carried. There are two

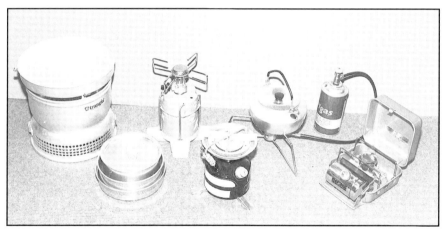

Camping stoves come in a variety of types. Each have inherent advantages and disadvantages

main types: those using resealable cartridges, and those using non-resealable cartridges. Of the two, those using resealable cartridges are arguably more convenient as they can be dismantled and carried more easily in the rucksack. Many of these stoves are highly efficient and, of course, they are very convenient. All you have to do is turn on the gas and light them (some will even do this for you!), so they are superb for making a quick brew in the early hours of the morning. However, they do have several disadvantages. Even if you disregard the fact that they are very expensive to run, the cylinders may not be widely available in remote areas, and you will soon find out that they tend to burn with an infuriatingly low flame once the cylinder is less than about half full. A half full cylinder, of course, takes up the same amount of space as a full one, and if you are away for some time, you may have to carry quite a few (as well as bringing the empties back). Even if you use a burner shield and a new cylinder, they hate draughts and tend to blow out at the slightest provocation. This is particularly apparent in cold conditions. Indeed, **butane** (the most common gas) is impossible to light in temperatures of below about freezing, and although it is possible to buy cylinders filled with **propane** which will burn at lower temperatures, it is fair to say that gas stoves and cold weather do not mix. One way around this problem is to sleep with your stove or its cylinders. Whilst this does work you should be aware of the danger of leaking gas. Not only could this suffocate you, but because the gas is heavier than air it can lie in a layer trapped within the tray of the sewn-in groundsheet just waiting for you to strike a match to make a morning brew.

Modern **methylated spirits** stoves bear little resemblance to the old fashioned picnic stoves. Indeed, the better models are cheap to run and surprisingly efficient, are quick and easy to light and give full heat within seconds. The most common models come as units complete with nesting pans (and even a kettle if you want one) which means that they represent excellent value for money, particularly for first time buyers. They are also the only type of stove available which thrives on draughts. On the negative side, although the fuel is reasonably easy to get it is heavy and fast-burning, so not only do you have to refill the stove at regular intervals, you also have to carry a fair amount of fuel with you. Additionally, the flame control on most models is fairly basic to say the least, the adjustments being full heat, simmer or off. Methylated spirits will seek out any weakness in the container in which it is carried, so use a proper fuel bottle with a well-threaded, deep neck (see below) and make sure the seal is in good condition. Although any spilled fuel will evaporate fairly quickly, refuelling should be done with the utmost care as the fuel burns with an almost invisible flame and accidents have occurred when people have tried to refill stoves which were still lit. To minimise the danger of this, refill your stove each time you come to use it and, whenever possible, allow it to cool down before attempting to refill it. Finally, meths will make the bottom of your pans sooty. Although this can be avoided by adding a small amount of water to the fuel, a blackened pot will absorb heat better than a shiny silver one so is therefore more efficient.

Pressure stoves come in a wide variety of models and types, some burning paraffin, some burning petrol, and some purporting to burn anything from sump oil to vodka. Generally speaking they are extremely efficient, very economical, and most have a stupendous heat output. The purr of a pressure stove is a comforting sound, especially if you are trapped in your tent during a storm! The fuel, either petrol or paraffin, is usually simple to obtain even in remote areas, but you must remember that these fuels are not interchangeable — a paraffin stove filled with petrol will behave like an incendiary bomb! On the negative side, most of these stoves are heavy, bulky and expensive to buy. There are exceptions to this, the most obvious being those stoves which come simply as a burner and tube with a pump of the end. These are designed to be used in conjunction with a fuel bottle, the pump being used to pressurise it. It must be noted, too, that pressure stoves are not the most convenient of stoves, for all but a very few require **priming** or **pre-heating.** Not only can this be frustrating if all you want is a quick brew, but it is also potentially extremely dangerous for if not done correctly it can result in a **flare** — in which a fountain of burning liquid sprays out of the burner.

Of the two major fuels, **paraffin** is the cheaper and the least affected by ambient temperature. Indeed, paraffin pressure stoves usually include a pump so they can be pressurised by hand, and these stoves will work well whilst sitting directly on snow. However, although the vapour is not flammable, if you spill paraffin it takes ages to evaporate and makes everything near it stink for weeks afterwards. Additionally, you will need to carry either meths or solid fuel tablets in order to prime the stove correctly. **Petrol,** on the other hand, will evaporate quickly, but please note that any spillage can be extremely dangerous because the vapour is explosively flammable. Only use unleaded fuel (or the more expensive camp-stove fuel) or else the jet of the burner will become blocked with monotonous regularity. Additionally, the petrol can, with care, be used to prime the stove, although many manufacturers recommend the use of a **priming paste** instead. Paste is certainly safer. On the down side, many petrol stoves are self-pressurising and can be difficult to light in cold conditions. Admittedly, some models have optional pumps which replace the filler cap, but even when these are used you need to insulate the stove from the ground in some way.

Although **multi-fuel stoves** would seem to solve many of the problems associated with fuel availability in remote areas, they vary widely in performance. Although there are some very efficient models available, others are quite complex and require setting up before each use. If choosing one of these stoves you would be wise to play with in the shop and to read the instructions before parting with any cash.

If using anything other than a gas stove, you will need something in which to carry the liquid fuel. This should be specifically designed for carrying fuel (not an old water flask). The most common **fuel bottles** are made of **aluminium** and have well-threaded, deep necks and plastic stoppers with replaceable sealing washers. The efficiency of the seal is very important, especially if carrying methylated spirits which will seek out any weakness and exploit it. Never use your fuel bottle for water nor your water flask for fuel; this could lead to obvious contamination and confusion.

Particularly with pressure stoves, it is important that you get to know how they work before you use them in the wild. If you have never used a pressure stove before, I advise you to light it in your back garden first, just in case you get a flare. Once you are happy with the lighting technique, try cooking yourself a meal on it in the comfort of your own kitchen, and then imagine what it would be like doing the same in the cramped confines of your tent during stormy weather.

Finally, it is of little use taking a stove if you have nothing with which to light it. Even if your stove is described as having automatic ignition you would be wise to carry something to use in the event that the technology fails. Non-safety **matches** are useful, especially if you dip them in varnish to make them waterproof, and a **cigarette lighter** can be worth its weight in gold, especially if it is a petrol lighter and you have a petrol stove. If you carry a lighter, you must keep it dry or the flint will refuse to spark. **Lifeboat matches** (which are both waterproof and windproof) are a useful standby for those really wet and windy nights.

Pans and utensils

If you have a methylated spirits stove, there will be no need for you to buy any pans as they are usually an integral part of the stove. However, with pressure and most gas stoves, you will need something in which to cook your food. In general terms you have a choice between mess tins, nesting billy cans (or dixies), and cooksets.

Of the three types, **cooksets** are the most convenient, the better ones containing a couple of deep pans with lids, a frying pan and, perhaps, a bowl and a universal handle. Although aluminium is the usual material, slightly heavier but more durable stainless steel cooksets are available in which one or more of the pans have copper bases. These transmit the heat far more evenly and are therefore arguably more efficient.

When it comes to eating your food, do you really need crockery? Why not eat straight from the pan? Alternatively, take a deep, bendy plastic plate which will double as a bowl. Plastic cutlery has the nasty habit of breaking at the most inappropriate of times, standard kitchen cutlery tends to be heavy, so the best option is a **cutlery clip-set** designed for camping. These are usually made from lightweight alloy and are reasonably cheap and durable.

If you are carrying a vacuum flask you can use the attached cup for your drinks. If not, or if you want something with more capacity, a bendy plastic mug is the best. Avoid metal mugs — it is virtually impossible to drink the contents whilst they are hot because the hot metal burns your lips.

Lighting

If you intend to camp, some form of lighting is essential. In its simplest form this will be a candle, stubby **long-life candles** being the most convenient. These give out a surprising amount of light and heat, especially if used in conjunction with a reflector made of silver foil. If using candles inside the tent, take great care and make sure they are kept well away from the fabric. Placing them on an upturned pan is a good ploy as they will usually go out if accidentally knocked over. Alternatively, there are some excellent lightweight **candle lanterns** available which fold down when not in use. One useful aspect of candles is that they give off heat as well as light.

A torch is obviously useful, but make sure it is robust and waterproof. Most convenient is a headtorch, those with the battery container as an integral part of the headband being the most practical. Remember to keep batteries separate from the torch when not in use, and take one or more spare batteries (and possibly spare bulbs) with you.

Rucksacks

Although it is possible to buy excellent gas and pressure lanterns, these are generally too heavy and bulky to be of much use during short trips to the wilds. However, they can be worth their weight in gold during extended trips at base camps.

All of the features needed in a good daysack (see section 2) should also be present in a good backpacking rucksack. It should, for example, be simple in design and construction, and shaped in such a way that the load is carried high on your back. However,

The fit of a larger rucksack is of vital importance

because you will need extra space and will be carrying a lot more weight, there are certain additional requirements.

A modern backpacking rucksack is a scientifically designed piece of equipment which should be chosen with as much care as your boots. Depending on the type of camping you intend to do, it should have a capacity of between 55 and 75 litres. Unless you are off on a mammoth expedition, if you feel you need a rucksack larger than this it is probably worth checking whether your packing technique could be improved or whether all the items you are carrying are essential.

Many backpacking rucksacks are split horizontally into two **compartments,** the upper one being accessible through the top flap, the lower one via a zipped opening about two thirds of the way down the body of the sack. This zip should preferably be two-way and well baffled. The two compartments are often separated by a baffle. It is useful if this is zipped (and therefore removable) or only attached at the front and the back so that long items (such as tent poles) can be slid down the length of the rucksack on either side. In addition, many models are available with side pockets (some of which are removable), and these can be useful for carrying things needed en route or keeping items such as liquid fuels well away from other objects which they could contaminate.

The most important difference between a daysack and a backpacking rucksack is the way in which the load is carried. In a daysack it is the shoulder straps which do most of the work; in a good backpacking rucksack, however, there should be some form of **load-bearing hip belt** which enables most of the weight to be transferred directly onto the pelvic girdle. In order for it to do this efficiently, your rucksack should fit you correctly. Not only should the back of the rucksack mirror the curvature of your spine, but also the hip belt should be in the correct position, fitting snugly across the top of your hips, not around your waist. Although some harness systems are adjustable, many rucksacks come in a variety of lengths and you should make sure you get one which fits you correctly. The main purpose of the **shoulder straps** is to prevent the rucksack from slipping backwards. Because they are worn fairly loose there are times when they can slip off your shoulders, so some rucksacks come with a short **chest-strap** which holds the shoulder straps in the correct position.

The body-hugging fit of the rucksack means that there can be problems with a build-up of condensation across your back. Some manufacturers have gone to great lengths to try and solve this problem, with chevron shaped panels and air vents. It has to be said that these are often less than successful, and if you go camping in warm weather on a regular basis, a damp back is something you will soon get used to.

Useful items

The equipment described so far represents the essentials — with it and your standard hill walking kit, you can exist in the mountains in relative comfort. However, most experienced campers take a few extra bits and pieces. These include food containers (made of plastic — never of glass), water purification tablets (sterilising water by boiling takes at least 20 minutes and uses precious fuel), collapsible water carriers, paracord, toilet paper, sharp knife preferably with a tin opener, soap-filled scouring pad, small sponge, jeycloth, toothbrush & comb, silver foil, plastic bags, inflatable pillow, basic tent repair kit, etc. Only you can decide what extra items you need; only you can justify the extra weight or the space they take up. Most people take far too much on their first few trips. Make a list of what you take and cross off anything you do not use. Do not take these the next time you go unless, of course, they would be useful or essential in an emergency.

5 CAMPING SKILLS

Although many people think of camping as "roughing it", the experience need not be an uncomfortable one. However, even if you have the very best equipment, you will still need certain skills if you are to get the most out of your stay. It is not the possession of the equipment that keeps you safe and comfortable so much as the knowledge of what to do with it and how to use it best. The following should give you some pointers.

Sites

Assuming you have the basic minimum of good quality equipment as outlined in the last section, the most important consideration is choice of site. Choose this with care. Try to find somewhere which is reasonably level, and place the groundsheet on a flat area where there are no lumps such as tussocks or protruding rocks which will make sleeping uncomfortable. The site should be well drained, but should be within easy walking distance of a water supply. Sites near streams and lakes can be idyllic, but they may also be cold, noisy, and damp, and at certain times of year you will be plagued by insects. Bear in mind, too, that mountain streams can rise very quickly during rain; your welcoming brookside site will not seem so pleasant if it becomes covered with water in the early hours.

The most important factor of all is that of **shelter,** particularly from the wind. Because weather conditions can change with frightening speed in the mountains, always choose your site with the worst in mind, and pitch your tent with its back facing the direction of the prevailing wind. It is far easier to secure your camp from the outset than it is to try and adjust everything in the pitch black in the middle of an unexpected storm. Think about the type of shelter you want — pitching your tent in the shelter of a large cliff may not seem like such a good idea if a rock lands on you in the early hours. Similarly, pitching beneath trees can be a frightening experience during a storm.

Camping **in winter** is a whole different ball game, and you should have a reasonable amount of summer camping experience before deciding to camp in the mountains in winter conditions. Choosing a sheltered site is critical, but beware the problems of drifting snow which always builds up on the leeside. If there is

A well-chosen, sheltered site is especially important in winter conditions

snow on the ground, stamp out an area slightly larger than the tent before pitching, and bank consolidated snow against the base of the flysheet to help prevent spindrift collecting in the gap between the flysheet and the inner tent. Remember that snow is very heavy, and can easily collapse a tent if allowed to build up on the flysheet. Some tents are more prone to this than others.

Cooking

The vast majority of camping injuries are burns and scalds. Take extra care when you are cooking and try to work methodically. Lay everything out beforehand so that everything you want is close to hand. If you are going to be at the site for any length of time, it is a good idea to prepare a cooking area where you can place your stove on a solid, flat surface. Cook outside whenever possible, and always hold the pan when adjusting the flame or stirring the contents. If you are forced to cook inside the tent because of awful weather, appoint one person to do the cooking, place the stove on a solid, non-flammable base near the doorway and keep everyone else well away, either in the back of the tent or, if there are a few of you, in another tent. Avoid putting hot pans directly on the groundsheet unless you want neat round holes! If your tent has space for you to cook beneath the flysheet, so much the better. Wherever you cook, keep the stove well away from any fabric or flammable material, and take extra care when refuelling. Always use lids as these save heat (and therefore fuel), and always boil slightly more water than you think you will need.

The quality of the food you produce can make or break a camping trip for you will undoubtedly have a ravenous appetite. Try to choose food which is nutritious and easy to prepare as well as being compact and light. If necessary, remove food from its original packaging and repack it to make it easier to carry, and remem-

Most camping accidents are burns or scalds. Choose a firm base for the stove, and always hold the pan when stirring the contents or adjusting the stove

ber that there is usually a fair amount of useful space inside cooking pans. Dehydrated foods are a good choice; freeze dried foods are even better as they require far less cooking time. Some things such as quick cook rice and pasta can be brought to the boil and then left to cook in their own heat whilst you prepare something else. Stews of any description are good, especially if you take a little curry powder with you. Whatever you take, make sure it is something you like — it is pointless taking something which is convenient if you do not feel like eating it. In particular, you should have plenty of high energy foods with you, and no matter how tired you are nor how awful the weather, always try to have a hot meal each night and a substantial breakfast each morning.

The food you carry is particularly important on extended trips when you plan to be away from civilisation for several days at a time. In this situation you would be wise to plan your menus and to read something about basic expedition rationing and nutrition.

Load packing and carrying

No matter how fit you are nor how good your rucksack, the way you pack your load will have a considerable bearing on both the psychological weight (i.e. the weight you feel) and comfort. The most important considerations are to make the best use of all the available space, and to pack the rucksack in such a way that the load is balanced and bears directly onto the pelvic girdle and thus onto the legs. Additionally, you should give some thought to the order in which you are going to need the various items you are carrying — it is not much use burying stuff you need en route beneath items you will not need until you have pitched camp. Try to avoid packing sharp or hard objects where they will dig into your back, and resist the temptation to strap lots of items to the outside of the rucksack where they will swing around or catch on things.

Although everyone has their own way of packing a rucksack, it is not insignificant that many experienced mountaineers pack in a remarkably similar way.

The sleeping bag, possible contained within a **compression sack**, goes at the bottom of the rucksack together with spare clothing, the tent, stove and possibly some food goes towards the top, and items needed en route are either packed in side pockets, the top pouch pocket, or at the very top. No matter how good the container, liquid fuels are best packed in side pockets well away from any foodstuffs. Sleepmats can either be rolled tightly and strapped to the top or bottom of the rucksack, or be opened out as used

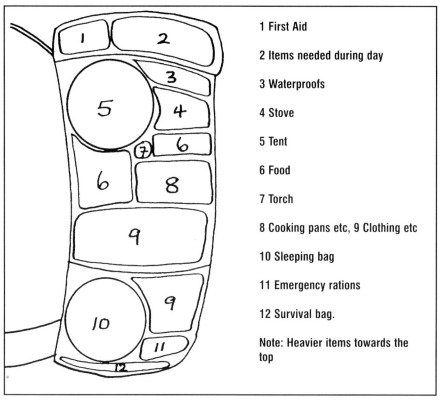

	1 First Aid
	2 Items needed during day
	3 Waterproofs
	4 Stove
	5 Tent
	6 Food
	7 Torch
	8 Cooking pans etc, 9 Clothing etc
	10 Sleeping bag
	11 Emergency rations
	12 Survival bag.

Note: Heavier items towards the top

Figure 19: Example of a packed rucksack

as a liner inside. A typical example of a packed rucksack is shown in figure 19.

Camp hygiene

A mild stomach upset which may cause only minor irritation when at home can be a serious problem when camping at a remote site several strenuous miles from habitation, so it pays to think about camp hygiene. Most of the hygiene factors are obvious. When camping at a lakeside site, for example, collect water from the inflow and do your washing and toilet near the outflow. Make sure your hands are clean before preparing or eating food, and wash the pans after you have finished. It is far easier to do this immediately than to wake up the following morning to find you have to get rid of congealed grease and burn-on food before you can have breakfast.

It's often the little things which make camp life comfortable!

Although it is not strictly necessary to dig a **latrine** if you are only using a site for one night, any faeces should be buried at least 15cms deep and used toilet paper should be burnt, the ash being buried with the faeces. If there are a group of you, or if you are staying at the same site for more than a day or so, you should dig a simple latrine. This does not have to be anything spectacular — a simple trench not less that 30cms deep will suffice. Remove the turves and stack them to one side so they can be replaced when you leave.

If you feel it is necessary to dig a latrine, you may also need to dig a **grease pit** in which to pour all your dirty water. This only need be a simple hole in the ground but remember to remove and save the turves and to replace them afterwards. Within 24hrs of you leaving a wild site it should be impossible to tell that anyone had camped there.

Personal hygiene is also fairly important. Any cuts and abrasions should be treated as soon as possible by washing and then using an antiseptic cream, and particular attention should be paid to the feet, especially on longer trips.

Camp routine

Although the very term routine may be anathema to some people who go off into the wilds to get away from that sort of thing, there can be little doubt that having some form of routine or sequence of events can go a long way towards making the camping experience less prone to discomfort or disaster. This is particularly true during **wet weather**, when movement in and out of the tent should be kept to the absolute minimum. Although different people will have slightly different routines, the following should give some idea of the type of things you should have regard for.

Unless you know the site well, try to arrive early so that you have plenty of time in which to set up camp. Assuming that the weather is not so bad that you need to get under shelter immediately, a brew on arrival is a great morale booster. While the water is heating, try to get the feel of the site and work out the best position for the tent(s). Pitching should be done carefully and methodically having first cleared an area slightly larger than the groundsheet of any sharp stones. Different tents are erected in different ways, and most are difficult to pitch in windy weather, particularly if you have never done it before. Make sure, therefore, that you are familiar with your tent before you use it in the mountains so that you can pitch it neatly and reasonably quickly. Ensure that pegs are placed firmly at an angle of between 60° and 45° to the angle of strain, and if you use boulders to weigh down dubious pegs, make sure the rock cannot chafe the guyline. No matter how tired you are nor how bad the weather, it is far easier to make minor adjustments at this stage than in the teeth of a storm at three o'clock the following morning.

Once you are satisfied with the tent, lay out your sleepmat and sleeping bag, and position all other items so they are readily accessible when needed. If it is **raining,** think carefully about what you are doing so as to keep movement in and out of the tent to a minimum, remove your wet gear before entering the tent and if any water does find its way into the inner tent, mop it up immediately before it has a chance to spread. In **winter conditions,** it is very easy to lose things when it is snowing, so put everything in a definite place and do not leave anything lying around. Do not allow snow to build up on the flysheet. Either clear it off from the outside or, if ensconced inside, bang the inner against the fly at regular intervals in an attempt to dislodge it. No matter what the weather, **never** wear boots inside the tent.

As has already been noted, a hot evening meal is essential, and you should make every effort to cook one no matter what. Before turning in, lay out everything ready for breakfast the next morning, and if it is cold, have a final brew and make sure everything (including a torch) is to hand so you can easily make yourself a hot drink during the night if necessary. Remove wet clothing and put on dry gear. Breakfast should, where possible, be a leisurely affair, and if conditions are kind it is a good idea to turn your sleeping bag inside out and air it over the ridge or a length of paracord.

As with pitching, striking camp should be done methodically. Clean your pans, wipe any mud from the bottom of the groundsheet, and make sure that everything is packed in its correct place. If you dug a latrine or grease pit, back fill them and replace the turves. In wet weather, leave one tent standing until everything else is packed away. If you are away for more than one night and you got wet the previous day, ensure you always have a set of dry clothing for use in camp, even if this means putting wet clothing on each morning.

Finally, when everything is packed away and you are ready to leave, cast your eyes carefully over the site to make sure **nothing** has been left. Within 24hrs of you leaving there should be nothing to indicate that anyone has camped.

6 MOUNTAIN NAVIGATION

Of all the skills of mountaincraft, it is undoubtedly that of navigation which has the greatest impact on mountain safety. Indeed, something in the order of 85% of all mountain accidents can be attributed to an initial error in navigation. Over the years I have found that the greatest problem in teaching navigation is people's prejudices — they think navigation is going to be complicated and feel they must be doing it wrong when they find that, in all honesty, the techniques themselves are simple.

As with the other skills discussed in this book, there is no way that you will become an accurate navigator simply by reading a book. You must go out and practice the skills in a realistic setting. In any case, I have room here only to give an overview of the major techniques. If you wish to find out more about navigation there are several relevant books mentioned in section 11.

Navigation should be, and can be, fun! If you find it a chore — if you become a slave to your navigation — you are not going about it in the right way. Skilled navigation should enhance the pleasures of the mountains, not detract from them. A common mistake is to think that navigation is the art of never getting lost. It is not! It is the art of working out where you are when you think you are lost. Perhaps the best way to put this in perspective is to say that a skilled navigator will never get lost although he may often be temporarily mislocated!

Types of map

By far the most important piece of navigation equipment, a map is simply a picture of the ground — nothing more, nothing less. In order to use it to navigate accurately, this picture needs to show as much relevant detail as possible, and for our purposes it is the terrain — the shape of the land — which is most important. The best maps are those made by the Ordnance Survey, both the **Landranger** series at a scale of 1:50,000 and the **Pathfinder** and **Outdoor Leisure Series** at a scale of 1:25,000. Specialist mountain maps (such as Harvey maps) are also extremely useful. Ideally you should be able to alternate between different maps without any problem. The Landranger and Harvey maps are useful when following good paths or definite ridges. If you are crossing trackless or more complex terrain, the extra detail shown on the 1:25,000 scale maps makes them indispensable.

Whatever type you use, do not forget that a map is out of date as soon as it is published. A map is a static thing whereas the landscape is dynamic. Forestry, in particular, changes at an alarming rate, and there may have been other changes which occurred after the map was surveyed. The only thing which does not change radically is the **shape of the land** — the terrain — so it is the shape of the land which becomes the most important consideration when you navigate.

It is a matter of personal choice whether you buy a standard map or a more expensive laminated, **waterproof map**. If you buy a standard map you must protect it from the elements in some way, even if this is only by placing it in a plastic bag.

Types of compass

Compasses come in all manner of shapes and sizes, only a few of which are ideal for use in the mountains. Although you may be able to work out a rough direction from a small button compass, it is not really accurate enough for our purposes. What is needed is an **orienteering** or **protractor compass** (figure 20). This will allow you to measure and follow bearings with great accuracy.

The orienteering compass comprises two major parts: the base plate and the compass housing. The **base plate** is a rectangle of clear plastic with scales along the front and one side. These scales can be in centimetres, although it is useful to have a set of **Romer Scales** in which the conversion from map distance to ground distance is done for you. Although Romer Scales are usually only found on the larger compasses, it is possible to buy these scales separately and these can be extremely useful. The base plate should be **at least 10cms long**, and should have a **magnifying lens**. Compasses with smaller base plates in which the magnifying lens is absent are available, but these are not recommended for serious mountain use. Engraved on the base plate are a number of lines running parallel to the sides, the central one of which has an arrow, the **Direction of Travel (or DOT) Arrow**, at its front end and intersects the rim of the compass housing at its rear end. It is from this point that you read and set your bearings (see below).

The **compass housing** is a liquid filled capsule containing a magnetic needle, on end of which is red (the **north-seeking end**), the other, white. The rim of the housing is divided into segments (each of which represents 2° of arc), and is engraved with relevant figures and the relative positions of the cardinal points (north, south,

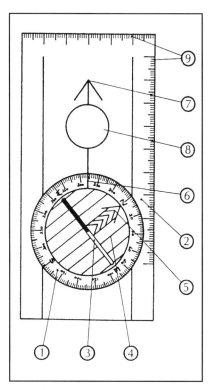

Figure 20: The Orienteering Compass. 1 Compass housing, 2 Base Plate, 3 Compass needle, 4 Orienteering lines, 5 Orienteering arrow, 6 Point at which bearings are read, 7 Directions-of-travel arrow, 8 Magnifying lens, 9 Scales

east, and west). The base of the housing is engraved with a series of parallel lines (the **orienting lines**), the central two of which are joined together to form an arrow (the **orienting arrow**). The tip of the arrow points to the north position on the housing.

Although this is the basic type of orienteering compass, other versions are available. For example, the **mirror compass** has a hinged lid which covers the housing, the inside of which contains a mirror engraved with a fine line. When open, there is a mark on the cover at the top of the line, and it is possible to site on a feature or object and adjust the mirror in such a way that you can read the bearing at the same time. Whilst this is undoubtedly a useful feature allowing you to follow and read bearings on the ground with considerable accuracy, there are two major disadvantages: firstly, few mirror compasses have base plates large enough to contain magnifying lenses or Romer scales, and secondly, it is very easy to get your bearings 180° wrong! Better is the **optical sighting compass,** in which the compass housing has been extended to make room for a lens and prism, and the compass needle has been replaced by a complex wheel. By sighting through the lens and using a hair-line on the prism, you can take and follow bearings extremely accurately. However, the complexity of the needle on some models makes it fractionally more difficult to calculate accurate bearings from the map. Increasingly available and coming down in price are electronic **GPS compasses**. These expensive hi-tech gadgets can be useful in the hands of experienced navigators when used in conjunction with existing skills. However, they should not be seen as a shortcut to accurate navigation, and will only be of limited use to people learning the craft.

Map skills

The most important skill in mountain navigation is the ability not just to read, but to interpret the map. There is a quantum difference between these two skills. **Map reading** is what you do when you drive from Dartmoor to the Cairngorms; **map interpretation** is what you do when caught in poor visibility on Dartmoor or the Cairngorms. Successful map interpretation requires you to look at your map in great detail. This is where the magnifying lens of your compass comes in handy. It is fair to say that the vast majority of people have no conception of the amount of detail shown on a map.

Maps are drawn to a particular **scale.** A scale of 1:25,000 simply means that one unit of measurement on the map is equal to 25,000 units of measurement on the ground. An easy way to judge scale is to ignore the final three digits, change the : to a = (i.e. 1=25) and work from millimetres to metres (i.e. 1mm equals 25m). A further way to get an impression of scale is via the grid lines, the series of parallel lines which divide the map into squares. No matter what the scale of the map, the grid lines are always 1 km apart on the ground.

By quoting its position relative to the grid lines (through a **grid reference),** it is possible to describe the location of any feature anywhere in the country. The procedure is described in the key of every Ordnance Survey map. Each grid line has a two figure reference number, and by quoting the reference number of the grid line to the left of the feature (e.g. 27) followed by the reference number of the grid line below the feature (e.g. 86) you can locate the feature to within a one kilometre square (e.g. 2786). If you wish to be more accurate, you can estimate how many tenths of a square the feature is from the left line (e.g. 274) and how many tenths of a square above the lower line (e.g. 863) which locates the feature to within a 100 metre square (e.g. 274863). You could also estimate hundredths of a square to give an eight figure reference if that amount of accuracy is required. This would locate the feature to within a ten metre square. These references are unique for the map but will be repeated at 100 kilometre intervals across the country. If this is a problem, quote either the map number or, more correctly, the **grid letters** which are to be found in the map's key.

In order to allow us to interpret our picture of the ground, map makers use a series of symbols (**conventional signs**) in an attempt to make things clearer. It will be helpful if we think of these symbols as falling into one of five categories. The first category of conventional sign is symbols for *things that aren't there* including "Site of Battle" and "European Constituency Boundary" — not very useful when trying to locate yourself in the middle of a misty moor! We can ignore all of these symbols bar one — the **spot height.** This is simply a dot on the map with a surveyed height. Although there is nothing to indicate its presence on the ground, by comparing two adjacent spot heights it is possible to work out the **aspect of slope** (i.e. which way a slope faces). This can obviously be extremely important!

The second category of conventional sign is *area symbols.* These include areas of woodland (deciduous, coniferous or mixed), water, bog, boulders, loose rock, etc. They also include different vegetation types (rough pasture, heathland, bracken, etc.). Whilst you will not be able to navigate accurately using only these symbols, they can be very useful when route planning, and you may be able to gauge your progress along a walk as you pass from one area to another.

The third category is *pinpoint symbols* (trig points, small pools, isolated sheep shelters, etc.). Many people will tell you that these are the most useful symbols as you can identify your position accurately by them. After all, if there is only one trig point shown on the map and you are standing by a trig point, you know precisely where you are. However, I feel that pinpoint symbols are of limited usefulness for one simple reason: they are so small relative to the landscape that you stand a good chance of missing them in misty conditions, especially if you are not sure precisely where you are in the first place! The next category of conventional sign — *linear features* — is far more useful.

Linear features comprise anything which is elongated (roads, rivers, field boundaries, etc.). If you are not sure precisely where you are and you notice from the map that there is a linear feature which lies roughly across your path, you have a fair chance of hitting it if you walk towards it. Granted you still do not know precisely where you are, but by following the linear feature (using it as a **handrail),** you may well come to another feature which you can use to relocate yourself.

Finally, we come to the most important category of them all — **contour lines.** It is these that show you the shape of the land, and it is the shape of the land which is the most important consideration when you are navigating in the mountains. Unfortunately, this is where many people switch off because they believe interpreting the contour lines to be difficult. This is not so. You only need to understand two basic principles and recognise three basic patterns to be able to interpret any landscape shape anywhere in the world.

A **contour line** is usually defined as a line which joins points of equal height. This does not really help us. Think, instead, of contour lines being imaginary paths (like a sheep tracks) which wend their way through the mountains never gaining nor losing height. All these paths are equally spaced, so the difference in height between one line and the next (and the next and the next) remains constant across the map. This height difference is known as the **vertical interval.** The vertical interval on 1:25,000 and 1:50,000 OS maps in mountain areas is 10 metres. Because these lines represent differences in height, the closer they are together, the steeper must be the slope (see figure 21).

When these contour paths run across a smooth slope, they appear as smooth lines on the map, but when they come to a valley or a spur, they have to curve around the head of the valley or the front of the spur thus showing as a V or U shaped pattern on the map. Thus more or less straight lines represent more or less smooth slopes, whereas V or U shapes represent valleys of spurs. If a contour line joins itself to form a circle, the path must go round and round in circles, and the pattern must therefore represent either a dome shaped mountain or a rounded basin (see figure 22).

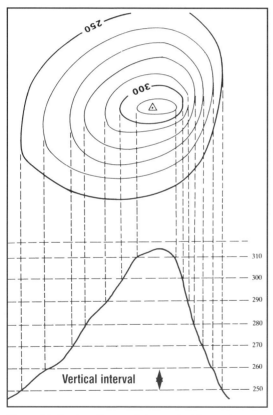

Figure 21: Contour lines and the vertical interval

Contour patterns mimic the landscape they represent. Wide, rounded, flowing contour patterns show a wide, rounded, flowing landscape; sharp, angular contour patterns show a sharp, angular landscape. Moreover, a single squiggle on a single contour line represents a similarly

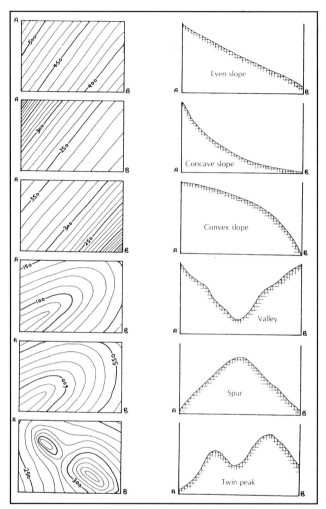

Figure 22: Contour patterns and landscape shapes

shaped squiggle on the ground. If you are working from a 1:25,000 scale map and there is a 1 mm squiggle on only one contour line, it represents a landscape feature which is at least 25m wide and up to 10m deep. Ask yourself whether this would be of significance in 20m visibility!

In order to interpret the contour patterns accurately, you need to know the **aspect of slope**. This is usually quite easy to work out as some of the contour lines will have the height they represent printed on them. Even if you can see only one contour marked in this way you can work out the aspect of slope because the figures on contours are always printed the right way up (i.e. with the top of the figure pointing towards the top of the slope). Alternatively, you can compare two adjacent spot heights. On those rare occasions where both these methods are impossible you can use other clues such as drainage. If you have a V or U shaped pattern with a river running down the middle of it, it is unlikely to be a spur!

One of the most useful but under-utilised techniques is that of **setting the map.** This involves turning the map in such a way that everything on the map is in the same relative position on the ground. In other words, if you are looking in a southerly direction, your map should be upside down. With your map set correctly, features seen to your left will be to the left of your position on the map, and direction finding can be done simply by line of sight. You can set your map in one of a number of ways. If you can recognise a number of features both on the ground and on the map, you can turn the map so that they all line up. Alternatively, if you are standing near a linear feature, you can turn the map so that the linear feature on the map runs in the same direction as the linear feature on the ground. Granted, you may be 180° out on occasions, but this should become immediately apparent once you start comparing other features. One further method makes use of the compass needle. Place you compass on the map so that the pivot of the needle lies on a north-south grid line. Now turn the map (not the compass) until the needle lies parallel to the grid line and the red (north-seeking) end of the needle points to the top of the map. Although this is not 100% accurate (for reasons which will become apparent later), it is usually sufficiently accurate to enable you to use the map effectively.

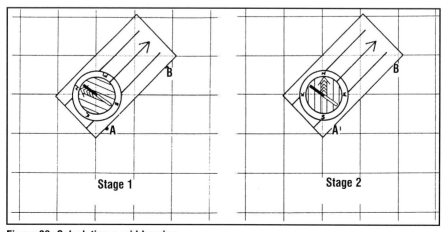

Figure 23: Calculating a grid bearing

Compass skills

In all but the worst conditions you should be able to navigate accurately using the map alone, especially if you learn to set it correctly and do everything by line of sight. However, there will be times, particularly in poor visibility, when you need a little help to travel in very accurate directions over precise distances. Having said this, I cannot overemphasise the fact that it is your map interpretation skills which are by far the most important. Compass skills and time and distance estimation are purely additional techniques which help to minimise errors. They are not the be all and end all of navigation. Indeed, you can be the best compass navigator in the world, able to calculate and follow bearings to within a second of arc, but unless you can relate all this information on to a map you will get lost!

The most common use of the compass is that of taking and following bearings. A **bearing** is simply the angle between two imaginary straight lines, one going from where you are to north, the other going from where you are to where you want to go. The convention in navigation is that bearings are always measured in a clockwise direction (i.e. in degrees east of north). To calculate an accurate **grid bearing** (i.e. from the map) you must be able to identify your current position and your proposed destination accurately on the map. Once you have done this, place your compass on the map so that one side of the base plate lines up precisely between these two points, with the DOT Arrow pointing in the direction you wish to travel. If you are heading towards a feature which is quite large (e.g. a mountain pool), head towards the middle of it. If you are leaving from a feature which is large, chose a definite point from which to leave it and line up the side of the baseplate with this precise position. Once you are satisfied that the base plate is as accurately position as possible, keep it firmly in position and turn the compass housing until the orienting lines lie parallel with the north-south grid lines and the orienting arrow points towards the top of the map. Double check that the DOT Arrow and the orienting arrow are pointing in the right direction and the side of the base plate is still lined up accurately between the two points. Once you have done this you have measured the angle and can remove the compass from the map (figure 23).

Now we come to a slight complication for, in order to use this information on the ground, you need to alter your bearing slightly. The problem is that you have measured the angle with respect

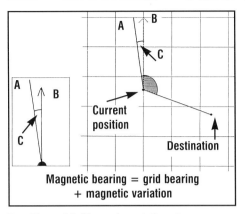

Magnetic bearing = grid bearing + magnetic variation

Top, Figure 24: Magnetic variation. A = Magnetic north; B = Grid north; C = Magnetic variation

Photo, a good position in which to hold the compass when following a bearing

to **grid north** (the position towards which the grid lines point). If there were grid lines running across the countryside you could simply line up the orienting lines with the grid lines and follow the direction indicated by the Direction of Travel Arrow. But, of course, there are not. The only other lines which can be used are the lines of magnetic force as shown by your compass needle. The problem is that grid north and **magnetic north** are at different locations (the difference being known as the **magnetic variation),** so you must make an adjustment to compensate for this. The value of the magnetic variation is printed in the key of every OS map. In the British Isles, magnetic north is currently to the west of grid north, and will be for some years to come. Because of this it is necessary to **add** the variation to the bearing shown on your compass (see figure 24). When you turn the housing to do this, remember that each segment represents 2° If you go abroad, you may find that the local magnetic variation is east of grid north. In this instance you would subtract the variation. It may help if you remember, when converting from a grid bearing to a magnetic bearing: *east means least and west means best*. Once you have adjusted for magnetic variation you will have converted your grid bearing into a magnetic bearing which can be used on the ground.

There is a definite technique when you come to follow your bearing on the ground. Hold the compass in front of you (in the position shown in the photograph) with the DOT arrow pointing

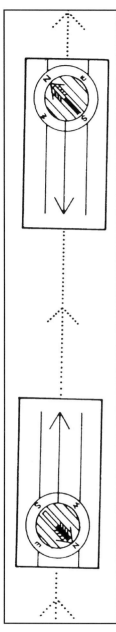

directly away from you. Keep the compass as level as possible. Turn slowly around until the red end of the needle lies directly over the orienting arrow. Assuming that you have calculated your bearing accurately, the DOT arrow will now be pointing precisely to your destination. However, it is insufficient simply to walk in that direction. What you need to do is sight between the pivot of the needle and the DOT arrow and find an object which lies on course. This should be something quite close by, and which you are going to reach. Avoid choosing objects which lie on the horizon. Once done, put away your compass and walk to that object, avoiding any obstacles which lie in your way. When you arrive, repeat the procedure, and so on until you reach your destination. This may sound simple (in essence, it is), but it takes practice to do accurately in any condition. The real art lies in choosing appropriate objects which remain recognisable as you approach them.

The art of successful compass navigation is being able to use the basic technique in all manner of situations. For example, you may be leaving a definite feature (say, a trig point) and heading across an apparently featureless moorland on which you are having difficulty in finding objects on which to sight. In this situation, a **back bearing** will save time and trouble. Head off in roughly the right direction then, just before the trig point disappears from view, turn around until the white end of the compass needle lies directly over the orienting arrow. This is known as Back Bearing. Site along the DOT arrow in the normal way, and see if it points to the trig point. If it does, you are on course. If it does not, move yourself to the left or the right until it does (see figure 25). Back bearings also allow you to **walk onto a bearing** without having to visit the originating point.

Another example is that of measuring the **aspect of slope**. This can be extremely helpful when, for

Figure 25: Top compass: Back bearing. The white end of the needle lies over the orienteering arrow, while the direction of travel arrow points to the position from which you have travelled. Bottom compass: Standard bearing. The red (north-seeking) end of the needle lies over the orienteering arrow, while the direction of travel arrow points towards the position for which you are making.

example, searching for the correct descent gully on a curving ridge or cirque, or estimating a point from which to begin a descent. Take a bearing with the DOT arrow pointing down the gully or at right angles to the slope at the point at which you wish to begin the descent, and convert this to a magnetic bearing in the usual way. As you follow the top of the ridge or cirque, keep pointing the DOT arrow into the valley at right angles to the edge. When the red end of the needle lies over the orienting arrow you have arrived at the correct point. Before descending, however, use your map interpretation skills to confirm that you are in the right position.

If you can measure the bearing between two points on the map (a grid bearing), you can also do the same when on the ground (a **magnetic bearing).** This can be an extremely useful way of locating your position, especially when you are standing on or by a linear feature. Let us say, for example, that you are standing on a narrow ridge. In front of you in the valley is a farmhouse which you can identify on the map. If you point the DOT arrow of your compass directly at the farmhouse, then turn the compass housing round until the orienting arrow lies directly beneath the red end of the needle, you have taken the magnetic bearing of the farmhouse. Assuming a westerly magnetic variation, if you now **subtract** the variation you will have converted this magnetic bearing into a grid bearing which you can now use on the map.

Place the compass on the map so that the front of one side of the base plate touches the farm. Without moving the compass housing, turn the whole compass around until the orienting arrow points to the top of the map and the orienting lines lie parallel with the north-south grid lines. Check to make sure the side of the base plate still touches the farm, in which case your position is where the same side of the base plate crosses the ridge on the map. The same technique can be used if you can see two features. Here you take a magnetic bearing on each and convert to grid. Your position will be where the two lines cross. Having said all this, if the visibility is good enough for you to see two features and you have set your map, you should be able to work out your position by line of sight and map interpretation!

All a compass does is show you the whereabouts of two invisible, imaginary straight lines, one running between two features of your choice, the other running from where you are to magnetic north. When using your compass, think in terms of straight lines. If you can work out a position or direction with straight lines on the map, you can work out the same position or direction with bearings on the ground.

Estimating time

An accurate compass bearing will show you precisely in which direction you should travel. What it will not do is tell you how far you have been or how far you have yet to go. Particularly in bad weather conditions it is easy to lose all track of time and distance, so the ability to estimate how long it is going to take you to walk between two points can be extremely useful.

In its coarsest form, estimating time is useful when planning your route. Particularly when visiting a new area for the first time, it is useful to be able to glance at a map and work out whether a proposed route is going be an easy dawdle or a strenuous yomp. Map distance and ground distance are two totally separate measurements in mountain areas because the map is flat whereas the ground is not. The ups and downs need to be taken into consideration.

The basic formula for calculating duration is known as **Naismiths Rule.** This is usually quoted as:

5 kph plus 30 minutes for every 300 metres of ascent.

This is a good starting block for calculating how long a proposed walk will take. However, it is too unwieldy to be of much use during micro-navigation in poor visibility, so it is necessary to chunk it down into manageable portions. Additionally, I work on the basis that if you are concentrating hard on your navigation in bad conditions, you will probably be moving slightly slower than 5 kph, so I always use 4 kph as the baseline. When chunked down this equates to:

1.5 minutes per 100 metres plus 1 minute for every 10 metres of ascent.

As the contour interval on most maps is 10 metres, you simply measure the horizontal distance using the scale or Romer on your compass baseplate, then add a minute for every uphill contour you cross. Generally speaking you can ignore descending contours unless the descent is very long or very steep, in which case add 1 minute for every second contour.

This baseline timing works well for me, but it will not necessarily work well for you as you may walk at a completely different pace. It is, however, a good starting block. Only you can decide what timing works for you — and you can only calculate your baseline through practical experience. You will also find that it varies slightly from day to day and depending upon the weather conditions, the load being carried, the severity of the terrain, and so on. With experience you should be able to adjust your time estimates accordingly.

Estimating distance

If estimating time is useful, then having the ability to estimate distance is a must. In its most macroscopic form this will involve judging distances on the ground. This is extremely difficult to do and even experienced navigators will get it wrong most of the time! Far more useful (and, luckily, easier and more accurate) is estimating distance on a much smaller scale, and this is done by **pace counting.**

Before you are able to pace count, you need to calibrate your pace. What you need is a measured distance of 100 metres. Although this can easily be found by visiting you local leisure centre and using the 100 metres running track, this is not the best way to calibrate your pace because you will take fewer paces to travel 100 flat and level metres than you will to cross 100 metres of rough heathland. Unless you have a companion who can pace count accurately, you will need to borrow a surveyors tape or use a 50m length of climbing rope to measure the distance. When you calibrate your pace, you count 1 step every time your left foot hits the ground. Neither exaggerate your pace nor walk in a group when you do this (if you walk in a group you will begin to affect each others' paces). Pace the distance three or four times and work out the average number of double paces you take to travel 100 metres.

This is an extremely useful figure. Let us assume that you take 65 paces per 100 metres and you are travelling a distance of 425 metres (as measured from the map) on a compass bearing in poor visibility. What you do not do is multiply 65 by 4.25! You pace count in terms of hundreds of metres rather than hundreds of paces. So pick up four pieces of straw, small pebbles, bits of grass, whatever comes to hand. Set off on your compass bearing and count your paces until you have reached 65. You now have travelled 100 metres, so throw away one of the pieces of straw (or whatever) and start counting your paces from one again. In this way you do not have to do any complicated mental arithmetic, and by glancing at the things you have collected you can always tell how far you have left to go. In this example, when you throw away the final thing you know you should be only 25 metres from your destination. Even if you are 3 or 4 paces out per hundred metres, you will be less than 20 paces out when you reach your destination. With practice you can be very accurate indeed.

Poor visibility navigation

Navigating in poor visibility should, in theory, be no more difficult than navigating in good conditions. However, confidence plays a big part and you may well feel waves of uncertainty pouring over you, especially if getting the right direction is critical. The best advice I can give is to remember the word **KISS** — which stands for **K**eep **I**t **S**hort and **S**imple. Each leg of navigation should be as short as you can possibly make it, certainly no more than 500 metres, even if this means heading to iffy points such as small squiggles on single contour lines. Try to get the feel of the terrain through your feet. Even on apparently level ridges and gently undulating plateaux it is possible to feel whether you are going uphill or down. Remember such information; it may be extremely useful.

Poor visibility navigation is an exercise in damage limitation. The further you go, the greater any compound error will be, so KISS! Double check your compass bearings by setting your map and seeing if the direction shown by the set map is the same as the direction shown by the compass. Work out timings and distances, and concentrate on what you are doing. Map interpret along the length of the leg to see if there is anything you can use to judge progress or give confidence that you are on route, look just before your destination to see if there is anything which will indicate you are nearing your objective, and look just beyond the point for which you are making to see if there is anything which will indicate that you have overshot.

When following a compass bearing you may find it difficult to find objects or features which lie directly on your route. If this happens, use your companions and **Leapfrog.** Send a companion on in front until he is nearing the limit of visibility then sight on him and, by arm movements, move him to the left or right until he is standing directly on course. Signal for him to stop, then walk to him. If he also has a compass set to the same bearing you can walk past him so he can sight on you, and so on.

The best features to aim for are **linear features** which lie more or less across your course. If you aim for a precise point on such a feature (for example, a stream junction), you will undoubtedly reach the stream but unless you have been accurate with your compass work, you may not be able to see the junction. Sod's Law dictates that in this situation you will always turn the wrong way! To save this happening, deliberately **aim off** to one side so that when you reach the stream junction you know which way to turn.

Whenever possible use map interpretation combined with natural features to aid your navigation. Linear features can be used as **handrails** which lead you towards an objective. For example, let us use a scene where you are walking towards a small pool and the mist comes down. You see from your map that to your right is an area of forest, out of which issues a stream which leads to the pool. Why use a compass? It is far easier to turn half right and find the forest edge, walk along this until you come to the stream then follow the stream to the pool. There may also be times when it is easier to approach your destination from a different direction, when, for example, there is a linear feature beyond it. Walk to the linear feature first (easy) then find some feature along it from where to reach your destination. This is known as using an **attack point**. Remember — KISS!

If the worst happens, don't panic! If, according to your pacing, timing and compass work, you should be at your destination, try doing a simple **line search** in which someone stays on the bearing whilst the other members of the party spread out in a line abreast, each person within sight of the next. The line then moves forwards along a standard bearing or backwards along a back bearing in the hope that the destination is nearby and will be within sight of one of the party. If you do not find it, you will have to relocate yourself as described later. Always keep someone on the original bearing as, if the worst comes to the worst, you can retrace your steps along a back bearing. If you loose the position of this bearing you will have lost all points of reference and relocating yourself will be that much more difficult.

Night navigation

There are many similarities between poor visibility navigation and night navigation. The techniques remain the same (including KISS), as do many of the problems. Judging distance can be virtually impossible when all you can see are silhouettes, so try to use physical features such as **breaks of slope** to keep track of how far you have travelled.

On a clear night there is nothing wrong with using a star as a feature to sight on, but make sure you can recognise it again. Because the **stars** move relative to the horizon, you should not follow the same star for more than about ten minutes at a stretch. Far more accurate if somewhat more time consuming is to **leapfrog** using pen torches to sight on.

Try to use map interpretation, handrails and attack points whenever possible, and if at all possible, allow your eyes to adapt to **night vision.** This will take at least 20 minutes to develop, and can be lost immediately if you turn on a torch. If there is insufficient light to see the map correctly, use a long-life bulb in your headtorch (this gives less light than standard or halogen bulbs) and close one eye so it remains dark adapted. Red light will not affect night vision, but it is pointless using a red filter over the lens of your

The real skill of navigation is the ability to relocate or work out your position when you think you are lost

torch because you will be unable to read the brown contour lines on your map!

Relocation

There will inevitably come a time when you suddenly realise that you have absolutely no idea of where you are. This is when you need a methodical relocation technique. First and foremost, don't panic! Tell yourself that you are not lost. You must know where you are to within a few kilometres, even if you cannot pinpoint your position. You know where you started from and you know how long you have been walking, so that's a good start. You may even have a rough idea of the direction in which you have been travelling, and that can help as well. If you are standing by a definite feature, you are almost home and dry and should be able to work out your position by a process of elimination (see below), but let us work on the basis that you are standing in the middle of a featureless plateau and can see absolutely nothing but rocks, heather, and mist.

The worst thing you can do at this stage is to stick your nose in the map, simply because there is no way that the map can show you where you are. Don't look at map for at least five minutes. Look around and try to get a feel for the area. Start by asking questions about the shape of the ground and the terrain. Are you high or low? Does the ground slope in any particular direction? What is the vegetation like? Use all your senses — listen for water or the breeze in trees, smell the air, probe the mist to see if you can sense a cliff or something nearby. You may laugh, but try it and you will be amazed how much information you can pick up about your surroundings. A small amount of information can go a long way in a situation like this, and you will soon be able to discount perhaps 95% or more of the map. Once you have worked out a rough location, look at your map to see if there is a linear feature in the area. If so, head towards it, taking great care if you are high and there are clifftops around. In winter, be aware of the dangers of cornices (see page 152) if there is any possibility that you may be walking towards the top of the crag.

If you have been following a bearing and you cannot find your destination, check to make sure the bearing was correct and that your compass has not been altered inadvertently during the journey. If the bearing is wrong, work out where the set bearing has put you. Once you have worked out a rough location, look at your map and see if there are any linear features in the area which would act as handrails. It is extremely unusual to find nothing.

Once you are standing by the linear feature (or any other feature for that matter) you are in a far better position to pinpoint your location. You may be able to do this simply by following the handrail to an obvious point. Alternatively you may find, having looked around and consulted your map, that you could be at any one of a number of locations. You should be able to distinguish one from the other by map interpretation or by measuring directions with your compass. If this proves impossible, you need to find something on the map which is within two or three hundred metres of your most likely position. Walk on a compass bearing towards this, pacing the distance. If you arrive at the feature you now know with 100% certainty where you are. If you do not arrive at the feature after the paced distance, turn around and regain your original position using a back bearing. In this way you now know where you are not (!). By continuing the exercise from all possible points you should eventually be able to work out your precise position by a process of elimination.

Route Cards

DATE:	START POINT:			FINISH POINT:		RETURN TIME:
FEATURE	GRID REF	M°	DIST (m)	HT ↑ (m)	TIME (mins)	REMARKS

FRONT OF CARD

SIZE OF PARTY:	(adults) +	(children).	No of LEADERS:
EQUIPMENT CARRIED:			

ESCAPE ROUTES:

BACK OF CARD

Figure 26: Example of a blank route card

It would be remiss of me not to mention route cards in a book about mountain safety. A route card is basically a list of grid references, bearings, timings, etc. which describe the route you are planning to follow when in the hills (see figure 26). From a safety point of view, you can leave a copy of this with a responsible person so that, in the event of your non-return, a mountain rescue team can be called out and will know where to look for you.

Route cards tend to be a contentious subject. Many people dislike them because they believe they destroy the spontaneity of walking. However, I feel they have several benefits. For a start, to write a route card, you have to sit down with your map and plan the route. In doing this you get a good idea of the bare bones of the area you intend to visit. Secondly, it is far easier to work out accurate bearings etc. whilst sitting at a table than it is to do the same thing across the fold of a map in strong winds! Thirdly, if things do go wrong whilst you are out, all your navigational computations are to hand, and this is one less thing you have to worry about.

I also believe that route cards need not destroy spontaneity. Let us assume you have made out a route card for a particular walk. You will undoubtedly start from the position intended, but during the first or second leg of navigation you decide to leave your planned route and make for a ridge which looks like it may have a good viewpoint. You then wander round the area, never actually on the route described — until something happens. If the unexpected occurs, you relocate yourself and head to the nearest point mentioned on your route card (if necessary, by walking on to a bearing as described on page 118), from which point life will become a little easier.

Whilst I do not believe it is necessary to make out a formal route card every time you visit the mountains, I feel you would be well advised to do so if you are in charge of a group or walking by yourself.

7 MOUNTAIN WEATHER

The prevailing weather conditions have a profound affect on your visits to the mountains, and unexpected changes in the weather can quickly turn a delightful day into a nightmare. It is essential, therefore, that you have a basic understanding of weather and the way in which it affects both the mountain environment and you. To take an extreme example, freezing conditions will affect you directly by making you cold; they will also affect you indirectly by making the ground icy. More mundanely, perhaps, rain will affect you directly by making you wet; it will also affect you indirectly by making the ground wet and slippery, raising stream levels, and reducing visibility. But individual weather factors cannot be taken in isolation — it is the combination of weather conditions, of wind and wet and cold, which can be of vital importance.

Generally speaking, the higher you go the more extreme will become the weather. Mountains are always colder, wetter and windier than lowlands. If there is drizzle carried on a light breeze at sea level, there could well be torrential rain (or sleet) carried on gale force winds on the tops. Before visiting the mountains, therefore, it is essential to get an up-to-date, local weather forecast (or, at the very least, a good national forecast) and know how to modify it to mountain conditions. To enable you to do this with any degree of accuracy, you should have a basic understanding of frontal systems, and a reasonable knowledge of the weather conditions associated with various airflows. It is also important that you have some conception of the ways in which the mountains affect the weather and the weather affects the mountains. Even with a limited amount of weatherlore you should be able to recognise the onset of bad weather before it arrives, although it will take years of practice before you can forecast it with any accuracy. After all, mountains make their own weather and even the experts get it wrong!

Airstreams

The British Isles experience some of the most complex weather patterns in the world. This is due largely to the fact that the islands are affected by six major airstreams, each of which comes from a different direction and carries a different type of weather (figure 27). If you know which airstream is affecting the country at any given time, you will have a good idea of the expected weather.

The most prevalent airstream is the **Polar Maritime**, which affects the country for about 35% of the year. Coming in from the west or north-west, it brings cool temperatures and heavy, often prolonged showers. If there is an area of low pressure (see later) in the North Atlantic, this airstream can loop around below it to arrive from the south-west, in which case it will bring warmer but cloudy weather with occasional squally showers.

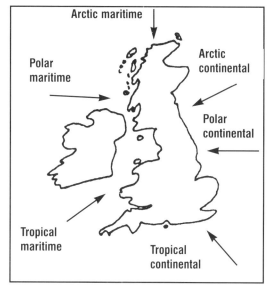

Figure 27: Air flows

The second most common airstream is **Tropical Maritime** which comes in from the south-west. In summer this usually brings warm temperatures, but is often associated with low cloud over western hills. In winter it often brings mild, moist, cloudy conditions.

Next comes **Polar Continental** air which blows in from the east bringing hot, hazy days in summer and bitter, Siberian conditions in winter. Also coming out of the east is **Arctic Continental** air. This only occurs in winter when it brings extreme conditions including blizzards and sustained frosts.

Arctic Maritime airstreams originate in the Arctic Ocean and come down from the north bringing unseasonably cold spells in summer together with frequent, often squally showers. During the winter months this airstream can be responsible for heavy snowfall in the mountains.

Finally, blowing up from the south is the **Tropical Continental** airstream which only occurs in summer, and then rarely. It brings extremely hot, heatwave temperatures together with a high risk of thunder.

Temperature

Generally speaking, the higher you climb, the colder it becomes. When air encounters the mountains it is forced to rise. As it does

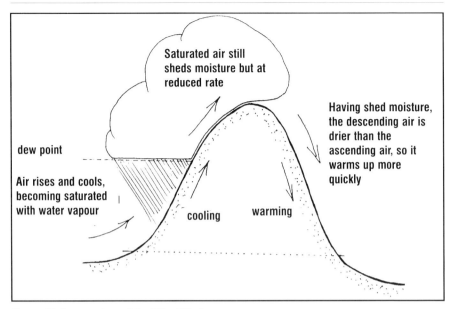

Figure 28: Lapse rate and the Föhn Effect

so it encounters less atmospheric pressure which allows it to expand, and as a consequence of this, it cools. The rate at which the temperature decreases with height is known as the **Lapse Rate,** and owing to their location, the British Isles have some of the highest Lapse Rates in the world.

The value of the Lapse Rate is not constant but depends upon the amount of water vapour in the air. In general terms, the more moist the air, the lower the Lapse Rate. The average Lapse Rate in Britain is of the order of **2°C per 300 metres.** During windy conditions (or if the air is particularly dry), this can increase to 3°C per 300 metres. On the other hand, if the air is saturated with moisture the Lapse Rate may fall to below 1.5°C per 300 metres. As a rule of thumb, the Lapse Rate will be high on windy days and low when the clouds are way down over the tops, and will slowly decrease with height. Additionally, because cold air cannot hold so much water vapour as warm air, the average Lapse Rate is lower in winter than in summer.

A further effect of the Lapse Rate is that of the **Föhn Effect** (see figure 28). As the air hits the mountains, it rises, expands and cools. Because cool air cannot hold so much water vapour as warm air, it may eventually become saturated. If this happens it is said to have reached the **Dew Point** and any further cooling or expansion will result in condensation of the vapour into clouds or even rain (see page 136). As the water vapour content of the air increases so there will be a corresponding decrease in Lapse Rate. As the air crosses the mountains it will obviously lose some of its water content in the form of clouds, drizzle or rain, so when it begins to descend on the far side it will be drier. Because the Lapse Rate becomes greater the drier the air, this descending air will warm up at a faster rate than it cooled down (the Föhn Effect), and this can result in the air

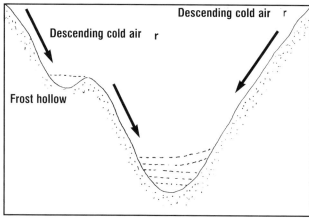

Figure 29: Temperature inversion

of the leeside of the British mountains being 1°C to 2°C warmer than it was on the windward side. In larger mountain ranges such as the European Alps, the temperature differences can be even more marked. Indeed, the turbulent Föhn wind in the French Alps is often the cause of wet avalanches.

The general effects of the Lapse Rate can sometimes be turned on their head leading the valley floors to be colder than the tops. When this occurs there is said to be a **temperature inversion** (see figure 29). These usually occur on windless nights when dense, cold air flows down the mountainside and collects in a layer in the valleys. As it flows down the slopes it will also collect in any sheltered basins on the way forming frost hollows. The effect can be marked, and temperatures in **frost hollows** can be in the order of 5°C colder than those on the open slopes. In the more sheltered valleys, the cold air can be several hundreds of metres thick and can result in dense fog, heavy dews and hard frosts. Most inversions will burn off shortly after the sun hits them in the morning. However, they can persist for days in deep, narrow valleys which rarely get the sun.

Wind

Days of total calm are rare in the mountains. Even if there is no appreciable breeze in the valleys, there will usually be a noticeable wind somewhere on the tops. This is due to a number of factors. As a general rule, the higher you climb, the stronger will be the force of the wind.

Wind speeds on general weather forecasts usually refer to the predicted speeds at sea level. This is one of the many reasons that you should always try to get a local forecast relevant to the mountains. On the better of these they will give you wind speeds and directions at various heights. Many people underestimate the effect of the wind on the mountains. For example, a force 4 wind will rip an open map to shreds whilst a force 6 will make sighting on bearings difficult. A gust of force 7 will blow you over, and if you get caught in a steady force 8 or 9 you will be unable to make any progress except, perhaps, by crawling. Further details are given in the **Beaufort Wind Scale** in figure 30.

The easiest way to understand the ways in which mountains affect the wind is to imagine that there is a ceiling above which the air cannot travel. Although air flows across the sea or the lowlands without much hindrance, friction with the ground will cause the surface winds to be lighter than higher winds. When the air reach-

FORCE	FORECAST NAME	SPEED	EFFECTS
0	Calm	<1	Water mirror-calm; smoke rises straight up; no effect on fresh snow.
1	Light	2-5	Wind just discernable; smoke drifts only fractionally; no effect on fresh snow.
2	Light	5-10	Light vegetation trembles; ripples on open water; no effect on fresh snow..
3	Light	10-20	Heather moves; small waves on open water; slight surface drifting of fresh snow.
4	Moderate	20-30	Small branches move; dry grass lifted on wind; spindrift up to 1metre high.
5	Fresh	30-40	Small trees sway; difficult to pitch tent; widespread drifting of fresh snow.
6	Strong	40-50	Walking requires extra effort; large branches move; spindrift above two metres.
7	Strong	50-60	Large trees sway; danger of being blown over; near blizzard conditions.
8	Gale	60-75	Walking near impossible with large rucksack; small branches break; blizzard conditions.
9	Gale	75-90	Crawling difficult; standing impossible; large branches break.
10	Storm	90-105	Body dragged along by wind; trees uprooted.

Figure 30: Beaufort Wind Scale

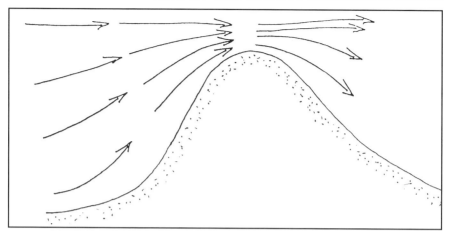

Figure 31: Effect of high ground on wind

es the mountains it is forced by rising ground to pass through a progressively smaller gap, and this causes it to speed up in a similar manner to water passing over a weir (figure 31). If the peak is isolated, the wind will tend to flow around it giving the highest wind speeds on the shoulders of the hill (figure 32).

The Lapse rate also has an affect on the way in which the air behaves when it reaches a mountain barrier. If the rate is high (as it often is on windy days), the air is unstable and will try to climb over the barriers. Conversely, if the rate is low (when the air is saturated as in low cloud), the air is unstable and will try to flow around barriers.

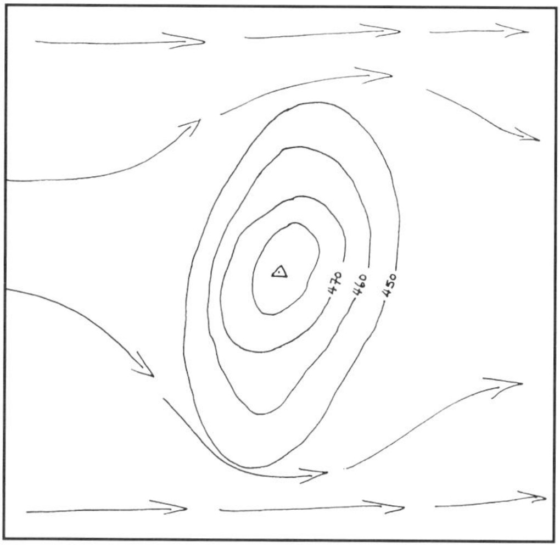

If there is a valley or a col lying in the same direction as the wind, this will act like a funnel which causes the air to speed up. If the valley curves around, the wind trapped within it will follow the line of the valley (figure 33).

Most mountain walkers will be familiar with the problems caused by **turbulence**. In its simplest form, this will simple be gusting winds. However, there are other forms of turbulence

Figure 32: Wind speed increase over shoulders

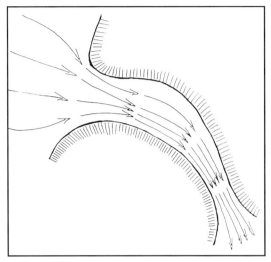

Figure 33: Topography causing change of wind direction

worth considering. Any sudden sharp change in the angle of slope will have an affect on the wind. This is particularly noticeable on sharp ridges and cliff edges. If the wind is blowing across the break of slope, the main wind will continue in its original direction for some time, and this will cause a **leeside eddy** (figure 34) — a weaker wind blowing in the opposite direction. This often results in a null point — a corridor of calm — along which it is

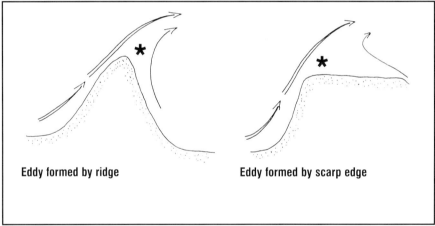

Eddy formed by ridge   Eddy formed by scarp edge

Figure 34: Leeside eddies and null points
(* indicates approximate position of possible null point)

possible to walk out of the wind. However, null points are neither constant nor continuous; when using them you should beware unexpected gusts especially when approaching the tops of gullies or changes in direction.

In areas where the wind has blown across a series of parallel ridges it can begin to flow in **waves**. Conditions such as this are often recognisable by parallel lines of stationary clouds. If these waves are large or extensive, the wind can become extremely tur-

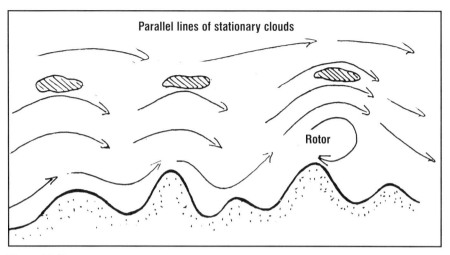

Figure 35: Rotor

Wind Speed (kph)	Ambient Temperature (°C)12						
0	12	8	4	0	-4	-8	-12
10	8	5	0	-4	-8	-13	-17
20	4	0	-5	-10	-15	-21	-26
30	0	-3	-8	-14	-20	-25	-31
40	-1	-5	-11	-17	-23	-29	-35
50	-2	-6	-12	-18	-25	-31	-37
60	-4	-7	-13	-19	-26	-32	-39
70	-4	-7	-14	-20	-27	-32	-40

Figure 36: Wind-chill chart

bulent and can sometimes form a **rotor** in which a gust comes unexpectedly from the opposite direction (figure 35).

Something people are far more aware of nowadays is **wind-chill.** This is simply the chilling effect of the wind. Contrary to popular opinion, however, the wind does not have to be strong to have a high wind-chill effect. Indeed, the greatest effects are at slower speeds, as can be seen from figure 36. Although this gives a fair indication of likely effects, rain will increase the temperature drops if allowed to penetrate clothing (see page 15) or fall on exposed flesh. In the same way that mountains are colder and windier than the lowlands, they are also wetter. The main reason for this has

Walking on the null point with a leeside eddy causing mist against the edge of the escarpment

already been explained when describing the mechanisms of Lapse Rate and the Föhn Effect.

Precipitation

As air flows across the sea it picks up vast quantities of water vapour. When it reached the mountains it is forced to rise, expanding and cooling as it does so. The cooler and less dense the air, the less water vapour it can hold, so there will eventually come a time when the air becomes saturated and any excess water vapour will begin to condense into droplets. The point at which it does this is known as the **dew point.** Above this point, water will continue to condense forming either cloud, drizzle, or rain. If it is already raining (caused, perhaps, by a frontal system — see below), the rain will become heavier. On the leeside of the mountains the air descends, compresses and warms up. It can therefore hold increasing amounts of water vapour and this can result in a **rain shadow.** The leeward sides of mountains are therefore often drier than the windward sides. However, this rain shadow effect is often negated during windy weather as strong winds will drive the rain on over the mountains.

In addition to the rainfall caused by topography, there is also rainfall associated with frontal systems. Mountains form an effective barrier to these systems and will slow them down. Therefore any frontal rain will tend to last longer over mountain areas than it will over the lowlands. To put all this in perspective, modern estimates put the average annual rainfall on the summit of Snowdon at twice that of Capel Curig (12kms east and 900 metres lower), and six times that of the Cheshire Plain (90kms east and 1000 metres lower).

There are two other forms of precipitation which will have a dramatic effect in the mountains. The first is **hail.** This is almost always associated with cumulonimbus clouds and often with thunderstorms. Although light hail may not cause any problems, being caught in a hailstorm can be a painful experience as some stones can have edges sharp enough to cut when driven on a strong wind. Few storms last long, so the best idea is to find some shelter and sit it out.

The other important form of precipitation is **snow** which will obviously affect the mountains in many ways. Most rain falling on Britain starts life as snow at high altitude, and if the temperature is cold enough, it will reach the ground. As it descends and meets air above freezing point, it will begin to melt, first clumping together to form large flakes, then turning to sleet and finally to rain. Generally speaking, the warmer the temperature, the larger the snowflakes. This **melting zone** may be over 250 metres in depth,

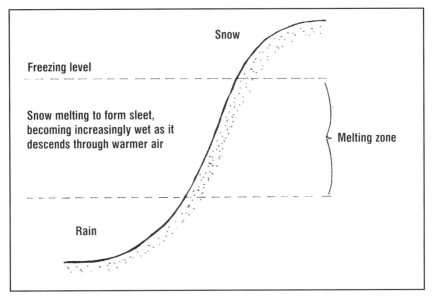

Figure 37: The melting zone

which means that the snow line is not necessarily the same as the freezing level (figure 37). It is also worth noting that because of the effects of variable Lapse rate and the cooling effect of rain, the snow line (and the freezing level) can drop by a significant amount during the day. This means that the damp path you followed in the morning can be snow covered and icy by the time you return in the afternoon.

The snow that you will meet on the mountains will not be uniform in consistency, but will vary from powder, through something resembling sugar, to stuff like porridge and finally consolidated snow which is almost as hard as ice. Different types of snow bring with them their own set of problems and delights. As I have mentioned before, your initial winter expeditions should be with an experienced companion or a suitably qualified instructor.

When recounting their experiences on the hill, people frequently talk about white out conditions when, in fact, they mean thick mist. A true **white out** can only occur in misty conditions when there is snow both in the air and on the ground. Under these circumstances everything becomes white — there is no differentiation between airborne snow and lying snow. Your companions will appear to float, and it will be impossible to tell what is up and what is down. Whilst conditions such as this are rare south of the Scottish Border, they can occur almost anywhere (see page 159).

A further potential problem is that of **spindrift** or airborne snow crystals which can cause a significant reduction in visibility. These get everywhere! It need not be snowing for there to be spindrift — even a slight breeze will pick up unconsolidated snow crystals. Given a slight breeze, the colder it is and the more recently it has snowed, the more likely you are to encounter spindrift. If spindrift is carried on a significant wind you can have white out conditions without there being any snow falling.

Arguably the worst condition you will ever meet on the hill is that of **blizzard.** This is more than just windy weather and falling snow, it is a snowstorm in every sense of the word. If it is really cold (which it is likely to be), the snow crystals can be so fine that they will make breathing difficult or even impossible when facing the wind. In any case, windblown snow is painfully abrasive; trying to walk into the teeth of a blizzard is like walking into a sandblasting machine! If blizzard conditions (snowfall and high winds) are forecast or suspected, stay off the hill. If the weather is working up to these conditions, retreat early, even if you have to descend into the wrong valley. If you get caught in blizzard conditions, seek shelter (see also section 10).

Frontal systems

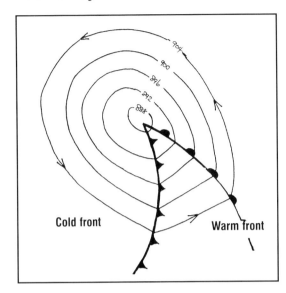

Figure 38: A frontal system

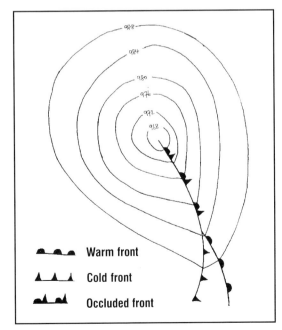

Figure 39: An occluded front

The airstreams which affect the British Isles each have different characteristics. When different types of air meet, particularly warm air and cold air, they form swirling areas of instability which lead to **depressions** (areas of low pressure) and **anticyclones** (areas of high pressure). These are shown on weather maps by **isobars** (lines joining points of equal pressure). In the same way that contours show the steepness of the terrain, isobars show the steepness of the pressure differences. Because air always tries to reach equilibrium, it flows from areas of high pressure and tries to fill areas of low pressure. The closer the isobars are together, the greater the pressure difference, and therefore the stronger the wind in that area. In the most general terms, depressions bring unsettled weather whereas anticyclones bring settled conditions. Air flows in an anticlockwise direction around a depression and in a clockwise direction around an anticyclone.

Associated with areas of low pressure are **frontal systems**. A front is simply the junction between air

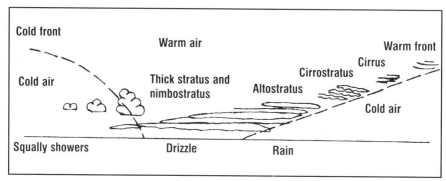

Figure 40: Section through a frontal system

masses of different temperatures. If warm air is advancing the junction is termed a **warm front**; if cold air is advancing it is known as a **cold front**. These fronts usually occur together in a depression, radiating out from the centre with the warm front preceding the cold, the whole system moving across the Atlantic in an Easterly direction at speeds of between 20kph and 80kph (see figure 38). However, cold fronts move faster than warm fronts so the two will eventually merge. When this happens the front is said to be **occluded** (see figure 39).

In theory, there is a definite sequence of events as a frontal system passes over a mountain range. The arrival and passage of the system can be seen in terms of the development of different cloud types and changes in wind direction (see figure 40). Indeed, the recognition of different cloud types should be seen as an essential skill. However, because mountains affect the weather in so many ways, this sequence may well be affected in detail and the differences and changes may not be so clear cut as described below. Nevertheless, a knowledge of the sequence can be extremely useful in predicting possible changes in the weather. The first signs of an approaching frontal system are usually long streaks of high **cirrus** clouds (**Mare's Tails**) which begin to appear up to 24hrs before the arrival of the warm front. The wind slowly increases and **backs** (changes its heading in an anticlockwise direction), and the high clouds continue to develop into continuous wispy sheets of **cirrostratus** which cast a halo around the sun or moon, and eventually into lower bands of grey **altostratus** which may herald the start of the rain. The wind continues to back and strengthen, and the nearer the front, the lower and darker the clouds. These eventually develop into continuous sheets of **stratus** and **nimbostratus** which often give continuous rain.

As the warm front passes, the wind suddenly decreases and **veers** (changes its heading in a clockwise direction), and the temperature rises. In lowland areas the clouds now start to disperse, but in the mountains they tend to hang around giving drizzle and poor visibility. As the cold front nears, the wind begins to increase again and **cumulus** clouds begin to form (although these may be hidden by lower clouds in mountain areas). As the cold front passes, the wind veers again, the temperature plummets, and there may be sudden squally showers. The clouds now start to disperse giving way to clearing skies and more showery weather.

If the fronts have occluded (as is common in the British mountains), the sequence remains essentially the same except that there will be no **warm sector,** the weather jumping straight from the band of rain to clearing skies with a marked veering of the wind.

Lightning

Although lightning is not a major cause of mountain accidents, it does kill two or three people each year. A basic understanding of the principles involved is therefore useful knowledge.

In simple terms, lightning is an electrical discharge from the atmosphere. During a thunderstorm, the clouds become charged with electricity which then **arcs** or jumps to earth causing a flash of lightning. Because electricity takes the line of least resistance, it tends to arc across the shortest possible distance and therefore almost invariably strikes the most prominent feature in its locality. A lightning strike is rather like dropping a raw egg onto a concrete floor from a height of about ten metres: it doesn't just break, it splatters all over the place! When the electricity from the cloud strikes the ground, it does not simply disappear; it spreads out from the strike in a series of **ground currents,** each one following the line of least resistance in an attempt to go to ground as quickly as possible. These lines of least resistance tend to be damp cracks and gullies, and if there are any breaks or obstacles such as caves or overhanging rocks, the electricity will arc across them in the same way as the electricity arcs in a car's spark plug.

There will usually be plenty of advance warning of an approaching thunderstorm for you should be able to see and hear it coming. As it gets closer, you will also be able to feel it! Your skin will prickle, your hair may literally stand on end, and any local projections may begin to glow with the bluish light of **St Elmo's Fire.** Perhaps more alarming, metal objects such as ice axes may spark and hum.

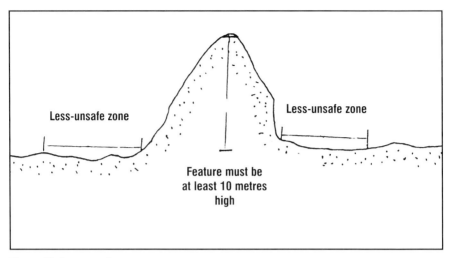

Figure 41: Less-unsafe zone

Because strikes tend to be concentrated on the most prominent features, there is a zone around these which is less prone to strikes. Although these zones have been described as a safe areas, the terminology is misleading and it would be better to think of them in terms of **less-unsafe zones**. These zones lie around features more than 7 metres high and have a diameter roughly equal to the height of the feature (see figure 41). When faced with an approaching thunderstorm, your priority should be to move away from exposed ridges, mountain tops and any prominent features and get into one of these less-unsafe zones. Try to find a relatively flat, open area within the zone, sit down on the driest object you can find (rucksack, rope, etc.), pull your legs up to your chin and clasp your hands around your knees. Although you have minimised the chances of a direct strike, there is still the problem of ground currents, so try to keep minimum contact with the ground and resist the temptation to lean back on your hands. If you do lean back and you are hit by a ground current, the electricity will pass through every major organ in your body. If you crouch or sit as described, however, a ground current strike will only pass through your legs.

By now it will be pouring with rain (or hailing) and there will be a great temptation to find shelter. On no account should you seek shelter in gullies or fissures as these are the most likely paths for the ground currents. Similarly, sheltering in shallow caves or beneath overhanging rocks can be extremely dangerous as, if met by a ground current, these can act like spark-plug gaps and you could be severely burned by electric arc. It may be prudent to place metal objects such as ice axes to one side, but they should not be discarded as they may be needed for a safe retreat. In any case, contrary to popular belief, they do not attract lightning any more than you do!

Finally, give some thought to secondary effects. For example, if you have taken all the precautions outlined above, it is unlikely that a ground current will kill you. However, it may stun you with potentially serious consequences if you are on steep ground. If you are scrambling on an exposed ridge with no possibility of retreat, try to find a flat area below the crest and sit it out. Moreover, during thunderstorms there is an increased chance of **stonefall.** Not only can lightning shatter rocks and boulders by vaporising the water trapped within them, but the noise and vibration from thunder can topple already unstable boulders.

Forecast sources

Because the weather plays such an important part in mountain safety, a basic requirement is that you should always get a weather forecast before venturing onto the hill. There are various sources for these forecasts, some better than others.

Forecasts in **newspapers** vary greatly in quality. All suffer from the disadvantage that they cannot be updated on a regular basis. Some are simply reports of what the weather has been doing, whereas others forecast the likely changes. If there is an accompanying weather map, check whether it is a report map of the recent situation or a forecast map of the predicted situation. Somewhat better are forecasts on **television and radio.** These are often updated between bulletins to take account of unexpected changes. Some television forecasts, in particular, are extremely useful as the accompanying satellite pictures give a graphic representation of what is happening and what is approaching. The Sunday **farming forecast** which gives details of the week ahead is particularly useful.

National forecasts are useful in that they give a general overview of the situation. However, it is desirable to have a forecast that is a little more detailed. **Local forecasts** are available on local radio stations and by **telephone,** and there are often special forecasts for mountain walking in the more popular areas. These give details such as mountain and valley conditions, temperature inversions, lapse rates, freezing level, cloud base, precipitation, wind speed and direction at various heights, etc. Details are available through

Take note of the forecast for wind speed and direction. Wind can have a dramatic effect on the day!

local telephone directories and are often publicised in outdoor magazines. Additionally, many of the better gear shops in popular areas have a weather board which is updated daily.

If you have access to a **fax,** it is possible to get forecasts direct from the Meteorological Office. There are a range of forecasts available both national and local, some with accompanying maps or satellite pictures. For further details telephone the Meteorological Office helpline on 01344-854435.

Self forecasts

Professional forecasting is a complex science, the weather is a fickle thing, and even the experts will acknowledge that they sometimes get it wrong! It therefore makes sense to have at least a basic working knowledge of frontal systems, airstreams, and the effects of topography. In this way you can modify the general picture to suit the local area, and can make some judgement of unexpected changes to the published forecast. In the same way that there are accident black spots on the roads, there are also weather black-spots in the mountains, so it always pays to ask local advice. People who live and work in the mountains are in a far better position to know the idiosyncrasies of their local hills than are visitors.

When out on the hill, be observant. Take note of any changes in cloud type, wind direction and strength, and temperature, and try to build up an overall picture of what is happening. When looking at your map, think about the ways in which the local topography may affect the general weather, and never be afraid to turn back if you think the conditions warrant it or may do so within the near future.

8 MOUNTAIN ENVIRONMENT

The famous Alpine guide, Gaston Rébuffat, maintained that there was more to being a mountaineer than learning how to climb. He believed that a good understanding of mountains and the mountain environment was equally important, if not fundamental. The truth of this is easily demonstrated by the fact that, when out on the hill, you can always recognise experienced mountaineers by the way in which they appear to move effortlessly, no matter what the terrain. Less experienced parties tend to go through periods where they stumble and stagger and generally flounder around.

As with so many of the skills of mountaincraft, learning to read the mountains and the terrain in order to choose a safe and suitable route is something which develops only after years of experience — you cannot expect to be proficient at route finding during your early sojourns into the hills.

Mixed ground

On the open fells there should be little difficulty in choosing a suitable route, but there will undoubtedly be times when you are faced with areas which contain a wide variety of features, from heather terraces through damp gullies to loose rock and small outcrops. The key to moving with the minimum difficulty through terrain such as this is to plan early, both through map interpretation and observation.

Try to work out a route which takes you along the lines of least resistance, and note the position of prominent features along the way which will help you keep to your chosen line. This can be difficult at first as things which look obvious from afar can often be far less obvious when you get closer. Do not forget, also, that you get a foreshortened viewpoint when looking at a slope from below, and an exaggerated viewpoint when looking down a slope. Particularly in conditions of low light, it can be extremely difficult to judge both depth and distance, and you will get a flattened perspective making it difficult to judge the best route.

When **ascending** through mixed ground where there are a profusion of outcrops, be aware of the increasing drop beneath you — it is very easy to scramble upwards gaining vast amounts of height without realising. In addition to route planning in broad terms, try to select a route in more detail as you go along. When

Walking through boulder fields is not the most pleasant of experiences!

descending, try to choose concave slopes (see page 56) which are as open as possible, and never jump down an outcrop. For one thing, it may be further than it seems; for another, you may not be able to climb back up the drop if you find your way on blocked. Always downclimb slowly and carefully — if you can descend in this way you should be able to re-ascend if necessary.

Boulder fields and scree

The best boulder field is an avoided boulder field! However, it is sometimes necessary to cross them. The best approach is a deliberate one, but move carefully, choosing your route and concentrating on your foot placements. Resist the temptation to leap from boulder to boulder, for not only can even the biggest of boulders move, but also the flat, inviting surface may be greasy. Be aware, too, that in certain areas, the edges of individual stones can be razor sharp. Take extra care where the boulders are overgrown with vegetation. Fronds of bracken and clumps of heather and bilberry can conceal gaps between the boulders which lie waiting to grab an unwary ankle.

Inclined boulder fields and scree slopes are potentially more hazardous, for if one boulder moves it is likely to set off a chain reaction (see also page 74).

Stonefall

Although it is not usually regarded as a major mountain hazard in Britain, stonefall does occur and people are injured by it each year. The three most common causes of stonefall are human action, freeze thaw action, and the effects of lightning. If scrambling, especially on big mountain cliffs, it would be prudent to wear a helmet.

When walking on or near a slope which contains loose boulders, be aware of other people. If there are people above you, work on the basis that they are idiots and take extra note when they are anywhere near vertically above you. If they are crossing above you, it may be wise to stop and watch until they are safely past so that if they do dislodge anything you get as much warning as possible.

Take great care, too, not to dislodge any rocks yourself, and if something starts to move, bellow *"Below!"* at the top of your voice. Do this even if you cannot see anyone below you — there may be someone hidden from view, and falling boulders can travel a surprising distance. Many people are unaware of the horizontal distance a falling boulder can travel — because it will glance off other rocks as it descends it is fair to say that a boulder can travel as far horizontally as it can vertically. Although the temptation can sometimes be almost irresistible, avoid trundling boulders deliberately.

Stonefall can also occur when there is no-one around to start it. This is usually due to **freeze-thaw action** in which water trapped in cracks in the rock freezes, expands, cracks the rock still further, and then melts. Freeze-thaw occurs most commonly in spring and autumn, and stonefall is most likely shortly after the sun has hit the crag. Where this is a common occurrence, there will be a build-up of loose boulders below the crag, the most obvious form being scree. If the scree is old and is only occasionally added to, it is known as **dead scree** and is recognisable by the fact that it has been colonised by vegetation. **Active scree**, on the other hand, has little if any vegetation which indicates that it is still being added to on a regular basis. If your route takes you up, down, or across scree, try to minimise the dangers (see page 74).

Freeze-thaw is not the only natural cause of stonefall. Heavy rain can wash away soil leaving rocks teetering on the brink; the vibrations from the noise of thunder can shake boulders free, lightning can literally shatter rock sending bits flying everywhere, and prolonged dry periods can cause the soil to shrink, freeing otherwise solid boulders. Therefore it makes sense to consider recent weather conditions when walking through areas where there is potential for stonefall.

Arguably the most dangerous areas for stonefall are gullies. No matter how well-used these are, they always contain a fair amount of loose material. Indeed, there are gullies which, once reasonably solid, are now becoming fraught with danger through the erosion caused by overuse. If you are caught in stonefall in a gully, there is very little you can do for the rocks will ricochet all over the place. If your route takes you into gullies, be aware of the different techniques you can use in an attempt to minimise the dangers (see page 74).

Bog

Bog is far more unpleasant than it is dangerous — indeed, the bottomless bog is more an old wives' tale than a reality. However, due to climate and poor drainage, many mountain areas contain large tracts of boggy land which are best avoided if possible. Admittedly, this can be difficult in areas such as Kinder Scout, Bleaklow, and parts of the Carmarthen Fan which appear to consist of little else.

If you must cross such areas, you may be able to keep out of the wettest areas by planning your route between patches of vegetation such as heather, heath and bilberry which do not like having their roots permanently waterlogged.

If you plan your route carefully you should never get into serious difficulties. However, looking on the black side (no pun intended), if you find yourself sinking deeper and deeper into the mire, don't panic, for if you struggle, you will only sink deeper. Take off your rucksack, place it on the ground in front of you and lean forward, spreading your weight over as great an area as possible, then try to ease your legs out of the ooze. If you cannot free yourself, rock backwards and forwards in order to create an airspace around your legs. If this does not work, try to form an air space by some other means (using you hands, tent poles, walking sticks, or anything else that comes to hand), then place your hands behind your thighs to give extra power to pull them out. If your companions have something to throw to you to give you some purchase, so much the better.

Flood

Mention of river crossing techniques has already been made on page 81, but it may be useful for you to know a little about the mechanisms of flood.

First and foremost, bear in mind that floods can occur even when you have not felt a drop of rain all day. For example, a localised rainstorm on a nearby hill can affect the state of a river many miles away. In winter conditions, you should also take into consideration the effects of the thaw. A sharp rise in temperature when the mountains are snowclad can have a significant effect on the level of streams in the area.

Mountain streams tend to rise and fall at an alarming rate due partly to the nature of the terrain they drain, and partly to the fact the rainfall in mountain regions tends to be more intense than in the lowlands. In simplistic terms (with apologies to any hydrologists reading), when rain falls on the ground it drains into small trickles which merge into bigger rivulets which merge into small streams and so on.

At each merging, the amount of water flowing increases dramatically. Alongside this, the banks of the river create friction which effectively slows water down, so that in a flood situation, the water behind eventually begins to overtake the water in front. The end result is a sudden rise in water level known as a **flood pulse** which can carry surprising amounts of debris before it. Not only can it uproot plants from banks and snap up overhanging branches, it can also roll sizeable boulders along the river bed.

Mountaineers in general appear to have only scant regard for the power of moving water. If you wish to know more about this, ask an experienced canoeist to take you to a bridge across a mountain river and read the water for you.

Ice

Ice can occur in many different forms in the mountains, from hard Black Ice, through brittle Blue Ice, to verglas, hoar and rime. All will have an effect on conditions underfoot.

Ice can be a hazard even when there is no snow about

Of course, there does not have to be snow around for there to be ice. Any water on the mountain will obviously freeze if there is a sharp frost, and sheets of **water ice** are a common occurrence in certain areas, especially on damp paths and below spring lines. If this only occurs in patches, it may be possible to detour around it. Alternatively, if the sheet is only thin, it may be possible to stamp through the crust. The wisdom of such action can only be judged at the time. If there has been a heavy dew, or if it has rained before a drop in temperature, **frozen turf** can present serious difficulties. This can make onward progress extremely difficult, and upward progress extremely hazardous, especially if there are any drops nearby. Indeed, progress may only be safely possible wearing crampons.

One of the most likely ice conditions to cause problems is that of **verglas.** This is a clear, wafer-thin layer of ice which coats rocks, sometimes invisibly. It can be caused directly by the freezing of meltwater on rock surfaces, or indirectly as when raindrops freeze immediately on contact with sub-zero rock. It can also occur in patches — one minute you are walking on rough rock, the next you are skidding on an invisible sheet of ice. Crampons are ineffective on verglas as it is generally too thin to provide any purchase for the points.

Atmospheric icing occurs in a number of forms, the most common of which are rime ice and hoar frost. **Rime Ice** is a soft deposit of ice which builds up on the windward sides rocks. It is formed from the water-droplets in clouds and, over a period, due to shifting wind directions, can build up into large, feathery flakes which totally cover rock pinnacles and flakes. It can also form on snow in which case it is known as **graupel.** Similar to rime deposits is **hoar frost.** This is a shimmering layer of fragile ice crystals formed by the crystallisation of water vapour direct onto freezing surfaces. If the vapour crystallises on lying snow it is known as **surface hoar.**

Ice is heavy, and broken ice can have razor sharp edges. In certain conditions you would therefore be wise to beware the danger of falling ice. This is particularly true after prolonged spells where the temperature hovers just below zero allowing a steady build up of water ice. Any thaw could precipitate the downfall of large quantities of ice, so be wary of walking below icy crags in such conditions. Bear in mind, too, the possibilities of stone fall (see page 148) and cornice collapse (see below).

Cornice

A cornice is basically a mass of unstable, overhanging snow which is formed by wind action at the top of a slope. Although in its textbook form it is often shown as being severely overhanging, it can be less obvious and may simply appear as a false edge. Cornices occur due to a build up of snow on the leeward side of a ridge or scarp edge. It is the angle of the windward slope which determines the size and shape of the cornice. If this slope is long, gentle and smooth, the cornice will be correspondingly large; conversely, if the windward slope is short, steep and uneven, the cornice will generally be far smaller (see figure 42). Thus you are far more likely to find large cornices on the edge of a plateau than on a knife-edged ridge.

Cornices present a potential hazard both when approached from above and below. When **approaching from above,** the most obvious danger is that of getting too close top the edge and falling through. However, the greater danger is that of your weight caus-

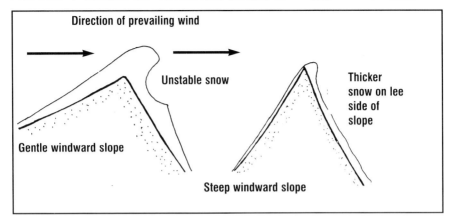

Figure 42: Cornice development and slope angle

ing a section of the cornice to collapse, for the **fracture line** is much further back from the edge than many people imagine (see figure 43). Even if you realise this danger, there are situations in which an apparently safe route can take you inside the fracture line (see figure 44). Good map interpretation is therefore of vital importance, and you should aim to gain a safe vantage point from which to view the edge whenever possible.

Particularly hazardous is searching for the start of a descent route. Sometimes the extent of the danger zone may be obvious from fracture lines, slumps and partial collapses; at other times it may be possible for you to gain a vantage point from which to judge the extent of the cornice. If you are unsure and must walk close to the edge in order to find the correct route, it would be prudent for you to rope up and be held on a belay. If there is no suit-

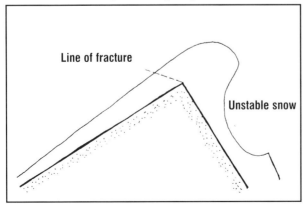

Figure 43: Cornice fracture line

able natural anchor available, you will need to manufacture one with your ice axe. Such techniques are beyond the scope of this book for the reasons outlined earlier when discussing winter skills.

When **approaching from below**, or simply passing below a corniced slope, the

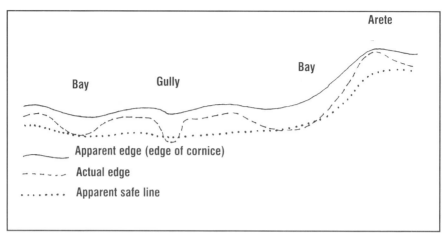

Figure 44: Cornice hazards

most obvious danger is that of the cornice collapsing on top of you. There are a number of factors to consider. Firstly, the fact that a cornice is there at all is an indication of potential avalanche conditions (see below) for there is often a build-up of unstable snow on the slope beneath. Secondly, all cornices are inherently unstable and may collapse at any time. Whilst physical examination from below is not recommended (!), a glance at neighbouring slopes for signs of recent debris may give you some clue as to the likelihood of imminent collapse. If a nearby cornice has collapse, it is likely that there will be further collapses in the near future. However, do not be lulled into a false sense of security if no other cornices have collapsed, for the one above you may be the first to drop!

The **weather conditions**, both current and over the preceding few days, will also play a significant part in the stability of any cornice. Whilst it should be obvious that thaw conditions spell danger, recent heavy snowfall or winds strong enough to cause drifting will result in a build-up of snow which may, in itself, cause the cornice to collapse. As it happens, heavy snowfall and strong drifting are also classic avalanche conditions. This simply magnifies the potential danger for if an avalanche does not occur independently, under these circumstances a collapsing cornice is almost certain to trigger one.

Avalanche

Over the past decade, much publicity has been given of the danger of avalanche, yet it is fair to say that a large number of hillwalkers still do not fully appreciate the risks. It is also fair to say that the mechanisms at work in avalanche are so complex that no-one fully understands them. Although this is an important safety consideration for anyone visiting the mountains under winter conditions, there is quite simply insufficient space here for me to do anything but give a brief overview of the main factors. Those of you wishing to know more will find details of a couple of relevant books in the bibliography.

We have already seen that different conditions will produce different types of snowflake. Thus the type of snow deposited in one snowfall may well be totally different to the type of snow deposited in the next. Additionally, the snow on the ground may well have undergone some changes before being covered by the new snow — for example, it may have been partially melted and have a crust on it or there may be surface hoar present. Over successive snowfalls one can therefore get a build up of several layers of snow, each with a different character. If two neighbouring layers of snow are of different hardness, or if layers are lubricated in some way (by a layer of unstable crystals or a sheet of water), a line of weakness is formed along which large masses of snow can slide.

A snowflake is inherently unstable and will change its shape as time goes by. There are three main processes at work in this situation. In **destructive metamorphism** (also known as equi-temperature metamorphism), the individual snowflakes become simplified, changing from angular crystals to rounded pellets. This initially results in a lack of cohesion between the individual particles, although eventually they will freeze together to form a layer. In practical terms, what happens is that the snow settles and then becomes more stable. This process happens most readily when the snowpack remains just below freezing. However, the colder the snowpack, the longer the process will take.

If the temperature oscillates around 0°C, the process of **melt-freeze metamorphism occurs.** During the day, when the temperature is above freezing, some of the crystals melt. When the temperature drops below freezing, the water so formed refreezes and bonds the crystals together. This process can result in a highly stable snow pack, but there are other considerations as well. For example, the water formed can percolate downwards through the snowpack until its reaches an impermeable layer, such as could be caused by destructive metamorphism. When this happens it will flow along the boundary between this layer and the one above, effectively lubricating the joint.

Constructive metamorphism (or temperature gradient metamorphism) occurs when temperatures remain below freezing for a considerable period of time. When this happens there is a temperature gradient from the ground to the snow surface, and this allows water vapour to rise through the layers. If this continues for any length of time, it can result in the formation of large unstable crystals which, in addition to forming a lubricating layer, also represent a weakness which can fail suddenly and cause an avalanche.

One final type of metamorphism is found during **sudden thaw.** Under these conditions the crystalline structure of the snow can be destroyed before the snow melts, causing the whole snowpack to flow down the slope. This can be extremely dangerous as large quantities of debris are carried with the slide. A further problem is that the whole mass may freeze solid within only a few minutes of stopping.

Theory is all well and good, but we should be more concerned with practicalities. For a start, given the right conditions, avalanches can occur anywhere. Although they are most common in the Scottish hills, they also occur on a regular basis in places such as the Lake District and Snowdonia, and have been reported from the Brecon Beacons and even the South Downs! Avalanches will only occur if there is sufficient snow. The greater the **amount of snow,** the greater the risk of avalanche. 80% of all avalanches occur during or within 24hrs of heavy snowfall. The **angle of slope** also plays an important part. Although it is commonly believed that the steeper the slope, the more likely the risk of avalanche, there comes a point where a slope is so steep that it will not allow large accumulations of snow and the risk therefore declines. The most dangerous slopes are those where large amounts of snow can build up. These are of medium angle, the highest risk being on slopes of between 30° and 45°, although there is a risk on any slope of between about 20° and 60°. Moreover, the **shape of slope** will have an effect. All snow will slowly migrate down a slope due to the effects of gravity. If the slope if uniform, the process is usually a slow one. If the slope if concave, there is compression of the layers at the point of concavity; however, if the slope is convex, an area of tension results and this can cause the layers of snow to fracture, and a significant number of avalanches start from such points. Another governing factor is the **type of surface** on which the snow pack lies. Slopes of long grass, mobile scree and smooth rock slabs provide little cohesion for the snow, and therefore the risk of avalanche from such slopes is increased.

One cannot assess the avalanche risk without taking past wind conditions into consideration. Not only will high winds cause large accumulations of snow through drifting, it will also deposit snow in layers of windslab. Generally speaking, the higher the wind-speed, the harder the **windslab.** Successive windslabs may only be marginally attached to one a another and therefore present a very high avalanche risk. Slab avalanches are the most commonly occurring type of avalanche in the British mountains. They are also the most difficult to predict. Do not underestimate their danger.

Although avalanches occur naturally, most avalanches involving people are caused by their victims. Before setting out on a winter expedition, **ask local advice.** Avoid the hills within 48hrs of heavy snowfall (or longer if it is particularly cold), and be wary of sudden changes in temperature, especially moving from cold conditions to mild conditions. If you think there may be a risk, keep to the high ground and avoid all convex slopes and those between 30° and 45°. Avoid gullies and narrow or enclosed valleys, and keep to windward slopes where possible. Look out for signs of recent or impending avalanche activity such as collapsing cornices, areas of subsidence, and cracks (especially when they run parallel to the slope), and take warning from small slides of slab when you move your feet.

You can also assess the risk by digging a **snowpit** using either a shovel or your ice axe. This should be dug in an area away from any risk of avalanche, but which is at about the same altitude and facing in the same direction as the suspect slope. The pit should be about 1 metre wide, and should ideally be dug down to ground level. The back wall should be smoothed so that there is a clear indication of any differences between snow layers. What you are looking for is large differences between hardness or water content in adjoining layers, and three tests should be carried out. Regarding **hardness,** it is usual to work on a scale of 1 to 5, 1 being soft powder snow and 5 being hard, consolidated snow-ice. If any adjacent layers have a difference in hardness of 3 or more, there is a high avalanche risk. With regard to **water content**, work on a scale of 1 to 5 again, 1 being dry powder which will not stick together, and 5 being wet snow which releases water when squeezed. Again, any large differences should be taken as warning signs, with the added proviso that the water in wet layers (4 or 5) can act as a lubricant and increase the chances of avalanche. Finally, look at the basic **structure** of the snow. Particularly dangerous are large cup-shaped crystals and rounded grains of graupel, both of which can form an ideal sliding surface. Once you have completed these observations, use the shaft of your axe to cut two vertical slots just under a metre apart in the back wall of your pit. Now get a companion to approach slowly from above, so that his weight causes the snow to slump. If a slab breaks away cleanly between two layers, this represents weak bonding and the ease with which it breaks indicates the ease with which an avalanche could occur.

If you find yourself in a situation where it is imperative that you cross a slope which you consider to be suspect, do so one at a time, choosing if possible the shortest route between two stable points such as trees or outcrops. Before starting to cross, loosen your rucksack, raise your hood and zip up your jacket to give some protection to your face, and remove any ice-axe loop. When crossing, move slowly and steadily, heading slightly downhill. If the slope does avalanche there is probably very little that you will be able to do. If you are on the edge of the slide, you may be able to escape, but if not you should try to stay where you are for as long as possible — the longer you stay still, the less material there will be to bury you. Try to keep upright with your back to the snow. If you start to move, get rid of your ice axe and rucksack, cover your face, keep your mouth closed and try to roll towards the nearest edge of the slide. The critical period for survival is as the avalanche slows. If you are still conscious struggle with all your might to make as large an airspace around you as you can and claw your way towards any light before the snow sets solid.

80% of avalanche fatalities are caused by suffocation, so keep your eyes on your companions as they cross a suspect slope, and try to track their position if they are engulfed. If they are buried, try to note the position at which they were caught and the position at which they were last seen, as this may give an indication of where they are. **Speed is of the essence**. As soon as the slope has stabilised, do an immediate surface search and dig in any likely places.

If you visit the hills in winter, it would be wise to consider carrying an avalanche beacon or, at the very least, an avalanche cord. **Avalanche cords** are long lengths of brightly coloured nylon which have arrows pointing in one direction along their length. You tie the end towards which the arrows point around your waist and leave the rest trailing when you cross a suspect slope. If you are avalanched, some part of the cord may rest of the surface and this will guide rescuers to your position fairly quickly. **Avalanche beacons,** on the other hand, are far more expensive, but they may save a life. These are simple radio transceivers which can be set either to transmit or receive. These should be carried on your person and not in your rucksack for you may be parted from your rucksack if you are avalanched. Under normal circumstances you should switch the beacon to transmit mode. When searching for an overwhelmed person, you set them to receive mode. Different models work in different ways, but most work on the principle that increasing signal strength indicates decreasing distance from the casualty. Different models also work on different frequencies, so it makes sense to check that all beacons in the same party work on the same frequency.

Whiteout

Mention has already been made of whiteout conditions on page 138. If you are caught in such conditions, accurate navigation becomes imperative, especially if you are in areas where there are drops and possible cornices. It is no exaggeration to say that you could be standing on the edge of a crag and not even know it is there! You will be disorientated, you will probably stumble and fall over a fair amount, and you will need to concentrate on what you are doing. Because you will have no horizon, your judgement of distance and time will be impaired, so use Naismith's Rule and pacing. Compass navigation will necessitate a leap frogging technique.

9 AILMENTS

I have strong views about First Aid training: I feel it should be a compulsory subject at both primary and secondary levels of education. Be that as it may, when you consider how far you might be from front-line medical assistance when you are in the mountains, it makes sound sense for every visitor to the hills to have at least a working knowledge of basic first aid techniques. I would therefore encourage you to get some training, preferably on a course aimed specifically at outdoor first aid.

Although it is not possible for me to go into a great amount of detail, no book about mountain safety would be complete without at least a passing mention of some of the more common ailments.

Mountain hypothermia

Of all the ailments met in the mountains, it is unquestionably mountain hypothermia, or **exhaustion-exposure,** which is the most insidious. Despite the fact that it is easily avoidable in the vast majority of situations, it responsible for a large number of deaths each year. One of the main reasons for this may be that, notwithstanding continual efforts by organisations such as the British Mountaineering Council, the condition is still largely misunderstood by many hillgoers. To give a classic example, most people associate mountain hypothermia with cold conditions, but the colder it is, the warmer you dress, and the more aware of the temperature you are. The sad fact of the matter is that mountain hypothermia most commonly occurs when the ambient temperature is between 5°C and 10°C.

When discussing the Layer System (page 17), I described the body as a machine with two main parts: the **core** (containing all the vital organs), and the **shell** (the skin, flesh and bones). It was stated that this human machine had a set of ideal operating conditions, the most important of which was the temperature of the core. Hypothermia occurs when the temperature of the core drops below its optimum value of 37°C, the immediate result being a marked decrease in the efficiency of the vital organs. The brain (and thus the personality) is one of the first things to be affected, so different individuals will react in different ways. Because of this, although there are several parallels, it is true to say that no two cases of mountain hypothermia have ever been exactly the same.

This, of course, presents us with a problem, because different people will display different symptoms! The most straightforward approach is to work on the basis that, in marginal conditions, any change of character or unusual behaviour should be regarded as indicative of possible hypothermia.

Several other factors will have an affect. Firstly, the word **exhaustion** is important here, because the body requires energy in order to produce heat. This is one of the reasons that a good, cooked breakfast and frequent high energy snacks are vital in poor conditions. Secondly, even on good days, people who have suffered an accident and have gone into shock are at greater risk from the condition, and should therefore have their heat loss minimised as a matter of urgency. Thirdly, psychology appears to play an vital role and the **will to live is essential**. Finally, always treat the condition as serious and provide treatment with the utmost urgency. It is not overly melodramatic to say that the time between onset and death can be less than two hours.

In order that you are able to treat mountain hypothermia effectively, it is necessary that you know a little more about cause and effect.

The body normally maintains its core temperature to within very fine limits, balancing heat losses and gains through a variety of mechanisms. In terms of hypothermia, it is the way in which the capillaries (tiny blood vessels) below the surface of the skin react which is the most important. If heat gain exceeds heat loss, these capillaries open up through the mechanism of **vasodilation**. This allows more blood to pass close to the surface of the skin so that heat can be shed. This is accompanied by **sweating** in order that evaporation can increase the amount of heat lost. If, on the other hand, heat loss exceeds heat gain, the capillaries close down through the mechanism of **vasoconstriction.** This reduces the amount of blood flowing to the shell and therefore reduces the amount of heat loss at the core. Additionally, because muscular activity produces heat, we start to **shiver** as a means of creating more heat. The reason your fingers feel numb and you fumble when you are cold is because vasoconstriction has reduced the blood flow to the muscles and reduced their efficiency.

It is when the heat loss continues that we enter the problem area. As mentioned above, everyone reacts in a slightly different way. Although we can identify a number of phases, the signs and symptoms may overlap or may even be absent in certain individuals, so the following is a guide to what you may see.

The first phase — **mild hypothermia** — begins as the core temperature drops below 37°C. Coldness and fatigue are obvious common symptoms, and many sufferers experience cramp as vaso-constriction begins to reduce the blood supply to the muscles. As the core temperature decreases past 36°C, vasoconstriction will increase to the extent that the muscles start to become seriously affected, and sufferers will stumble, fumble, and display a general lack of co-ordination. Shivering becomes uncontrollable, and the skin may take on a pallid appearance. The efficiency of the brain, too, will start to deteriorate, and sufferers may become lethargic, apathetic, and withdrawn. At this stage, further deterioration can often be prevented simply by reducing heat loss (see later). Beyond this stage, however, the situation becomes far more serious.

As the core temperature drops below 35°C, we enter the stage of **moderate hypothermia.** The situation has now become very serious indeed, and the most insidious aspects of the condition will begin to take affect. The brain will, by now, have become so affect-ed that the sufferer may refuse to acknowledge that there is a prob-lem, and may become abusive and even violent if you try help. As the body tries even harder to prevent further heat loss, vasocon-striction will increase to the extent that shivering will cease. Muscular movement will become sluggish and erratic, stumbling and pallor will increase, and it will take a long time for the suffer-er to recover after increasingly frequent falls. At about 33°C, the vital organs will deteriorate rapidly, the most marked effects being on the brain and the visual cortex. Irrational behaviour (many peo-ple start taking off their clothes) and incoherence together with hallucination and other forms of visual disturbance are commonly reported, and many victims start suffering from amnesia. Make no mistake about it: people suffering from moderate hypothermia are very ill. Damage to the vital organs will be such that prevention of further heat loss will be insufficient to promote recovery, and the sufferer will have to be actively rewarmed.

As the core temperature drops below about 31°C, the sufferer enters the stage of **severe hypothermia** — a critical condition in which both heart beat and respiration will begin to weaken. Stupor becomes increasingly apparent, and the pupils may begin to dilate. Below about 30°C, the heartbeat will become weak and irregular, and the sufferer will drift towards unconsciousness. Even if the heat loss is stopped immediately, death will occur within a matter of a few hours unless medical help is available. Indeed, by this stage, chemical changes will have taken place within the body which can lead to fatal complications on rewarming, so it is imper-ative that anyone who reaches this stage gets expert medical help as a matter of extreme urgency.

When the core temperature drops below 29°C we reach the stage of **acute hypothermia** in which most reflexes cease to function. Heartbeat and respiration will continue to weaken and become increasingly erratic. Below 28°C the autonomic nervous system governing heart beat and breathing will start to fail, and the sufferer may exhibit no noticeable pulse or breathing. However, it is imperative that you do not take the absence of breathing or pulse to indicate death. Extremely low core temperatures reduce the body's need for oxygen, and there are documented cases in which acutely hypothermic people have made a full recovery after having exhibited neither pulse nor respiration for over an hour.

The most common mistake after having diagnosed the onset of the condition is to head urgently for the nearest habitation, forcing the sufferer along. Unless this is at the earliest stages of mild hypothermia and habitation is very close to hand (under, say, an easy kilometre), this is totally the wrong thing to do, for any additional expenditure of energy by the sufferer can cause the core temperature to plummet with possibly fatal results. In the most basic of terms, **treatment** is simple. No matter where you are, the most important thing to do is to stop any further heat loss, and the simplest way to do this is to find some sort of shelter from the wind, even if you have to make this yourself. This is where your cheap plastic **survival bag** can literally become a life saver.

Once in shelter, replace the sufferer's wet clothes with dry ones (but see below), and place him in a survival bag which has been insulated from the ground with a sleepmat, rucksack, clothing, or anything else which comes to hand. You should now attempt active rewarming, the easiest way being to get someone to join the sufferer in the survival bag. If you can also give hot drinks and some high energy foods (your **survival rations**), so much the better. A sleeping bag would also be useful, but make sure that someone else has warmed it first as the sufferer's shell temperature will be so low that he will be unable to warm a sleeping bag himself. Rewarming should be gentle and general — on no account should you attempt massage or vigorous rubbing, nor should you place warm objects against the sufferer's skin. Doing so would reverse the effects of vasodilation, causing the local capillaries to open allowing warm core blood to be replaced with cold shell blood. Giving alcohol to a hypothermic person will also have the same effect, for one of the effects of alcohol is to promote vasodilation. Do not forget, also, that psychology plays a part in the treatment of any ailment. Give plenty of TLC (tender loving care) and calm reassurance no matter how worried you are. Think also of yourself and the other members of the party: if conditions are such that one person is suffering, chances are that others may be at risk especially if they are hanging around doing nothing.

Recovery from mild hypothermia can be rapid and may appear to be total. Even if this occurs, there should be no question of pushing on, as the sufferer will have been severely weakened by the condition. You must get him off the hill by the easiest and most sheltered route — this will not necessarily be the quickest. If recovery does not occur within two hours, or if the condition worsens, you should work on the basis that the moderate hypothermic stage has been reached and any further heat loss could prove fatal. Although the treatment continues to be the same, there are now other factors to consider. For example, if on initial diagnosis you suspect the sufferer has already reached this stage, you will have to think very carefully before removing any wet clothing, for this will contain a small amount of heat and provide a small amount of insulation, albeit minimal. Removing wet clothing may therefore result in an overall heat loss, and this must be avoided at all costs. Far better, in this situation, to place the sufferer in a survival bag, wet clothes and all, and then provide additional insulation over the top of the wet clothing. Additionally, no matter what the situation, moderate hypothermic casualties should always be regarded as stretcher cases, and a mountain rescue team should be called. Self-help is not advised.

Recovery from moderate hypothermia will not occur without the application of some form of external heat. If the sufferer is conscious, by all means administer hot sweet drinks and high energy foods. If you are carrying a tent, pitch this and place the sufferer inside together with as many other members of the party as is comfortably possible. Also extremely useful in this situation are KISU's (see page 181).

If the sufferer reaches the severe or acutely hypothermic phase, the situation has become extremely grave indeed. No matter what action is taken to reverse the heat loss, death is inevitable within a few hours unless specialist medical help is available. Summoning a mountain rescue team therefore becomes a matter of extreme urgency. All you can do on site is provide shelter, prevent any further heat loss, and provide general rewarming.

Finally, three points are worth reiterating. Firstly, assuming you know the sufferer reasonably well, the occurrence of any uncharacteristic behaviour in marginal conditions should be regarded as being indicative of exhaustion-exposure. Your usually mild-mannered companion may, for example, start to swear and curse and become belligerent. Secondly, assuming that you are not suffering, you are in a far better position to judge the condition of the sufferer than he is himself. Despite any denials on his part, it is essential that treatment begins as early as possible. Prompt action at an early stage is the key to successful treatment and recovery.

Last but by no means least, in 99% of cases, mountain hypothermia is totally avoidable. If you wear the correct clothing and are neither over-ambitious nor foolhardy, it should never occur.

Heat stroke

Going back to our analogy of the human machine, in the same way as a drop in core temperature will lead to serious problems, so too will a rise in core temperature. If you think of mountain hypothermia lying at one end of the temperature scale, heat stroke lies at the other. Indeed, whilst there are many similarities between the symptoms of the two conditions, the treatments are at opposite extremes.

When you visit the mountains in hot weather, and particularly in humid conditions, the heat gained through muscular exertion can be so intense that the body is unable to maintain its heat balance. The response to overheating is **vasodilation** accompanied by sweating. As the amount of overheating increases, so the amount of sweat produced increases. Even if this reduces the overheating, the loss of the fluid and the salts contained in the sweat can result in several problems, most noticeably **heat cramp,** which can be regarded as the first stage of heat stroke.

Heat cramp usually affects the stomach and leg muscles, and is excruciatingly painful. Not only are the effects exacerbated by vasodilation, but the increased blood flow to the shell may cause a decreased blood flow to the brain resulting in a general feeling of weakness, dizziness and possibly fainting. The condition should be taken seriously as it is a warning sign that heat stroke is a distinct possibility, and treatment should be immediate. The sufferer should be put in some form of shade and allowed to rest. If there is no natural shade available you must create some with a survival bag or something similar. Cramped muscles should be eased by stretching and massaging the affected areas. It is also essential that the sufferer is given plenty to drink. Because of the salt loss, the ideal liquid is some form of electrolyte replacement drink, but water to which salt has been added at the rate of a couple of pinches per litre is just as effective (and far cheaper). Do not add more salt than this as at greater concentrations the liquid becomes emetic!

Prompt action will almost always result in rapid recovery. However, as with hypothermia, there should be no question of continuing as the sufferer will have been severely weakened by the experience. He should be led slowly off the hill by the easiest and most shaded route, and allowed frequent rests and drinks.

If heat cramp is ignored, or the level of sweating is not reduced, there will be a real danger of **dehydration.** Additionally, any further physical exertion could cause the core temperature to rise, and the inevitable result is **heat exhaustion,** a far more serious condition. The symptoms are in many ways an extension of those of heat cramp: the sufferer will complain of nausea and headache, will feel fatigued and light headed, and may vomit or faint. Additionally, both pulse and respiration rates may increase as more and more blood is pumped to the shell but, somewhat paradoxically, the skin may feel cold and clammy. Again, some form of shade is of the utmost importance, but now the essential liquid should only be given in sips as the sufferer may not be able to keep it down. Moreover, it is important actively to assist the body to lose heat, and this is best done by loosening or even removing clothing, fanning, and applying wet clothes to the skin and particularly to the forehead. Given shade, active cooling and liquid, recovery will usually occur given time, and this will be assisted by giving more frequent drinks once the nausea has dissipated. Even when the sufferer appears to have recovered, it is important that he be given plenty of time to rest before being led slowly homewards by the easiest and coolest route, for not only can heat exhaustion recur with frightening ease, but it is also only a small step away from heat stroke.

Heat stroke is an extremely serious condition and anyone suffering from it will be critically ill. In this final stage the core temperature has increased to such an extent that the vital functions start to deteriorate. Unfortunately, one of the first things to malfunction is the mechanism of vasodilation which results in the body being unable to lose heat. Consequently, the core temperature will rise rapidly and death will result within a very short period of time. As victims of heat stroke are suffering from a breakdown in their vital organs, they often display many of the symptoms of mountain hypothermia, particularly those of irrational behaviour, aggression and abuse, in addition to most of the symptoms of heat exhaustion. Somewhat confusingly, the skin may either be red, hot and dry or cool, pale and damp. The core temperature could well be as high as 41°C, and immediate and active cooling is imperative for otherwise the sufferer will go into convulsions and die. It will not be sufficient simply to put the sufferer in shade; you must remove his clothing, apply wet clothes or, if available, cool water to the forehead and the back of the neck, and fan him vigorously. Only give him liquid if he is conscious or regains consciousness, and then only in sips. Victims of heat stroke are critically ill and should always be regarded as stretcher cases, even on the very rare occasions that they appear to have made a total recovery. Medical advice should be sought in all cases.

As with hypothermia, the condition is avoidable. On particularly hot days avoid strenuous walking whenever possible, particularly around noon, and drink far more liquid than you feel you need, a little at a time but often. If you eat a balanced diet you should not need salt tablets, but some people, particularly those who sweat profusely, will find them useful. They should be taken in the morning as a precautionary measure rather than being used as first-aid items on the hill.

Many people suffer from mild **dehydration** when they visit the hills, relying on the traditional evening social sessions to get them out of water debt! Whilst mild, short term water debt will not cause too many problems, it is not good practice, and you should always take plenty to drink and sip little but often in order to maintain a good fluid balance.

Frostbite

Like heat stroke, frostbite can be regarded as a progressive condition ranging from frostnip (a far more common condition than generally realised), through superficial frostbite (a common occurrence in emergency situations), and finally to deep frostbite (rare in the British mountains). It is caused initially by a reduction in blood flow to the extremities such as occurs in vasoconstriction or if you wear clothing or footwear which is too tight. As the warm blood flow is reduced, so the surrounding flesh begins to cool, and if the air temperature is low enough and there is insufficient protection, ice crystals will being to grow between the cells and the tissue will literally freeze.

The first stage of the condition, in which the tissue has just started freeze, is **frostnip.** Most commonly affected are the toes, fingers, ears, nose and cheeks, so if you are out in particularly cold conditions and any of these areas begin to feel warm or numb after having been painfully cold, you should suspect frostnip and investigate further. Frostnip is easily detectable as the affected part will be numb and white. Treatment is simple and effective — you should rewarm the afflicted part. Do not rub the area, however, as this could cause more damage. Cheeks, ears and nose can be warmed with the hands, and fingers can be placed under the armpits, preferably beneath a couple of layer of clothing. Rewarming toes is somewhat more problematic and generally requires outside help from someone who is a true friend! The best results are gained by removing socks and placing your feet under

A typical winter's day! The potential for hypothermia, frostnip and snow blindness should be taken into consideration

their jacket, preferably on their stomach, under their armpits, or in their crutch. Recovery is usually fairly rapid, but it may be accompanied by stinging pins-and-needles sensations, and is often painful. The damage caused to the tissue will also result in increased susceptibility in the future, so prevention is far better than cure. If you cannot get the feeling back to the area within about an hour, you should treat the condition as frostbite.

If you think you may have frostnip, particularly frostnipped feet, it is important that you stop, investigate, and take appropriate action even if the removal of gaiters, boots and socks seems like a lot of bother. If you press on regardless and ignore the warning signs you could do yourself some lasting damage, for if the freezing is allowed to continue, **superficial frostbite** is inevitable. This is far more serious as the cells now freeze, rupture and start to die. In addition to being numb, the skin will have the appearance and possibly the texture of white candle wax, and small blisters may form. The immediate treatment is the same as that for frostnip — the affected part should be rewarmed. On no account should you rub the affected area, especially not with snow (a common misconception). Doing so is a bad mistake on three counts: firstly, you could rupture the cells which are already damaged, secondly, snow crystals act as an abrasive on the damaged skin, and thirdly, the resultant moisture evaporates leading to further cooling.

Recovery from frostbite is not so easy as from frostnip, and if feeling has not returned within about half an hour, there is little else you can do without medical help. In this situation you should get off the hill with the part still frozen. If you do succeed in regaining colour and feeling to the affected area, you must make every effort to ensure that it does not re-freeze as you retreat as this will cause greatly increased damage. In all cases, even when recovery appears to have taken place, appropriate medical advice should be sought as soon as possible for there may be lasting damage to tissue and nerves.

Like so many of these conditions, both frostnip and frostbite are avoidable in the vast majority of cases. If you are clothed correctly and discipline yourself to stop and check if you suspect the onset of the condition, there should be no problem. It is particularly important that you avoid wearing any clothing or footwear which restricts movement or circulation. Bear in mind, too, that wet socks and mittens will increase the effects of wind-chill, and can result in frostbite occurring when the temperature is only just below freezing. For this reason, overmitts and gaiters are essential items in winter conditions. On a more positive note, constant fiddling, wriggling your fingers and toes, will result in a small amount of muscular heat and better circulation, and will therefore reduce the risk to these parts.

Finally, when camping in winter conditions, be careful not to spill stove fuel (which freezes well below 0°C) on bare hands, and avoid contact between flesh and bare metal.

Snow blindness

Snow blindness is an excruciatingly painful condition caused by overexposure to ultra-violet radiation. Although there can be similar effects after a long day on the hill in bright sunshine, the condition is mainly associated with sunlight reflecting off snow so that the UV radiation hits the eyes from below. Contrary to popular belief, the condition is even more likely on cloudy days as the cloudbase will itself reflect UV back down again! A major problem is that the damage is done before the symptoms make themselves felt.

Symptoms start with itching, dryness and irritation of the eyeball which quickly develops to the stage where it feels as if there is broken glass under the eyelid. Blinking becomes excruciatingly painful and in severe cases the eyelids may swell. Tear production often increases to the extent that the eyes water permanently. The condition is temporary and will go away of its own accord, given two or three days. During this time, the best relief is gained by lying quietly in a darkened room with cold compresses on the eyes. Analgesic may be taken to reduce the pain, but anaesthetic eye drops should be avoided as they tend to increase the recovery time. Avoid rubbing the eyes.

Once again, prevention is far better than cure, and is simply done by wearing good quality sunglasses or goggles. These should have lenses which filter all the harmful rays, and which are sufficiently tinted to reduce all the glare. If glasses are worn, they should be close fitting and have some form of side baffle to prevent unfiltered light from entering.

If you are caught in snowy conditions without suitable protection, or if you lose your glasses, you can get temporary protection by cutting a narrow horizontal slit in the cardboard cover of a map. This can be used to cover the eyes, held in place either with a spare bootlace, or by a jacket hood.

Sunburn

No matter how much of a sun-worshipper you are, nor how well you tan, sunburn is potentially a serious problem in the mountains. The air is generally much clearer than in valley areas and this leads to greater amounts of UV radiation which may cause you to burn far more readily. The situation is particularly hazardous in winter conditions when snow reflects the radiation upwards.

Avoidance is easy through the regular application of a good **sunscreen** with a filter factor of at least 8. Higher values are necessary for people with fair skins, and a total sunblock is advisable if you have sensitive skin. The sunscreen should be applied to all exposed skin, and in winter conditions you should ensure that you apply it to the underside of your chin, the base of the earlobes and the nostrils. It is better to carry sunscreen in a pocket rather than in a your rucksack as this encourages regular application. Lips should be protected with a suitable lip salve with a high filter factor.

Blisters

Blisters are probably the most common complaint suffered by walkers, and their seriousness should not be underestimated. Although they usually cause nothing more than discomfort, they can be debilitating and can slow you down sufficiently to increase the possibility of benightment. If treated badly (or left untreated), they can also lead to serious problems if you are camping in the wild.

A blister is simply the result of friction, the most common causes being badly fitting boots, ill-fitting socks, sensitive feet, or foreign bodies. Avoidance is simple — before the blister forms you will feel a **hot-spot** or soreness. You should discipline yourself to stop immediately this occurs and pad the area with zinc oxide plaster or a proprietary blister pad.

If you are weak-willed and continue until the blister is allowed to form, you should treat it by bursting it with a sterile needle, draining the fluid, and then covering it with a pad. Do not remove the blistered skin.

Particularly effective are pads made from artificial skin — a special gel layer which provides not only padding, but also has antiseptic and lubricating qualities. Alternatively use a dressing held in place with zinc oxide plaster. If the blister has formed on a toe, the most effective way to pad it is by using micropore or tubular bandage. If the blister is particularly large, you should cut the plaster in such a way that it does not crease when applied.

Once you arrive home (or at your campsite), remove the dressing, wash your feet to reduce the chance of infection, and let the blister breathe. If you are visiting the hills again within the next few days, cover the affected area with artificial skin before you set out.

More serious injuries

And so we come back to first aid training. Everyone who visits the mountains should have a working knowledge of the ABC of First aid, for if something happens it could be some time before qualified medical help arrives. At the very least you should know the recovery position, how to give CPR, what to do in cases of severe bleeding, and how to deal with fractures. One problem you may meet is that most standard First Aid courses are run on the basis that you can dial 999 and expect an ambulance to arrive within a matter of minutes. I would therefore advise you, if you wish to go on a course, that you find one which focuses specifically on practical techniques which are of use when dealing with casualties in remote situations.

10 EMERGENCY PROCEDURES

Accidents can happen to anyone, no matter how experienced or well equipped. It therefore makes sense to have thought a little about what you would do in the event of an accident — before it occurs. The problem is that no two accidents are ever the same. There are so many variables (weather, location, terrain, people, nature of injury, time of day, equipment available, etc.) that every accident is unique. There are thus few, if any, hard and fast rules governing what you should do.

Having said this, there are certain areas where we can draw definite conclusions. For example, if you are the leader of a party, the order of your priorities is quite clear. Your first priority is to the rest of your party — it is pointless going to someone's aid if this results in further casualties. Your second priority is to yourself — it is of little use trying to help someone if you end up injured yourself. As cynical as it may sound, the casualty comes third. If you are a member of a party, the order still applies, for you should keep your eyes on your colleagues who may well be unable to cope with the situation as well as you. This is particularly important in marginal weather conditions when hypothermia is an ever-present risk for all members of the group in any emergency situation.

Similarly, you should try to stay cool, calm and collected at all times. Granted, it is easy for me to write this sitting comfortably in front of a word processor whereas it is a totally different proposition when clinging to a heather ledge above an awesome drop in a howling gale. In any case, no-one knows how they will react to an emergency until it actually happens, but whatever the situation, you will not help matters by panicking. If you feel yourself losing control, try to focus your attention and "centre" yourself (to use the modern phrase). Calm yourself by consciously controlling your breathing, drawing in deep breaths and releasing them slowly.

Rescue call-out procedures

Self-evacuation is never an easy option. Whilst there are certain things you can do you to help yourself and the casualty (see below), you should never delay in calling for help for fear of embarrassment or recrimination. The situation will be far worse if you try to do it all yourself and fail. In the most general of terms, you would be wise to summon assistance in all situations except those where the casualty is reasonably mobile, where the injuries are superficial, or where the journey off the hill is exceptionally short. Most mountain rescue teams would rather arrive to a situation which is less serious than was reported than be called out later to pick up a corpse. Having said this, there have been a number of situations over the past few months where people with mobile phones have called mountain rescue when in all honesty, their situation was not that serious. Whilst a mobile phone can have obvious advantages in a real emergency, it should not be seen as an easy way out of trouble.

Your initial call for help will probably be to people who may be nearby, and this is best done by giving the **alpine distress signal.** This consists of six good blasts on a whistle followed by a minutes silence, repeated as necessary. You should continue giving the signal until you are in visual contact with people coming to your aid. If you hear this signal, you should acknowledge the fact by giving the reply — three good blasts on a whistle followed by a minutes silence, repeated as necessary. Once again, you should repeat this acknowledgement until you are within visual contact with the distressed party. As it happens, any whistling in the mountains may be construed as being a distress signal, so never blow your whistle unless in distress or answering a distress call. If for some reason you have no whistle, the same signal can be given by shouting or waving a bright object such as a white handkerchief, orange survival bag or similar. At night, flashing a torch (in conjunction with blasts on a whistle, if possible) could be useful. Having said all this there are two points worth bearing in mind. Firstly, if you are in distress it may well be that the weather conditions are so bad in terms of visibility and wind, that people only a couple of hundred metres away may not hear or see you. Secondly, whistles have been abused to such an extent that many people may well ignore anything but a clear alpine distress call or SOS (three quick blasts/flashes/waves followed by three long blasts/ flashes/waves followed by a further three quick blasts/flashes/waves then a short pause before repeating the sequence all over again).

It is a great tradition of the mountains that the mountaineer looks after his own. If you suspect that a party may be in distress, try to investigate further. If you can reach them easily and safely, all well and good, but on no account should you jeopardise your own safety or that of your companions. If you hear a distress signal but for some reason cannot find out any more, give the acknowledgement a few times, then make your way quickly but safely to the nearest telephone or rescue post and notify mountain rescue. You will almost always be asked to stay by the telephone and await either further instructions or the arrival of a team member. This is because face-to-face discussions are invariably more informative than telephone conversations.

The **call-out procedure for mountain rescue** is simple. Either visit a manned post or (more likely) get to a telephone, dial 999, ask for the police then ask for mountain rescue. In order to proceed promptly and efficiently with the rescue, the team will need a lot of information. In particular, they will need to know the precise location of the incident. Although this is best done by giving a six figure grid reference, there may be times when this is not possible (when, for example, you have heard a distress signal but have been unable to investigate further). In such cases, give as much information as you can, by giving your position when you heard the distress signal, the direction from which it came, etc. If the incident has taken place on a rock climb, you should give the name of the crag, the name of the climb and the pitch on which the accident happened. Similar information should be given if the accident occurred on a scramble. Ideally, the rescue team should be able to go straight to the incident site from your description, and should know whether to approach from the top or bottom of a climb or scramble.

In addition to the location, the team will want to know such things as the time the accident occurred, the number of people injured and the nature of their injuries, the weather conditions at the incident site, the number of people remaining at the site, etc. Whether you are a member of the party or someone who has gone to their aid or is reporting their distress, many of the questions asked may seem irrelevant at the time. However, all these questions will be asked for good reasons.

Self-help

It may sound trite, but the best way you can help yourselves is not to let the accident occur in the first place! Although unforseeable accidents do occur, the vast majority are avoidable. As mentioned earlier, I think that a good philosophy for mountain activities is "Bottle out and run away, live to climb another day!". Unfortunately, it often takes more courage to turn back than to push on regardless, especially if you have been planning the weekend away for some time.

Do not take unnecessary risks; if the weather looks threatening or something is going wrong, either turn back or modify your plans accordingly. After all, the mountain will always be there —

there will always be another opportunity — and you will probably enjoy the experience all the more if you wait until the circumstances are more favourable.

If an accident does occur, try to stay cool, calm and collected, make sure that there is no risk to yourself or other members of the party, then go to the aid of the casualty. Administer immediate first aid as necessary, checking bleeding, breathing and heartbeat. If the casualty is unconscious, move him into the **recovery position** unless you suspect neck or spinal injury, in which case you should not move him unless not doing so will seriously prejudice his chances of survival. If the casualty is conscious, give him plenty of reassurance and TLC.

Do not underestimate the effects of medical **shock,** and always work on the basis that an injured person is far more likely to succumb to **hypothermia.** If you are able to move him, get him to a sheltered position, the most important consideration being protection from the wind. If you cannot move him, it may be necessary to build some form of shelter around him (see below). Give him extra warm clothing (dressing him yourself if necessary), and place him in a survival bag. Do not forget to insulate him from the ground. Reassure him at regular intervals.

Now is the time to use your emergency rations. If you can also provide a hot drink (either from a flask or, if you have the equipment, by starting a brew), so much the better. Hot, sweet drinks are of enormous benefit in cases of hypothermia and shock, and are a good morale booster for the remaining members of the party. Never try to give food or drink to an unconscious casualty or to anyone suffering from head, chest or abdominal injuries.

If you are alone with the casualty, you will have to make an extremely difficult decision — whether to stay with him, signal your distress and hope that help will soon arrive, or whether to leave him alone whilst you go and summon help yourself. There are no easy answers here — the decision can only be made at the time and will depend upon such things as location, nature of injuries, weather conditions, time of day, etc. If you decide to go and he is conscious, make sure he is as warm and as comfortable as possible. Reassure him once again, leave him your spare clothing plus a flask and emergency rations if possible, and make sure he has a whistle and a torch so that he can signal to any approaching rescue team. If you are carrying one, leave him a stove and pan so that he can make a hot drink himself. It may be several long hours before a rescue party arrives. If he is unconscious, do all of the above and, if possible, tie him to an anchor so that if he regains consciousness he cannot wander off in a daze. This is particularly important in the event of an accident on a rock climb or scramble, or if there is steep, rocky ground in the near vicinity. It is also a good idea to leave a reassuring note explaining what you are doing. Before you leave, mark the precise position as prominently as you can using bright objects as markers. If you have a climbing rope, run it out in a line across the hillside so that there is a good chance of finding the position again, even in bad visibility. Once you have done as much as you can, make your way carefully to the nearest telephone by the easiest route, always remembering that his safety now relies on your safety. Never take unnecessary risks.

If you are a member of a larger party, you must decide how many people should go for help and how many people should stay with the casualty. Again, there are a number of considerations, the most important one being that, wherever possible, at least two people should go for help. If the weather conditions are marginal, anyone who stays is at risk from hypothermia, so it may at first glance appear that as few people should stay as possible. However, the other side of the coin is that the more people there are in a shelter, the warmer it will be, and this will not only reduce the risk of hypothermia but will also help a conscious casualty.

There are never any easy decisions in a mountain emergency. All you can do is think about the effects of the weather, the surroundings and the situation both on the casualty and on the remainder of the party. In the heat of the moment, do not neglect to think about the effect on yourself.

Improvised shelters

Even where there has not been an accident, you may have made an error of judgement and still be left high on the hill in gathering darkness. Indeed, benightment is an especially high risk in winter when mountain days are short, and you would do well to think about finding shelter earlier rather than later, for trying to build a shelter in unknown terrain in the dark can be a nightmare. Having said this, try to get as far down the mountain as you can, but once benightment is inevitable, stop as soon as you see anything which can be used to provide shelter.

In some areas it is possible to find superb natural shelters formed by overhanging boulders or piles of huge rocks. If there is natural shelter, use it. However, the chances of you coming across one of these by accident at the precise time you need it are slim. Even if there is natural shelter, you may well be able to improve it. In any

Never underestimate the difficulties of self evacuation

case, some form of shared activity can be a great morale booster. Having people hanging around doing nothing is not going to help matters, and could well precipitate further problems. Getting people involved and doing something will not only take their minds off the blacker side of the situation, but the physical activity may keep them warm and thus help to prevent them from becoming hypothermic.

If there is no natural shelter nearby, you will have to construct some yourself. Innovation is the key as you must make the most of what is available. At its most simple, a shelter may well be a polythene survival bag or breathable fabric bivibag, but if you can also get to the leeside of a boulder or build a low wall of stones, so much the better. Indeed, if you have a casualty who cannot be moved, building a sheltering wall of stones may be your only option. If everyone in the party has a survival bag, particularly if some people have the larger double bags, there is nothing to prevent you from getting two people to share a bag. Spare bags can then be cut along one long side and the bottom to form a large sheet of plastic which can be used to form added protection. This can be draped across the top of a boulder or a low wall, secured between two low walls, etc. Shelters of this type are best kept low as this reduces the danger of the wind getting underneath and blowing them apart. Make sure that the sheets are secured in such a way that any boulders securing them cannot be dislodged onto people sheltering. The most important consideration is protection from the wind.

Improvising shelters in **winter conditions** is a different ball game. Not only are conditions likely to be far more harsh, but there is also often a superb shelter-building material all around you — snow. However, here again it is better to use some form of natural shelter than to spend time and energy in digging a snow shelter. Natural snow shelters are often to be found around rocks, stone walls and trees (see figure 45), and many of these can be enlarged, adapted and improved by the application of a little ingenuity.

Digging a good snow shelter is not easy unless you are well practised. It can also consume a considerable amount of time and energy. You may feel hampered by a lack of digging equipment, although it perfectly possible to dig a snow shelter with an ice-axe. Whatever the disadvantages, snow shelters are an extremely effective way of sheltering from winter conditions.

There are basically two types of emergency **snow shelter**: those dug into banks or slopes of snow, and those formed on level ground. Regarding those in snowslopes, it is generally true to say that the steeper the slope, the easier the digging. It is also better if the entrance is a short way up the slope so that the removed material can be disposed of without too much difficulty. Start by digging a round tunnel just wider than your shoulders and begin to enlarge it once you are about 1 metre in. We are not concerned with textbook snowcaves here so much as something to keep you alive, so as long as you include the basic features, almost anything will do (see figure 46). The main considerations are that the entrance should be small and should be below the main area so that the colder air can escape. The main area itself should only be just large enough to accommodate everyone in the party, and should contain a snow bench on which to place insulating material (rope, rucksack, sleepmat, etc.) on which to sit. If the party is large, it may be advisable to dig two entrances which lead to the same main area. Ventilation is very important and should not be overlooked. Most people will want to seal the entrance(s) in some way (with blocks of snow or rucksacks), but ventilation must be maintained both here and, in larger snowcaves, by forming ventilation holes in the roof or walls with the shaft of an ice axe. These ventilation holes should be checked regularly as they will easily become blocked by falling or drifting snow.

On level ground, a **snow trench** is probably the best option. This simply involves excavating a trench in the snow about 0.75 metres deep, piling the snow into one or preferably two walls to either side. Spare survival bags (formed into sheets as described above) can be set into these walls to form a roof. The problem with a snow trench is that there is nowhere for the cold air to escape, and unless you design it very carefully, you have a large amount of contact with the snow. Although it will provide shelter from the wind, it will be an extremely cold experience. Wherever possible, use a snow trench in conjunction with some form of natural shelter.

Whatever type of snow shelter you build, once constructed try

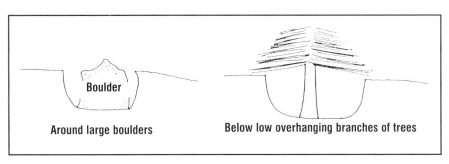

Boulder

Around large boulders   **Below low overhanging branches of trees**

Figure 45: Natural snow shelters

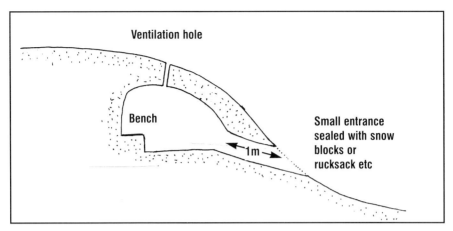

Figure 46: Basic features of a snow hole

to keep movement in and out to a minimum and insulate yourself from the snow by whatever means come to hand. If you have a sleeping bag or bivibag, now is the time to use it. Once in, stay in! If you need to use a stove to heat drinks, you have a ready supply of liquid all around you, but avoid cutting snow from the inside of the main area as this will only result in everyone becoming covered in pieces of snow ice. Beware, too, creating too much condensation as this will initially freeze and subsequently drip! The most important consideration if using a stove is to make sure there is sufficient ventilation.

Mention must be made of **KISU's** (Karrimor Instructors' Survival Units). These are like large dome-tent flysheets. In use, the party get into a huddle and the KISU is thrown over the top of everyone and secured by having its edges sat on! Although not widely available, they can be found if you look for them, and usually come in a range of sizes from 2 man up to about 12 man. They are very effective, the people within them creating a surprising amount of heat. This will obviously be increased if a small stove is lit in the middle to boil water for a brew.

No matter what type of shelter you are in, if it is very cold you should try to keep awake. This is simply because the body's metabolism slows down during sleep and there is therefore an increased danger from hypothermia. Prepare for the night by putting on your spare clothing and insulating yourself from your surroundings, especially from the ground and any surfaces of snow or ice. If your clothing is wet and you have dry gear with you, now is the time to change. Loosen any clothing which could restrict your circulation, and untie your boot laces so as not to restrict the circulation to your feet. Throughout the long night (and it will feel like an eternity), exercise your fingers and toes, and arms and legs at regular intervals by simple clenching, hugging and stretching movements. Try to maintain morale with stories and jokes and reassure any worried people in the party. Remember that survival is predominantly an attitude. No matter how good your survival techniques, the will to live is vital.

Improvised stretchers

Figure 47: Rucksack carry

Although self-evacuation is never an easy option, there may be times when it is necessary to move a casualty a short way in order to get him to a more sheltered position. It may also be possible to effect a self-rescue if an accident occurs within easy striking distance of a road. Piggy-backs and fireman's lifts are not the easiest options, especially on rough terrain. They are exhausting and upset your balance. Various techniques can be used to make the carry more comfortable for both the casualty and those people moving him. A rucksack can be used as an improvised harness to help with a piggy-back type of carry. This is generally only possible with larger rucksacks. The basic idea is to transfer most of its contents to other rucksacks in the group, then loosen the shoulder straps to the extent that, when worn, the casualty can sit on the body of the sack (with extra padding in place if desired) with his legs through the straps (figure 47). This **rucksack carry** is only possible where the casualty has minor injuries and is able to help himself into the correct position. It will help if he sits on a boulder above the carrier, or is upslope at a steep angle.

If you have a climbing rope with you, this can be used to great

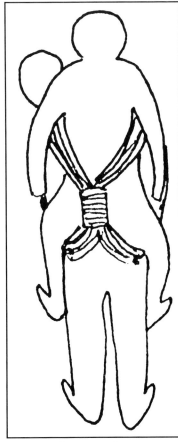

Figure 48: One man split rope carry

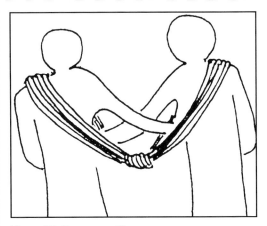

Figure 49: Two man split rope carry

advantage. Although it is possible to tie a rope stretcher, this is a time consuming procedure even for experienced persons, and there are often better alternatives. A better way to use the rope is in some form of **split rope carry** There are two basic techniques, both of which require the rope to be coiled in a mountaineers coil (see page 60). If the coils are split down the middle, the rope can be worn like a rucksack and a form of rucksack carry can be undertaken (figure 48). Some form of extra padding is desirable in this case. A less exhausting technique, perhaps, is to split the coils and share them between two people, the casualty sitting on padding on the rope between them and supporting himself by placing his arms over their shoulders. If this technique is used, the rope should be recoiled so that the coils are long enough to fit over the shoulder opposite the casualty (figure 49). However, although this shares the load, it can be unstable over rough ground and there is always a danger that one person may slip or the casualty may fall off. Moreover, the people carrying the casualty should be of roughly the same height.

Perhaps the most useful improvised stretcher is one formed from a **survival bag.** In this technique, a standard polythene survival bag is used, with or without padding, carrying being facilitated by placing pebbles inside the bag then tying tape slings or climbing rope around them to form carrying handles or shoulder straps. This is quick to make and reasonably easy to carry, but it does rely on having at least four, preferably six or more people available to assist. It will also slide easily on snow covered ground. However, the lack of friction can be disadvantageous as well as the casualty can slide around with alarming ease. If using this technique, ensure that there is sufficient support for the casualty's head, and if carrying on a slope, ensure that he is carried head up and cannot slide off the downslope end of the bag.

Basic search techniques

One of the problems faced when searching for a missing person is that injured people tend to go to ground. Survival instinct takes over, and they seek shelter, even if this means they are not easily visible to a search party. If involved in a search of this nature, do not make the assumption that the victim will be easily seen or will have made an effort to leave some easily visible clue as to his whereabouts. Sadly, this is rarely the case.

The most simple search technique is that of a **token search**, in which you follow the intended route of the missing person looking for some sign of them. If this is not productive, a more comprehensive technique will have to be employed, and this usually involves some form of sweep search. In its basic form, a **sweep search** is conducted by a group of people spread out in a long line, the distance between each person being dependent on both the nature of the terrain and the visibility. The line controller usually places himself somewhere near the middle of the line. Discipline within the line is very important, as is communication between the individual members — it is all too easy for it to become a collection of individuals and this will dramatically lessen the effectiveness of the search. The line must work as a cohesive unit, and it is therefore important that everyone within the line keeps their eyes on their neighbours so that as straight a line as possible is maintained. In particularly difficult terrain where there are many places which could hide the casualty, it may be difficult to maintain line discipline as two or three people may be involved with a detailed search of a chaotic, boulder strewn area whilst the other members of the team are on more open terrain. In such situations the distance between searchers may have to be reduced. Whatever the terrain, shouting and calling should be done at regular intervals, but there should also be definite periods of silence so that any cries for help can be heard.

In a large search, the area is usually divided into a number of sec-

tors, each one usually being defined by a linear feature such as a stream, a long field boundary, or perhaps a ridge. Each sector is then covered by a line search. Perhaps the most important consideration in a search of this type is that the line search within any sector should be conclusive. In other words, if the casualty is there, he must be found. To put it another way, if you search a sector and find no casualty, you must be 100% certain that there is no possibility whatsoever that you have missed him.

To be effective, searches require a fair amount of manpower. It is unlikely that you will need to use these techniques in a casual way. However, a basic knowledge of how searches are organised may be of great benefit if ever you are asked to assist with a search by a mountain rescue team. In any event, if this happens you should be well briefed by a team leader.

11 FURTHER INFORMATION

Nowadays there is a wealth of information available about all sorts of mountain and mountaineering related topics, as a browse through the bookshelves of your local gear store or public library will show. The following should get you started, and I hope it will whet your appetite.

Selective bibliography

Avalanche & Snow Safety,
Colin Fraser, Murray, 1978

The Avalanche Book,
Armstrong & Williams, Fulcrum, 1992

Modern Snow & Ice Techniques,
Bill March, Cicerone, 1973

The Backpackers' Manual,
Cameron McNeish, Oxford Illustrated Press, 1984.

Wild Country Camping,
Kevin Walker, Constable, 1989

The Handbook of Climbing,
Alan Fyffe & Iain Peter, Pelham, 1990

A Manual of Modern Rope Techniques,
Nigel Shepherd, Constable, 1990

First Aid for Hillwalkers,
Renouf & Hulse, Cicerone, 1982

Mountaineering First Aid,
Lentz, MacDonald & Carline, The Mountaineers, 1985

Medical Handbook for Mountaineers,
Peter Steele, Constable, 1988

Mountain Navigation Techniques,
Kevin Walker, Constable, 1986

Mountain Hazards,
Kevin Walker, Constable, 1988

Safety on Mountains,
British Mountaineering Council, BMC, 1991

Mountaincraft & Leadership,
Eric Langmuir, MLTB, 1984

Mountaineering (The Freedom of the Hills),
ed. Peters, The Mountaineers, 1992

Mountain Weather for Climbers,
David Unwin, Cordee, 1978

Mountain Weather, David Pedgley,
Cicerone, 1979

The Weather Handbook,
Alan Watts, Waterline, 1994

There are also a number of excellent monthly publications including High, Climber & Hillwalker, TGO, and Trail Walker.

Useful addresses

BRITISH MOUNTAINEERING COUNCIL
177-179 Burton Road
West Didsbury
MANCHESTER M20 2BB
Tel 0161-445 4747
Fax 0161-445 4500

KEVIN WALKER MOUNTAIN ACTIVITIES
74 Beacons Park
BRECON
Powys LD3 9BQ
Tel/Fax 01874-625111

MOUNTAIN LEADER TRAINING BOARD
Address & telephone as BMC

THE RAMBLERS' ASSOCIATION
1-5 Wandsworth Road
LONDON SW8 2LJ
Tel 0171-582-6826

SCOTTISH SPORTS COUNCIL
Caledonia House
South Gyle
EDINBURGH EH12 9DQ
Tel 0131-317-7200

DALESMAN
Publishing Company Ltd

THE NORTH'S LEADING PUBLISHER
FOR MORE THAN 40 YEARS

With more than 150 books to choose from the **Dalesman** range covers subjects as diverse as:

WALKING, WILDLIFE, HUMOUR,
TOPOGRAPHY, ANTHOLOGIES, HOLIDAY GUIDES,
GHOSTS AND SPORT

For a catalogue of all **Dalesman** titles please send your name and address to:

DALESMAN PUBLISHING CO LTD
FREEPOST
CLAPHAM, VIA LANCASTER, LA2 8EB

Tel 015242 51225

Here is a selection of other books that may interest you:

Map Reading
(ISBN 1 85568 042 4)

Dales Way
(ISBN 1 85568 0072 6)

Cumbria Way
(ISBN 1 85568 000 9)

Complete Dales Walker Vol 1
(ISBN 1 85568 070 X)

Complete Dales Walker Vol. 2
(ISBN 1 85568 071 8)

Complete Lakeland Walker
(ISBN 1 85568 053 X)

Complete Yorkshire Coast and Moors Walker
(ISBN 1 85568 085 8)

Northern Caves Vol. 1
(ISBN 0 85206 927 8)

Northern Caves Vol. 2
(ISBN 1 85568 033 5)

Northern Caves Vol. 3
(ISBN 1 85568 083 1)

Caves of the Peak District
(ISBN 1 85568 034 3)

Rejection&Reven

Book 1 of the Fox Pond

by KM Neale

©2022

With love and thanks to Peter. Always.

Chapter 1

The sun was low behind the line of darkened green Scots pines that towered over the garden of *Fox Pond*, firmly demarcating it from the New Forest that stretched for miles beyond. There was a February, Winter chill in the air, and the dog and cat looked from her to their bowls and back to her.

"You'll have to wait a bit – let me get this first chapter down, then I'll sort you both out."

She began typing:

Kilroy crouched down, head to one side, taking in the girl's lifeless face. The lipstick looked like a blueberry stain smeared across the grey skin; the force of the strangulation had exploded her eyes into a bloodshot network of red. Jenkins and her side-kick were already there, measuring, swabbing, poking at the girl's thigh which flopped to one side, the green skirt rucked up across the stomach.

> *"Any idea of the timings?" Kilroy asked.*
>
> *"You know I don't speculate, Kilroy," Jenkins said without looking up from the thigh.*
>
> *The sidekick risked it: "I'd hazard a guess at six hours ago – 1 a.m.?" He felt Jenkins' glaring displeasure, adjusted his heavy-framed glasses and scurried off with his sample bag.*
>
> *Kilroy looked at the handbag they'd already bagged up and labelled – several smaller plastic bags beside it. No keys, but there was a key chain: a small yellow bird with one or two feathers for its tail – the kind you win from the arcade machines on the seafront. A magazine – French. Hairbrush. Phone. He pulled on his latex gloves and tapped at the screen. Locked.*

"Collins!" he called to his sergeant. "Get this to George. Tell him I want it unlocked – fast."

"But, sir, it's Sunday…"

"Really?" Kilroy frowned. "Religious restrictions, Collins? The Lord's day of rest?' He paused for effect. 'Get it to George and get me all records – I don't care if you have to drag him from the church!"

Jenkins smiled at the image of the old electronics specialist in church, whisky in one hand, coughing on his cigarette.

Kilroy looked around. Uniform were busy taking statements from the locals standing on the other side of the police tape. A dog watched the proceedings through the split plank of a wooden gate. What a desolate, lonely place to die, thought Kilroy. An alleyway linking one sad street to the next; one row of terraced houses leading to the next, leading to nowhere.

He'd transferred up to Kingsmouth 12 years ago – London had lost its pull and he imagined a smaller place might sidestep the darkness he'd experienced in the Capital. He was wrong. This town was classic, English seaside postcard. Its once busy harbour now attracted a small number of visitors in the Summer – the generic, faded amusement arcades shouted out loudly to them - but during the colder months, the place subsisted in a kind of low-wattage neon glow that was both tawdry and sad. The majority of the town's inhabitants had turned to Social Welfare; then the drug dealers moved in like roaches, and it had become increasingly common to see women selling themselves in the ancient winding alleyways.

The dead woman's French magazine might mean foreign student? Certainly, these houses were, for the most part, rooms-to-rent for the small colleges of 'International English' or 'International Hospitality' that sprung up all along the English coast and issued Diplomas with a flourish of raised gold letters from awarding bodies whose acronyms were as recognisable as hieroglyphics.

Kilroy's team were already doing door-to-door; it would be a day before the girl was reported missing. Maybe longer. He hated the idea of showing her photo – her dead face – to all and sundry, but he needed to know who she was before he could find her killer.

> "Kilroy! Detective Kilroy!" Vera Kennedy shouted from the crowd, waving her notebook in the air. "Any idea who she is? A name?"

He ignored the reporter and walked toward the café that backed onto the lane; the smell of coffee and bacon reminded him he hadn't eaten since yesterday. All last night he'd been prowling Queen Street, watching the working women ply their trade – watching for 'John'.

The first letter he'd received from John had been, he thought, the work of a crank. The mad poetry, the biblical prophecies of death and retribution to harlots, the sick drawings – remarkably good, often embellished with idiosyncratic twists. But Friday's letter disturbed him deeply – this retribution was now aimed at a specific harlot – Marie – an old friend of Kilroy's, and one to whom he owed his life.

Chapter 2

Livia hit 'Ctrl' and 's': Chapter 1, draft 1 of book 1 was underway.

> "Right!" she said, closing the lid of the laptop. "Come on, then, Clochette – walk first, then eat. Here, cat," and she sprinkled biscuits into the bowl.

She took the lead from the coat hook and opened the front door as the dog skidded across the stone floor and scarpered out between her feet. The lead was unnecessary: Clochette was too much Border Collie to ever harm the creatures that wandered the New Forest. She raced ahead, across the track down to the wooden footbridge across the stream and up, in a wild run, through the dry heather, browned and bruised by hoar frost, up to the crest of the hill.

They met at the peak and stood for a moment, Livia taking in the scene below. The watery sun was low, a faded, butter-yellow smear of light behind the wood to the right of her cottage. *Fox Pond* looked so welcoming in this last light, the timer lamps on the gate already glowing soft amber. Beyond the wood, about half a mile away through the Beech trees, chimney smoke rose in quiet, damp curlicues above the six houses that made up her neighbourhood.

There had been a dwelling on this site since the 1700s, but today's structure was mostly the rebuilding that had taken place in the early 1900s. It was wide, two-storeys gleaming white with a dark, slate-tiled roof, and a weathered barn standing at its side. The property was accessed via a narrow, gravel track that broke from a larger road about two miles away. The pond, no more than 20 feet across, shone like a dark, silver disc in the shallow valley at the front of the cottage; it was a regular watering hole for the ponies, and, of course, the foxes. Clochette barked and danced, beginning her trek home, back down the hill, with a short detour through the edge of the wood.

Later, the night-time hush of the Forest descended; the cat stretched out across the lounge chair closest to the fire, her head lolling over the edge of the cushion and the dog on the rug just below. Livia logged into her emails – a strictly once-a-day affair, since she suspected that someone had hacked her account and was monitoring
her activity.

Only four emails. Justin Latché's perfunctory, weekly chase checking-in on how the draft was going – not pressuring, just checking, 'We did agree end-of-May?' To those who didn't know him, Justin was a slick, shallow, highly polished media type, purposefully remote, despite the kiss at the end of every email or text. Livia had met him at a writers' workshop, 20 years before, when he was just plain Justin Latchy. He'd already realised, he told her later, that he was never going to be a successful writer, but that he 'had a gift for spotting talent' when he saw it in others: he'd paid for a place on the course in order to find 'the next big thing' and carried, for the sake of authenticity, a battered old manuscript of something he'd once started.

Being forced to endure the other attendees' readings of their depressingly confessional tomes every day – a monologue they continued on into the late, wine-filled evenings – drove Justin and Livia to one another.

> 'I swear!' he said, throwing his hands in the air with exasperation, 'if I have
> to endure another description of lost virginity I will not be responsible for my actions! And doesn't anyone read Larkin, anymore? Your parents failed you – move on!'

He demanded Livia show him her work, and the next morning he delivered his verdict: he was certain Livia was not The One (teachers rarely were). Even so, their friendship had endured.

A few years later, he'd found success with Robert Langley, a hard-drinking ex-soldier who'd written a novel based on his time in Afghanistan. Justin had edited the manuscript and knocked it into, what he thought was, a Hollywood blockbuster. Eventually, he'd settled for a deal with a small, English production company who successfully sold it to ITV as a 10-part mini-series. The next year, Justin scooped the award for best TV adaptation at the National TV Awards. He'd made it. Langley, however, hadn't – he died peacefully in his sleep, after a particularly heavy drinking session of his old regiment.

From that moment, Justin was inundated with new ideas, novels, scripts and he managed to sell them on, establishing his reputation as an agent and producer. But he was becoming uneasy with the rising success of the murder mystery – lone female detectives solving increasingly grisly murders in increasingly grimy northern towns. Or grizzled, cynical male detectives solving the same grisly murders in the leafy suburbs of elite University towns. Justin needed a detective, and knowing that Livia was back in the UK and unemployed, he'd put his proposal to her.

'I know it's not your thing, darling, but how hard can it be? If you could just knock off a draft – 30,000 words? – follow all the rules: detective/sidekick/churlish/pathologist/ corrupt police chief/etc.... and get it to me, I can make it work...'

For a small retainer, she'd accepted: short of signing up for supply teaching, what else did she have to do? (She shuddered as she recalled the slow death of teaching the English Curriculum.)

> 'And one last thing,' he'd warned her gently. 'Don't get too *clever* on me – I loved the stuff you showed me at the workshop, but it's still looking for its moment, right? This one has to appeal to Everyman. And woman, of course (they make up about 67% of our audience). X.'

Clochette sigh-growled in a dream and adjusted herself on the rug.

The next email was from Livia's sister; she scrolled down.

Next, Alex Marchal, her husband. He was not a natural on email, in fact, he wasn't a natural on any kind of electronic platform. The note was brief: attached, last quarter accounts. Business was going well; the accountant had transferred the money into her account. He hoped she was well and he asked after the repairs to the barn – had Martin been able to recommend a builder?

Alexandre Marchal was 10 years older than her; they met through her friend, Claire, who was the marketing manager of a wine consortium – Alex was in the UK promoting his father's vineyard. Livia sighed - it seemed like a life-time ago. They'd
imagined their own vineyard here, in the New Forest, where Alex could make a name for himself, introduce some of the French magic to this comparatively new territory. Buying *Fox Pond* had been the first tentative step. However, not long after their wedding in France, Alex's father died suddenly. The New Forest vineyard plans were shelved, *Fox Pond* rented out, and Alex and Livia became the new keepers of *Chateau Marchal*.

Over the next ten years, they'd revolutionised the brand; Alex in the vineyard, Livia turning her communication skills to introducing their product to the traditional wine markets in America and Australia. She typed a quick response and reassured him that everything was fine.

The last message was from the Library; her requested texts were awaiting collection.

Chapter 3

The waitress finished mopping up the spilled coffee and hurried back with a pot to refill Kilroy's mug.

'I'm so sorry! My nerves...' she tried to smile.

'Don't worry,' smiled Kilroy, trying hard to sound sympathetic. 'It's been a shock hasn't it....?'

'Oh, yeah. I mean it's quite rough round here... you know, the pubs at closing, and lately there's been some new lads moved in... black – oh, not that that makes a difference... but... well....'

'Yeah,' said Kilroy, unfolding his badge. 'What time did you open this morning?'

'Oh!' the badge startled her. 'Oh, around 5 – usual time. You lot were already here...'

'And last night? What time did you lock up?'

'7. Always 7. My husband collects me – doesn't like to be kept waiting.'

'Notice anything unusual? Any new customers?'

She thought for a moment.

'Janice!' The cook called from the kitchen. 'Full breakfast ready to go!'

'Alright, already!' Janice shouted as she walked toward the serving window.

She returned with Kilroy's breakfast.

'A pretty normal day,' she said, frowning. 'There was that woman, though...'

'Yes?'

'Oh, it was nothing, really... she came in and asked if she could use the phone. Said hers had been stolen .... her bag.'

'And, did she...'

'Oh, yeah, Jack, the cook, told her she'd have to pay, so I let her use mine... I mean, her bag had been pinched! How the hell could she pay? She was already more than upset!'

'Upset, how? What time was this?'

'Oh, 5-ish, maybe?' She shouted back to the kitchen: 'Jack, what time did that lady come in? The one who had her bag pinched?'

'Quarter to five...' he shouted back.

Janice turned back to Kilroy.

'She was crying... shaking.... said she'd only put it down for a bit, on a bench down on the Prom.'

'Did she see who did it?'

'No – just turned around and it was gone! She kept saying: 'Oh no, not this again!'

'What did she mean?'

'Dunno.... she was so upset....'Oh no, not this again!''

Kilroy felt an uneasiness, the usual edginess he got before a case broke, or before something went very wrong. He pushed away the greasy, half-finished breakfast.

'Did you get a name? What did she   look like?'

'No... no name... she was, I'd say... 40s? Nice enough looking. Too much make-up... skinny.

Vera Kennedy was making her way to his table, click-clacking her scuffed heels on the linoleum floor.

'What number did she call, Janice – did you check your phone?'

The reporter sat down.

'What was the number?' Kilroy repeated as he stood up.

'Foreign,' answered Janice. 'I checked. France. That'll teach me to help someone out, I s'pose... but I had to help her. She was so upset.'

Kilroy handed her £10.

As he left, Vera called after him in   exasperation. 'Oh, come on, Kilroy!'

Kilroy called back to her: 'Janice has a scoop for you, Vera! Bag snatch!'

He left through the front door; he'd walk back to the station via The Promenade.

Chapter 4

Clochette whined eagerly by the car, waiting for Livia to open the passenger door of the Porsche Boxster. As the wheels crunched the gravel drive, the dog barked joyfully, anticipating the long drive into town.

On Wednesdays, Woodbridge's centre was a pedestrianised mall, a market selling fruit and vegetables, meat and fish, batteries, bin liners, disposable razors and woven rugs of the Persian style. The High Street still housed some of the original 19th-century shopfronts, but there were too many charity shops opening and closing and re-opening again when the exorbitant council rates became too much for local businesses. Two cafés served those who shopped at Waitrose, and one or two fast food places attracted the local youth or the punters from the market. On Sundays, the chic little micro-brewery hosted a jazz session, and an art supplies shop struggled on, tucked between a unisex hair salon and a mobile phone shop. But despite all of the activity, there was a sense of stagnation in the air.

She left Clochette in the car, despite the pathetic half-hearted yowls, and went into the library. The librarians were getting to know her. They knew she was researching for her novel – at least, she hoped they believed her, when she ordered *'The Art of the Post-Mortem Pathologist'* or *'The Killer's Mind'*. The woman behind the counter smiled. 'Here you are, Mrs …. Olivia Bowman-Marchal.' Livia winced, wishing her Council Tax identification didn't have to carry her married name; it made her feel like some matronly horse-rider who took *'The Telegraph'*.

At 56, she felt neither matronly nor horsey. She was long-limbed, taller than average, a good weight and she often walked for miles. She had never considered herself attractive – Alex had failed to convince her that she was beautiful – but she knew her warm chestnut hair and her deep brown eyes did attract some attention. She did not like the whisper of dotage that crept up on her whenever she heard her name in full. In her mind, she was still Livia Bowman – a thirty-something, left-leaning, street-smart woman of indeterminate provenance. Surely, that attitude would ward off the years?

She threw the books on to the passenger floor, grabbed the straw panier and hooked Clochette's lead to her collar. The smell of fresh fish, coffee and flowers coming from the High Street's weekly market made her think, for a moment, that she could be in France. She wandered slowly, buying tomatoes, cheese, and thinking about a coffee before she returned home. The small tables of the newly-opened Café Italia spilled out onto the pavement. She took a newspaper from the table by the window and sat down.

The waiter, a big, round man who she assumed was the owner greeted her warmly in a French accent.

'Madame?'

'Espresso, please.'

He returned, placed the coffee on the table and surveyed the market.

'It's lovely, non?'

'Yes,' she smiled. 'I imagine it reminds you of France?

'It does! You know, I think you're the first person to recognise me as a Frenchman – most customers assume I'm Italian.'

She pointed to the sign above the door. 'Café Italia?'

He laughed. 'Yes, I know, but the English seem more open to the Italians... at least I think so, judging by the people who come in. And who is this?' He reached down and stroked the dog's head.

'Clochette.'

'Ah! Clochette! Little Bell! And so, I see you have a French connection yourself!' He raised his eyebrows in a demand that was softened by his kind grey eyes.

She explained that she'd spent 'a few years' in Bretagne; she was glad when he sensed that she did not want to discuss details.

'Well,' he extended his hand. 'I am Henri - pleased to meet you.'

She shook his hand – 'Livia.'

On the way back to the car, she popped into the Co-Op for some biscuits for the cat – hoping they had the one brand, in the one flavour the cat tolerated. As she was leaving, a young lad, clearly out of it, pushed past her in the doorway, cursing under his breath. Outside, three more youths were waiting: one smoking, one scrolling through his phone, one sucking back on a can of cider. They smelled of strong body spray, their trainers were immaculately clean, new. They were restless, agitated and they hardly saw her as she untied Clochette's lead from the wall and headed back to the car.

That evening, she returned to her emails… she should respond to Alex; she would, as soon as she'd added another chapter to the book.

Chapter 5

Kilroy pulled his old Mac about him; the wind was picking up, skipping crisp packets along the beach front. Pensioners huddled in the weathered shelters looking out to sea, wordlessly, faces lifted hopefully to the chilly sun. A man threw a ball across the sand and his dog raced after it, its back legs spinning in mechanised circles, like a hare in a Warner Brothers' cartoon.

The arcade was already open, the thumping music of the games grinding out against the day. A few boys lingered outside, smoking, laughing loudly like gun fire. The detective breathed deeply, back at the station he'd check if the woman had reported her bag stolen – he doubted it, for some reason – and, looking up at the CCTV, he'd have his team check out yesterday's events.

He was also mulling over the last letter from John – and the very real threat to Marie. He'd met Marie nearly 20 years ago, in London. She was fresh out of training, fast-tracked through the system and her first assignment was shadowing his team of detectives as they investigated a series of high-profile, betting shop robberies. She was a petite brunette and she was beautiful – a fact not lost on the team. At first, they'd laughed at her – this pretty little thing, a degree in French Literature, for God's sake! One or two asked her out, but they were rebuffed pretty swiftly; it wasn't long before the nastier banter started up. He was worried, at first, that the constant attention would prompt her to ask for a transfer, but watching her brush off the crap with a sharp – and always amusing – response, he relaxed. It soon became obvious that she was a bloody good cop; she proved herself definitively the night she took out a shooter just before he would have pulled the trigger and sent a shower of lead into Kilroy's back.

About six months after she joined them, she asked him out for a drink. They went to the local and spent the night talking – like he'd never talked to anyone before. She was

10-years younger than him, but she seemed to understand his life: his father walking out on the family, problems with his alcoholic wife, the huge disappointment of being a police officer. So, really, she had saved him twice.

His phone buzzed in his pocket. 'Kilroy.' It was Collins; the Chief Super wanted an update on the investigation. Now. He put his phone in his pocket, and turned off the Prom. into the town. He hated being at the beck and call of an idiot; the Chief had graduated from the Academy ten years after Kilroy and had fast-tracked to the top, making valuable friends from local government along the way. He knew nothing about real police work; it was impossible to teach him anything. And he hated Kilroy. Passionately.

Chapter 6

Livia arched her back in a long stretch and re-read the email to her husband.

> Cher Alex,
>
> Thanks for the email – and for the updates. Yes, Martin's people are starting next week. Luckily the weather's been good – cold, but no rain. I've asked him to look at the wall in the spare room, too. I think there's damp there.
>
> Not much happening, here. I've started the manuscript for Justin – he sends his regards.
>
> How's the team? Say hi for me?
>
> Talk soon,
>
> Livia.

She pressed send and shut down the computer; so much was unspoken and it weighed heavily on her. Topping up her tea, she settled down into the old sofa. The fire was burning low, enough to keep her warm for another hour. She opened one of her library books: '*The Mother Behind the Psychopath*'.

She knew she didn't want to get too deep for Justin, but she knew she needed to understand more about her characters if the idea was to feel real. Kilroy's 'John' had to be a believable killer – well, believable to *aficionados* of the tv genre. And it was common knowledge that serial killers held a grudge against women - a grudge, really, against their mothers. She smiled ironically; sure, blame it on the mother.

The first case involved a series of murders that had happened in between 1943 and 1947. The bodies of four young women, believed to be prostitutes, were found in the dunes on the coast between Camber Sands and Dungeness. Eventually, the police declared the killer to be Damian Short, a strange young man who'd disappeared from Dungeness around the same time the murders had stopped.

Everyone in the village agreed he was 'not right' and over the years it became accepted that Damian Short had probably killed himself, perhaps by walking out to sea. His mother and his sister withdrew in their shame and were rarely seen outside of their ramshackle house by the beach. Their bodies were found, in 1955; it seemed the mother had killed her daughter before killing herself with a shotgun.

Livia shuddered slightly. It was past 11; she bookmarked her page and made her way to bed, followed noiselessly up the stairs by Clochette and the cat.

Chapter 7

The Press Conference was scheduled for 15h00, said the Chief. He wanted facts – proof that his force was doing its utmost to bring the woman's depraved killer to justice. He wanted answers. And he wanted them now.

Kilroy watched the man pace back and forward behind his desk, eyes staying level, focused on some imminent glory, never looking at Kilroy. He was a tall man, good-looking in a white teeth and smoothed hair way – certainly his wealthy wife must have thought so – and he pushed his chest forward when he spoke, as if continually receiving a medal.

He'd been appointed to the station five years ago. Old Chief Mackinson had retired, making way for the new kind of policing he could never have understood – the computers, the younger and younger officers, the barrage of political correctness that restricted every policing instinct he had in his sixty-year-old bones. Kilroy missed him.

Chief Gillam was now sitting down, and pushed a document across the desk.

> *'We have a mock-up of her face for tonight's news. I expect we'll have a name not long after. Any news on her phone?'*
>
> *'George's just messaged me; I'm on way down there now.' He looked at the face staring up from the sketch.*
>
> *'Well, no chance he'll have anything near useful – he's getting slower by the day. We'll need something for the press – see what you can get out of him, chivvy him along.'*
>
> *'I don't think it's wise to 'chivvy' George, Sir. Last thing you want is for him to lose his focus.'*

Gillam stared at him coldly.

'I think, Detective, it's wise to do what I ask – if George isn't up to the job tell him I'll gladly accept his resignation. And what about pathology? Jenkins must have something by now...'

Kilroy said nothing, but got up and headed for the door.

'Oh, and Kilroy? I'm throwing everything at this – I expect to be kept in the loop. None of this 'independent investigation' – you know where that got us last time.'

Kilroy nodded and left the door open behind him. 'Arsehole,' he thought. 'It's that independent investigation that keeps the crime figures down – and gets you brownie points with the mayor.' He hoped George had been able to unlock the phone. And he hoped the call he put in to the CCTV boys might make a link – even a tenuous one – between the murder and the bag snatch on the Prom.

George Reynold's cubby hole was deep in the building, a windowless office overcrowded with computers and monitors and always smelling of cigarettes, despite the non-smoking rules. He didn't look up when Kilroy entered; just continued tapping away on his keyboard, watching the screen for a response.

'George. What have you got for me?'

'You mean for the Press Conference – yes, I've already had Gillam busting my balls...'

Kilroy smiled sardonically. 'And?'

'Well. Was it you who said she was foreign? Don't know if you're right, but she's called a lot of foreign numbers.'

'France?'

'Yes – and some local.'

'I'll need those numbers printed out. What about messages? Photos?'

'No selfies, which is unusual for a young woman. A couple that look like surveillance shots.' He opened a new window on his screen.

The first picture was a blurred, grainy shot – as if it had been zoomed in on from a long distance. It looked like buildings, lights were on, so night time – was that a car? And at the bottom, a white shape – a person of indeterminate gender.

The next one was definitely of a man. He was close enough to make out a suit. The background was a brick wall, and to one edge, someone was leaning forward, sheltering under their umbrella.

'Can we do anything with them?'

'Maybe,' said George. 'I've sent them to the lab to sharpen them up – they'll never be great, but they might give us something.'

Not enough, thought Kilroy, to keep the Chief off his back.

His phone buzzed; it was Collins.

'Sir? Preliminary autopsy results are in. Jenkins is waiting for you in the lab. Oh, and Sir? That bag snatch – the CCTV is in. I'm looking through it now.'

Chapter 8

Martin Carrick and his Golden Retriever, Floss, followed the stream, up through the wood and out on to the heath that rolled down towards Livia's cottage. She was already up, and he could smell the coffee brewing, wafting out on the low sunbeams bouncing off the frosted grass.

She opened the door and Clochette sprung forward, greeting Floss like a long-lost friend. They circled and tumbled through the living room, into the kitchen and out through the kitchen door, running wildly in the back garden.

Martin laughed and sat down at the table; Livia brought their coffees over.

'How's Rachel?' she asked.

'Fine, fine. It's a struggle to keep her still!'

Livia smiled. Rachel's baby was due within a month, and she'd been told to take it easy.

'Honestly, I had to sneak out this morning, or she would have come with me!'

'Not long now, though. How's work?' Martin was a thatcher, as his father had been.

'It's been steady... a lot of repairs after the snow; it'll pick up when it warms up a little. I'm doing a place up near Andover next week – that reminds me, are you still ok for Matthews and his boy to come up to look at the barn? Friday, he said, didn't he?'

'Yeah – he phoned yesterday.' From the garden, Clochette yelped.

'Floss!' Martin shouted, and both dogs came scattering in and looked at him quizzically. 'Out! And play nice!' The dogs barked joyfully and scampered out again. The cat watched, nonplussed, from the kitchen window sill.

'You're not going in to town today are you? Had a call from my brother – there's no access this morning – police everywhere. Some trouble last night.'

'Oh, no I wasn't going in - what happened?'

'No idea – Dave said the air ambulance was on the scene, too.'

'Hmmm. Thanks for the heads-up.'

A little while later, Martin and Floss set out across the stream and began the climb up the hill. Martin had lived in The Forest all his life, and he walked different routes every day, checking on the ponies, the cattle and the state of the land - particularly in the Summer, when the 'grockles', the tourists, descended, leaving their rubbish and their half-extinguished disposable barbeques behind.

She shooed the cat from the sill and rinsed the coffee pot under the tap. The blinking light of the answer-machine reminded her that her sister had called. 'Call me back!' Rose had ordered. 'You ignored my email! I'm worried! I'm coming down to see you. Tomorrow. Can you make up that spare bed? I should be there by lunch – I'll stop at Waitrose on the way. Don't call me back, this evening I'm ….' The recording timed out.

Rose had the ability to make a welfare call sound like a disciplinary tribunal – only those closest to her didn't take offence. Others found her incredibly difficult to deal with. Widowed at 55, she had carved a new life for herself with committees, volunteering, the University of the Third Age, and, after 7 years, she was where she wanted to be: too busy to grieve.

Despite the presumption, and despite Rose's imperious tone, Livia was looking forward to the visit. She smiled: 'presumption', 'imperious'. God, she sounded just like her sister.

Chapter 9

The autopsy lab smelled, as it should have, of someone trying to disguise the scent of dead bodies. Even after all these years, Kilroy was surprised at the way the chemicals rose like a greasy wave of gas, finding their way into your nostrils and down the back of your throat.

'Ah, there you are!' Jenkins was washing her hands in the deep sink. The girl lay on the stainless-steel table, the blue-tinged neon lights adding an even greyer pallor to her face. She couldn't have been more than 25.

'So,' she said, wiping her hands on the paper towel, 'the Chief needs something for 3 o'clock?' Kilroy bristled: Gillam had clearly done the rounds. 'I've sent him a file, so his comms. people will have something to run with. Tattoo.' She pulled back the rubberised sheet and there, on the right hip bone, was the small, colourful tattoo – a butterfly. Kilroy turned his head to one side, peering through squinted eyes.

'That's good. Thanks. Any signs of sexual assault?'

'No – they pulled up the skirt to make us think so, but no fluids.'

'Tox. screen?'

*'Anti-anxiety meds – not excessive, high enough dose. I'd say our girl
was stressed.' Jenkins pulled the sheet up to cover the face. 'She doesn't fit the bill of the average working girl, that's for sure.'*

'I agree. The skirt, the blouse, the bag she was carrying... doesn't ring right.'

'She didn't have any money on her – mugging gone wrong?'

'No,' he shook his head. 'They could have snatched the bag and run, put a knife to her to hand it over... No, this is something else.'

'Well, we've got a few more tests to run – I'll let you know if we come up with anything. You should get some sleep – you look like shit.'

'Thanks,' he smiled wearily. He looked at his watch; he'd be gone before the Press Conference started.

Chapter 10

Rose arrived at 2 p.m., the wheels of her Renault scattering the gravel at the side of the house. She was immaculately dressed: lilac linen trousers, over-sized white linen shirt and nude pumps. She dropped her Hermes Birkin on to the sofa and looked around the room.

At 62, Rose Gilbert was still an attractive woman – the sort of 'attractive' that took a lot of maintenance. Her hair was a natural-looking platinum bob and her make-up was the expensive kind that made one question if she was wearing it. Her sheer pink lip gloss matched the soft pink of her nails.

> She clapped her hands. 'You've made it look good! I <u>love</u> the tiles…'
>
> Livia smiled and filled a jug with water. 'Thanks! Put the flowers in here, I'll put this in the fridge – what is it? Oh, lovely, I love Waitrose ready meals!'
>
> 'Well, I didn't want you cooking – I want us to have a good catch-up! I've got to be off tomorrow at 9 – but that gives us all afternoon and into the evening! There's a good cake in there, too – from my local café. All organic.'
>
> 'Great. I thought we'd go for a walk this afternoon… after a coffee - and cake?'
>
> Rose took her travel bag to the guest room and changed into her trainers. Soon after, they were climbing the hill and looking out across the heath.
>
> 'You should see this when the heather blooms, Rose. It's the most amazing purple! Are you up for a five-miler?'
>
> 'Great! I haven't been for a good stretch in weeks!'
>
> Both of them, and their three sisters, had inherited a love of walking from their parents. They laughed as

they recalled their toddler-selves being dragged about the Lake District or up Ben Nevis.

'Their strategy might have had the opposite effect,' said Rose. 'We could have been deeply traumatised!'

'Yes! I guess they knew what they were doing.'

They smiled fondly. Their father had come from a poor background, but his parents had realised that he was a bright child and, in the way working class parents of the 1950s did, pushed him to get the University education they never had. However, he found academia too limiting, too narrow; he joked that he was more of a Renaissance Man. He changed courses a couple of times, but then dropped out entirely, taking up an administration role in local government. He did well enough to raise his five daughters in a leafy village in Hampshire, but he never really stopped learning; the house was full of books and there were many weekend trips to London's galleries and museums – when they weren't climbing mountains.

Their mother often lamented that she'd been born ten years too early, when she saw the opportunities and life that was available to her girls. She, too, was a greedy reader and temperamentally she and her husband were well-matched; but she always exuded an underlying air of bitterness that she was trapped by her gender. Livia sometimes wondered if that's why she'd married later, and was that why she hadn't had children? But none of her sisters had been put off and they had produced enough grandchildren to camouflage Livia's choices.

Rose laughed. 'I did the same thing to my two, you know – I don't think they ever had a free weekend! They haven't thanked me. Yet.'

'How are they? I got a parcel from Patricia last month – a little Peace Lily. House-warming. Is Taylor still enjoying America?'

'Oh, yes. I'm starting to think he's never coming home! It seems the Yanks do Pathology better than we humble Brits. He's just about to wrap up his Ph.D. If they offer him a job, I think he'll stay. And I suspect there's a girl on the scene… God Forbid he marries a Californian or something.' She paused. 'I miss him.'

'Oh, Rose! You don't have time to miss him!'

And while Rose chatted about the Parish Council, her U3A course on Victorian architecture and the work she did at the local Food Bank, they wound their way across the heath, finishing in the wood, the Birch trees standing dark and smooth in the dark mud and decaying leaves, Clochette driving large circles around her flock of two.

After supper, Livia cleared the kitchen while Rose sat on the lounge, sipping on a glass of Cabernet. She was leafing her way through '*The Mother Behind the Psychopath*'.

'Good Lord, Livia!'

'I know, light reading, eh? It's research for the novel – the script.'

'Listen to this,' cried Rose. 'Everyone in the village agreed he was 'not right' and over the years it became accepted that Damian Short had probably killed himself, perhaps by walking out to sea. His mother and his sister withdrew in their shame and were rarely seen outside of their ramshackle house by the beach. Their bodies were found, in 1955; it seemed the mother had killed her daughter before killing herself with a shotgun.'

'Sad, right? I couldn't finish reading that chapter…'

Rose continued scanning the page, reading out short snippets of the text: 'Autopsy revealed that the daughter was – in fact – a male! Damian Short had not disappeared but had, in fact taken on the identity of his sister. The villagers were astonished, but they later realised that they had never seen the two children together at any one time. My God! He lived as both himself and his sister! You couldn't make it up! Seriously, should you be reading this stuff? It's very warped! I worry about you being on your own, reading such things!'

Livia smiled and sat down in the arm chair with a mug of Earl Grey.

'How's Alex doing?' Rose tried not to sound obvious and failed miserably.

'Yes, Rose, he's still talking to me. He's fine. The business is fine.'

Rose pouted a little. 'Well, I don't want to pry – I'm just not used to all of this 'Continental Liberalism'.

Livia laughed. 'Liberalism? What on Earth are you talking about?'

'All this 'civility', all this impersonal separation! It's quite... unusual. Definitely not normal.'

'I've told you; we need some space, that's all.'

'Livia, be careful what you wish for... space gets lonely. It's been 7 years since I lost David... but it feels a lot longer.'

Livia felt a rush of sadness for her sister.

'I'm sorry, Rose. I forget. You miss him terribly, still, don't you?'

Rose's eyes filled with tears. 'I do. The house seems empty... especially now the children have gone.'

Livia got up and hugged her sister tightly. Later, as she lay in bed, she wondered if she and Alex were being selfish, or tempting fate. To the outside, she supposed it did look like they'd separated – they'd worked hard to make sure it did. But only they knew that this charade of separation was more a matter of survival than a glitch in their marriage; whoever was trying to drive them apart needed to believe they had actually succeeded. Maybe then, the intruder would show himself.

Chapter 11

Kilroy fell back onto his sofa, enjoying the warm flow of the whisky down his throat. Digger sat by the fire, his eyes fixed on Kilroy, expressionless. The day the police swooped on the run-down farm of a group of dealers, five years before, Kilroy had found the dog in the barn. It was clear the creature wasn't fed often and the collar and chain were worn and rusty. There were several holes under the wall where the dog had tried to escape but had been held back by the chain. As Kilroy had approached him, the dog had barked loudly, bared his teeth and growled roughly. 'I think you'd best come with me,' Kilroy had said softly, releasing the chain from the wall. Once back at Kilroy's cottage, and after some cold chicken, the dog had agreed to a bath and slept soundly on the smooth stones in front of the wood stove.

'I suppose you need your real dinner,' said Kilroy.

The dog stepped lightly after him and waited by his bowl. The kitchen was low-roofed with heavy beams; one small window looked out onto the drive and the dunes that made a yellow curtain between the house and the sea. On warm Summer days, with the front door open, you could smell the waves as they splashed softly onto the sand. He'd bought the place about 15 years ago, gutted the kitchen and put in two new wood stoves. The wooden cupboards and shelves were not beyond repair and he'd found the grand, old oak table in the barn under damp canvas sheets; he'd sanded it and brought it back to a golden glow.

He'd planned for his wife and him to move into the house eventually, but Kristin's enthusiasm had waned – for both the house and the marriage. He loved the silence of the place; his neighbours, all three cottages, were far enough away to keep their distance.

The hot shower had made Kilroy realise how tired he was; he'd have a look at the CCTV segment Collins had emailed him, and then he'd sleep – hopefully. The footage was *grainy, crap quality, but it was easy to see the few people emerging from shops or walking their dogs along the Prom. He fast-forwarded to 4.30 – Collins said that was the point when the skinny woman first appeared. She came out from a side street, looking both ways, nervously. She checked her watch. Looked down the road. She checked her watch. She pulled her bag forward from her shoulder, looked inside, checked her phone. Pulled the bag back onto her shoulder. Then she hurried across the road to one of the sheltered seats, and she was out of view, just a blur through the dirty, scratched plexi-glass of the side window.*

The man appeared just then, from the same side street. Tall. Suit. He crossed the road, without checking the traffic. He was in the shelter, and minutes later he was out – carrying the woman's bag. He didn't run. He crossed back over the road and made his way along the Prom., disappearing.

About 30 seconds later, the woman emerged, looking left and right erratically and then behind her. She made her way back up the side street – to the café where she used the waitress's phone. Collins would soon have the blown-up images of the man and the woman. She had not reported the crime, the CCTV did not show a mugging. But Kilroy was certain the woman was acting under duress, and he wanted to know why.

He unfolded the letter again; the one that was waiting on his desk when he got back from Pathology. John had drawn an image of a young woman in an alley, her skirt hiked up, her mouth a smear of lipstick. He'd entitled it:
'The End of Harlots'.

Chapter 12

After she'd waved Rose off, Livia made a second pot of coffee. She had taken ages to fall asleep last night, and when she had she dreamed of Alex, of the vineyards and a shadowy intruder who stalked the long rows of rich, red grapes. She wanted to call Alex, to check in on him, but she knew that they had to maintain this charade that she had, indeed, abandoned her husband and returned to the UK to start a new life without him. The plan had to work: the intruder had to believe that Alex and Livia's marriage had ended. Maybe then he would leave them alone.

The 'campaign', as the French police had called it, had begun two years ago. At first, the silent phone calls to the office – at all hours of the night. They'd switched the phone off, diverting it straight to answer phone. Shortly after, the same thing began happening on Alex's private mobile.

Then came the postcards: strange, abstract collages of brides and grooms, of ideal families, the kind used in 1950s advertising. The messages were all about everlasting love, the bonds of family, the strength of union. But over time, the messages became darker, lamenting the passing of love, the destruction of family. And then they became threatening – for those who thought they had found everlasting love, there would be an avenging angel who would steal it away from them. Alex had called in the police, but they had written it off as nothing more than a nasty hoax – perhaps the work of a rival vigneron? An old flame of Alex's? So, they tried to ignore the letters that grew longer and longer, expressing pain and explaining the only solution possible: those who had love must lose it, before it was ripped from them.

After a few months, the stakes were raised.

It was Winter. Alex and Livia had returned from dinner with friends, and were settling in for sleep when Clochette let out a low, warning growl from the landing where she usually slept. The growl soon rose into a full-on, defensive bark and she sprinted down the stairs. Alex and Livia were awake immediately. The main door to the house was wide open, a cold wind blowing in, the lounge lights were blazing. Clochette was somewhere down the drive, chasing, barking. 'Call the police!' Alex ordered as he ran after the dog.

Livia called the police and moments later Clochette came running through the door, followed by Alex, panting and breathless. They looked across the hall into the lounge – the floor was strewn with torn paper, which, on closer inspection, turned out to be the photos taken from their frames; the photos of their wedding day, their friends, Alex's parents.

The police surmised that the intruder had destroyed the lounge while the couple were at dinner. When Alex and Olivia had gone straight upstairs on their return, it was likely the intruder was still in the house. Of course, security was tightened and Livia once again reviewed the letters, looking for clues, but there was no logic in the crazy, rambling messages.

The next break-in confirmed their drastic plan of action.

She shook her head, refusing to get lost in these memories. No. It was only a matter of time before this would be over, and she and Alex would be together again. But, for today, she would visit the Library and, maybe, take another coffee at Café Italia – Henri was a welcome distraction.

*****

The market was not as busy as usual, and Henri was subdued as he served her an espresso.

> 'Bonjour, Livia! How are you? Eh, Clochette, ca va?'

> 'Bonjour, Henri. It's quiet today.'

> 'Yes, this dreadful business with the police has made everyone afraid!'

'Oh, yes, I heard there'd been a commotion the other night... what happened?'

Henri explained that there had been a stabbing! Yes, a stabbing in their little town! It seemed that some young men had had a disagreement and they all had knives. Drugs might have been involved.

'That's awful,' she said, sadly. 'We don't expect it down here, do we... it's so out of the way.'

Henri nodded. 'Oui, it's so sad. The boy was only 15. Too young to die!'

'Die? Oh, no...'

'Yes, here, you can take this to read more,' he handed her the local newspaper and hurried to greet another customer.

Chapter 13

"Twenty missed calls!? My God, how long have I been asleep?" It was 5 a.m., and Kilroy sat up on his sofa where he'd fallen asleep. He had four messages on his phone – one from Collins to say the enhanced images were back, but they weren't good enough to identify anyone. One from his ex-wife, drunk. Delete.

Then a message from the Chief. He was congratulating himself on the Press Conference, while railing at Kilroy for bringing no new information to the table and for leaving the Chief to front up to those piranhas from the local press. He was sure that Kilroy would be receiving calls from the public as he'd instructed the Comms Team to run Kilroy's number at the bottom of the screen. He wanted an update. Immediately. Kilroy hit delete.

And one message from a woman – she started to say something, paused and rang off. She sounded scared. He returned the call. The phone rang several times before it was answered. There was a pause, breathing.

'Hello? This is Inspector Kilroy…'

'He -…. Hello?'

'Yes? This is Kilroy. Who is this?'

'I… I am Anna. I see the dead woman. The one on TV last night… the news.' The woman had an accent.

Kilroy told himself to take his time. 'Hi Anna. What's your last name?'

'No, this is not important. I see her, the girl.'

'What's her name?'

'I don't know – but I see her a lot.'

'Where? Where did you see her?'

'Off the High Street, Canford Mansions.'

'Anna, can I meet you somewhere? Can we talk? I need to...'

'No, no talk. She is very nice, smiling. I am very sad for her.'

'That's great, Anna, if we could meet, you could tell me...'

The line went dead.

Chapter 14

On Friday, Shaun Matthews, the builder, arrived bright and early, his teenage grandson still asleep in the passenger seat.

'Mrs Marchal? Shall we have a look at that barn?'

They walked across the yard to the solid wooden structure that edged the garden.

'It's a fine barn,' he nodded. 'Original?'

'Near enough to,' she said. 'It's only used for a little storage at the moment, but the roof is giving up on us.'

'Yes, from in here it doesn't look too bad... I'll get up and have a look. Probably broken tiles – might have to order them in. And you said there was some damp inside the house?'

The boy was now standing beside the truck, hands in his overall pockets, looking like he hadn't slept much last night. He had light grey shadows under his eyes.

'This is my grandson - Arthur. Say hello to Mrs Marchal.'

The boy nodded and started unloading the ladder from the back of the van, while Livia took Matthews inside and up to the guest room. The back corner of the room had a shadow across it, a faint stain.

'Oh, yes. Yes... I think...' and he opened the window and leaned far out, making Livia want to grab hold of his short legs to stop him falling. 'Yes, the seal on the window's broken... it'll be easy enough to sort out.'

After Matthews had been on the barn roof and after Arthur had climbed the ladder to look more closely at the outside seal of the window, they appeared at the kitchen door. She looked from the grandfather to the grandson; you could definitely see the family resemblance. Matthews, too, looked like he didn't sleep well. His face was tired and worn, deeply lined by the sun and by worries. His hair was wiry and full, shot through with grey, pushed flat by the worker's cap he lifted off as he came inside.

'Can I get you some tea?' She offered.

'A tea would be lovely,' he said. 'He'll have a cold drink if that's possible …'

Once the tea and Coke were sorted, they sat at the table and Matthews explained the cost of the work, reading from his small notebook.

'Oh, that sounds fine,' Livia said. 'How long will it be before the tiles come in?'

'A week, maybe two. I'll call when I know.'

'Great.'

They sat in easy silence, Clochette staring at Arthur, her head turned slightly to one side. The boy looked at her, looked away, but then looked back at her again.

'She's trying to hypnotise you, trying to get you to go out and throw her ball around,' Livia offered.

The boy smiled shyly. 'Is it ok if I…'

'Sure! She'll show you where it's hidden!'

As Arthur pushed back his chair, Clochette gave a short bark and hurried to the back hedge, re-emerging with a well-chewed tennis ball. Matthew watched fondly as his grandson threw the ball across the garden and the dog leaped and tackled it gracefully.

'Oh, no! I'm done for! He's been on at me to get him a dog for months!' he grimaced.

'Oh, it's all my fault!' she laughed.

'No. It's about time. And to be honest, it might be welcome company for him, now…'

'Now?'

Matthews shifted uncomfortably. 'He's a good boy. My wife and I raised him after his mum died – dad took off when he was a baby. But he got in with the wrong people at school, you see. Got himself into trouble and, well, they threw him under the bus, so to speak…'

'I'm sorry – is that why he isn't in school?'

'Yes – I took him out. The town's getting rougher, you know…'

'I read about the stabbing…'

'Exactly! Arthur knew the kid! Poor lad got in with some serious characters from London and, well…' he pulled his cap back on firmly. 'Anyway, we'd best be going. A few more calls to make today. Thank you for the tea.'

Livia looked out at the boy and the dog, now both rolling around on the grass, fighting over the ball. Clochette was in her element.

'Come on, lad!' Matthews called as he walked toward the truck.

'Mrs Marchal,' called Arthur, 'what's her name?'

'Clochette… it means little bell….'

'Little bell,' he repeated, smiling. For that short moment, he looked like a carefree child.

Chapter 15

Canford Mansions was a tall, ugly, dark-red brick Victorian building, with tiles on the front step like a grimy black and white chess board. There were twelve door buzzers, each with a name tag, smudged pen on paper, with several layers of over-writing. Collins pressed them, one after the other repeatedly, until there was a 'click' and the front door opened.

In the dark hallway, tiled in mustard and red squares, there were 12 post boxes. Once again, the names and numbers in smudged ink – some crossed out and replaced with new, equally anonymous, names: Jones, Smith, Allan – Moulin. The name sounded French. Flat 8.

They made their way up to the second floor and found the door. They knocked, but no answer. Kilroy tried the handle of the door – it was unlocked. Collins looked apprehensive; they didn't have a warrant.

'Police,' Kilroy called as he pushed the door wide.

The small room was musty and airless; the window was firmly shut, and on the sill, there was a picture of their victim, smiling broadly into the camera, arm-in-arm with a young man. They had the right room. Kilroy pulled on his latex gloves. The fold-out sofa bed was unmade, but the coverlet was pulled up to the pillows. There were a few dishes on the small sink in the kitchenette. In one corner of the room, a suitcase functioned as a coffee table, covered with a paisley silk scarf. Kilroy picked up the A4 notebook and opened it carefully – dates, time... notes in French.

> *Collins looked at the picture. 'Boyfriend?'*

> *Kilroy had noted the familial resemblance in their eyes and noses. 'Don't think so....'*

> *Collins opened the fridge. 'Long-life milk, that's about it.'*

Kilroy opened the top drawer of the dresser that was propped up, under one leg, with a small block of wood. He opened the EU passport: Stephanie Moulin. She was 24.

> 'Get on to this,' he handed Collins the passport. 'Notify next of kin - one of them will have to come over for the identification. And get uniform out here – the neighbours might know something.'

Taking the notebook, he hurried downstairs, calling Marie on the way. Her phone went to message: 'Hey,' he said quietly. 'It's me. I need a translator…'

Chapter 16

She put Justin on speaker, only because she knew the call would be a long one, and she wanted her hands free to continue preparing her supper while he gave his feedback on the first chapters of the manuscript she'd emailed him.

'My God, Liv, I think you're on to something! I'm already casting Kilroy – in my mind, of course – what do you think about... Clive Owen!?'

'I haven't seen him in anything for ages,' she answered. 'Yeah, he looks a little like a Kilroy... yeah, I can see that...'

'I wondered about Gabriel Byrne... but he's too –'

'Intellectual,' Livia offered.

'Old! And there's Liam, of course, but we'd never be able to afford him....'

'Well, I'm glad it's excited you,' she laughed.

'Oh, sure, there's lots to do, though – Collins, for example – you need to make more of him.'

'Really? I thought he was a foil to show off Kilroy's depth of experience and wisdom?'

'He does that, but as he's going to be our pull for the younger audience – he needs to be more rounded. Think Harry Styles...'

'OK,' she said, hitting her forehead with a celery stick in mock despair.

'And Stephanie's mother –'

'Her mother? Where did you read that?'

'I didn't. You're going to include her – the relative that comes over to do the ID. Hot. French. Widow – maybe a bit of *tension* –' he said this in a French accent – 'between her and Kilroy… might get us some interest from the French market …. Jane Birkin?'

'Hmmmmm. I'll think on it…' she answered without conviction.

'Anyhoo, how's life on the farm? I guess it's not so different, you coming from the vineyard, right? Oh, sorry, didn't mean to –'

She laughed. 'It's fine, Justin, I'm doing fine. Alex and I chatted last week – it's all very civilised.'

'I'm glad, I really am. You're made of tough stuff! You and I are both life-time members of the broken-hearts club, girl, and we are both survivors!'

She quickly changed the subject. 'How's the new series going? Are you still on set, or have they marched you off for too much interference?'

He laughed, delightedly. 'They tried, honey, they did, but I said to them: 'Are you looking for a National TV Award, because I've already got one and trust me, I know the direction we should be heading in!'

By the time the call had ended, the small pot of soup was ready to simmer and Clochette was bouncing about by the kitchen door.

'Ok, come on, then! Into the wood!'

The sun was gone, and a soft, grey light descended. Clochette didn't wait for the lead, and ran full throttle into the trees. Livia followed after, enjoying the occasional snatches of end-of-day bird-song. She loved hearing from Justin – his voice took her back to a time when things were more … fun. She laughed at herself – 56-year-olds were beyond fun. After the writers' workshop, they'd met up often for drinks and evenings out. Justin's love life was a colourful series of grand passions followed by the inevitable dramatic break-ups; she enjoyed helping him get over them.

She pulled her padded jacket about her as the damp chill settled.

'Clochette? Come on, girl!' The wood was silent.

'Clochette? Come!' Nothing, but the cold air.

She felt a rising panic, just as she had that last night in France. She hurried along the path in the direction she'd seen the dog run. Suddenly, a bird flapped wildly, exploding into a clearing. She stood still, listening for what had given it a fright.

From up ahead, Clochette barked.

'Clochette!' she called as loudly as she could.

More barking, and now she could hear footsteps, a heavy tread making its way through the ferns. She stood still again, staring into the shadows when Clochette suddenly appeared, ears flying backwards as she ran at high speed toward her, and, right behind, Floss barrelled into the clearing.

Martin raised his hand in greeting. 'Livia! Alright?'

She smiled and raised her hand back to him. 'Yes, yes, just taking the girl out for a run before supper.'

He called out to Floss and continued his proprietary walk through the wood. Livia hooked the lead onto Clochette's collar and hurried back along the path. Once inside, she double-bolted the door and drew the heavy curtains.

Chapter 17

Sylvie Moulin nodded to the attendant to draw back the curtain so that she could formally identify her daughter's body. She stared for a moment at the girl's pale form, then she nodded slightly. Kilroy had seen the muscles of her back tense painfully on recognition.

She placed her hand against the glass for a moment, and then turned to Kilroy.

'Oui,' she said. 'This is my daughter.'

'I'm sorry,' he said. 'Please, come this way.'

They walked along the drab corridors, a jaundiced yellow under the strip-lights, and out into the evening air.

'Madame, I would like to ask you some questions, but I understand if you need time to…'

'Non, that's fine,' she said. 'Do you think we can find a drink?'

The bar of The Grand looked out across the sea from the first floor of the faded Victorian hotel. Kilroy knew it would be quiet. On the Prom., the orange floodlights settled softly on the flat waves that rolled in monotonously. A fret was closing in, obscuring the pier.

Sylvie stared out to sea, past her reflection, back, Kilroy imagined, to the years when Stephanie was a toddler, running on the sand of another beach, somewhere far away.

'Why was Stephanie here, Sylvie? I mean, she wasn't enrolled in any of the colleges, no employment we know of…'

Sylvie turned back to face him, her eyes full of sadness.

'I don't know, Inspector… I did not know she was in England.' She saw his frown. 'Stephanie is… was… her 'own person', I think you say in English? When her father died, she was only 18, she turned in on

*herself... I could not reach her. She moved away –
Paris.'*

'And her brother?' Kilroy was following his instincts.

*'Etienne?' she sipped her brandy. 'I have not seen
Etienne for ten years, Inspector.'*

*Kilroy took the picture from his pocket and offered it
to her.*

*A light flush appeared on her white throat. 'Mon
Dieu, but how... where did you find this? Why did
Stephanie not tell me she had found him?'*

*'It was in her room. Why would she not tell you she
was in contact with him?'*

*Sylvie seemed distracted, her mind racing. 'Etienne is
four years older than Stephanie – when he was 16,
he was involved in... he ... he is a drug addict,
Inspector.'*

Kilroy nodded sadly. 'I'm sorry.'

*'Thank you. His father and I tried to help – the
doctors, the rehabilitation – but he did not want to
be helped, Inspector. A la fin, after my husband died,
it was a case of 'tough love' – I couldn't do it on my
own. I had to let him go.'*

*Kilroy sipped his whisky, sickened by the sadness of this
story. A young girl, finally reunited with her brother – just
before she's strangled in a filthy alley, in a foreign country.
Kilroy watched Sylvie Moulin's heart breaking in her
reflection in the darkened window.*

Chapter 18

The librarian raised her eyebrow, as she always did: '*Drug Addiction and Youth*'. She scanned the spine and passed it to Livia.

'More 'research', Mrs Bowman-Marchal? You know, that title's not as incongruent in our very own town as one might think.'

'Sorry?'

'Well, I'm referring to the 'Drug Problem' we have, here, in the town.'

'Oh, the stabbing...'

'The stabbing is only the latest thing, I assure you.' She leaned forward, confidentially. The local constabulary don't want us to know, of course, but there have been several 'incidents' over the past year, in fact, one of –'

'Morning, Margaret!' A tall, uniformed police constable leaned forward on the counter. 'Please, go on. Which 'incident' were you discussing?'

Margaret looked a little flustered, but quickly regained her composure. 'Officer Cummings! You startled me! I was just telling Mrs Bowman-Marchal about the ...'

'Yes, I caught your drift, Margaret. I'm a little concerned that you feel we 'don't want you to know' about such things?' He smiled and turned to Livia. 'Hi, I'm Michael Cummings.'

'Livia Bowman,' she said, shaking his hand.

Michael was tall, over 6 feet, with short sandy red hair cut close. His blue eyes smiled out of a square face that wouldn't have looked out of place in a 1940s Western: the Sherriff. A few freckles across the bridge of his nose, and a fullness to his lips, softened the look.

'Quite heavy reading,' he nodded to her pile of books as they headed out to the car-park.

'Yes, I'm researching … for a novel.'

'Really! Well, if you want to talk about 'the incidents' we've been dealing with here in Woodbridge, feel free to contact me,' he passed her his card. 'Do you live in the town?'

'In The Forest, *Fox Pond.*'

Later that night, as she tried to create the drugs network Kilroy would be dealing with, she opened her email and dropped Michael a line: 'I'm struggling with how the drugs 'get into' small towns like ours? Do organisations spring up spontaneously? Where do the drugs originate? In the UK?'

She was surprised when he responded almost immediately: 'The dealers are London-based. They send one of their guys down to small towns like ours, for a week or two. While they're here, they introduce themselves to the local kids, splash a little cash around, hand out some drugs. Once they're 'in' with the locals, they start asking for help in supplying – say, they'll ask a 15-year-old to take some junk to a party, sell it and bring back the profits. This goes on for a while, then they tell the kid he can make a lot more if he takes over a slice of the 'business'. Before you know it, the kid's travelling to and from London once a month to restock. Any more info. you need… call me. Maybe we could meet up for a drink…'

Chapter 19

Marie Hallet threw off one high heel, then the next, falling onto her sofa and rubbing the balls of her feet. As Kilroy poured them both a drink, she slid off her blonde wig, went to the bathroom and pulled two or three make-up wipes from the pack. The bright red lipstick and the candy-coloured rouge were gone in minutes. She peeled back the false eyelashes and, finally, washed her face with soap and water. The tight PVC dress unrolled and she slipped into a soft, grey tracksuit bottom and white t-shirt.

Kilroy watched her as she stretched her arms to the ceiling and let out a long sigh.

> 'You've lost more weight, Marie.'

> 'No, just maintenance now – not many fat addicts out there.'

Detective Sergeant Marie Hallet had transferred from London and had been undercover, here in Kingsmouth, for nearly a year. She mingled with the working women on the streets, close enough to be accepted as one of them, but not close enough to be outed as a fraud. She kept a room just off the high street, and, allegedly, had a select few clients who met her there. Her focus was the dealers who supplied the girls, and who were rapidly spreading their junk into the wider community. Like Kilroy, she knew the scale of the problem, but unlike Kilroy, she believed they had a chance of turning things around.

He sat beside her on the sofa; she looked up into his eyes and kissed him softly on his mouth. He returned the kiss.

> 'So, this translation?' she smiled, disentangling herself from his arms.

He passed her Stephanie's notebook and she flipped through the pages. 'Diary?'

'Looks like it. I need the details, though... what are the dates and times about?'

Marie squinted at the page. 'Pick up. Taxi. Drop off. It's strange - it seems to be in a sort of code?'

'What do you mean?'

'Well, I've got a 'parrot' here – 'perroquet' – and an 'armadillo' – 'tatou'. Can you give me some time with it?'

He nodded. 'Sure. I want to know her secrets. I want to show you something else – John's back on the scene.'

'More fan mail, Kilroy?'

'Yes, but a little bit of love for you, too.' He handed her the letter.

She frowned as she read. 'Hmmmmm. I'm the only 'Marie' I know. Have you got anything else on this guy?'

'Nothing... he says he killed the French girl...'

'You don't believe him?'

'I don't know. He called her a 'harlot', but she wasn't a worker. He saw the body, that's all.'

'He's rattling your cage...'

'I need you to be careful, Marie.'

'It's you he's rattling, Kilroy,' she patted his arm gently.

'Maybe, but he knows that you're my Achilles heel,' he frowned.

She leaned over, lifted her t-shirt over her head, and kissed him again.

Chapter 20

Matthews' truck crunched the gravel drive, triggering Clochette's barking, until she saw Arthur.

'Hey, little bell! Clochette, come here!'

Livia laughed and waved to Matthews as he began unloading the new tiles.

At lunchtime, Livia put aside her research and called out to Matthews that the kettle was on. He sent Arthur in with his sandwiches, saying he'd be a few minutes more. Arthur sat down at the table.

'You're a good team!' Livia smiled.

Arthur blushed. 'No, granddad does all the work. He's teaching me loads.'

'Are you going to do an apprenticeship?' Livia asked.

'Yeah, I've gotta pass English and Maths, as well… because I left school early.' He looked sad, suddenly like a boy.

'Yes, your grandfather told me. That must have been hard…'

'Oh, I don't miss school.'

'You miss your friends?'

He bit into his sandwich. 'I don't have many friends, now …'

Livia felt a pang of sympathy. 'Me neither.'

'You've got Clochette,' smiled Arthur. 'How long have you had her?'

'Since she was a pup – 8 years, now. Her mother lived on the vineyard next to ours in France.'

'How many other pups were there?'

'Six. They all went to good homes.'

He chewed thoughtfully. 'What's it like in France?'

'Great – it has its moments, like we do.'

'I want to go to Paris. There was a school trip, but I wasn't allowed to go after….'

'Well,' she smiled gently. 'I think going with a school would ruin it – best you do it on your own – independent travel's the way to really see a place.'

He smiled back at her, nodding.

'Hey,' said Matthews, stamping his boots on the doormat. 'That dog's looking at you for a game! Go on! Ten minutes!'

Once they were outside chasing madly around the lawn, Matthews turned to Livia. 'You've been very kind to him. Thank you.'

'Of course! He's a good kid. The boy who died, his friend? How are his parents coping?'

'They're devastated.' He looked angry. 'They came to this country for a better life! Didn't plan on their boy getting in with that lot!'

Livia's curiosity rose. 'Who are 'that lot'? The older lads?'

'Not lads. No. They come down from London.'

'And did Arthur know them?'

'Only to say hello to – he'd see them at parties and such…'

Her mobile buzzed from the lounge. 'Oh, sorry….'

It was Martin; his wife had given birth, last night, to a girl. Livia would drive into town and get some flowers this afternoon.

Henri was incandescent! The front window of Café Italia had been smashed, some time the night before. There was little money in the till, as business had been slow for weeks now, since the stabbing. The café was dark and unwelcoming with a huge piece of chipboard hastily nailed in place early this morning. Livia did her best to console him, but he was all over the place with grief and rage.

'Non! Non! Clochette! There is glass on the floor! Livia, she will hurt her feet!'

Livia rounded her up on the lead and tried to guide Henri to a seat.

'Henri, please sit down, let me get you something to drink – you look exhausted!'

He was; he had not slept well for weeks. His small flat on the edge of the town offered little comfort; he wondered if he shouldn't just pack up and return to France.

'Yes, yes. Just some water, please.'

By the time Michael arrived, Henri was calmer.

'Well, I've got a little good news for you. CCTV from the newsagent across the road – we have an image of one of them, at least. Not the face, but it looks like a male, small frame. Probably a teenager.'

'That's something,' said Livia.

'Yes,' sighed Henri. 'It is. But will it pay for my window to be fixed? I'm sorry officer, I am grateful, but… my business is dying since all of this trouble has come to town.'

Michael nodded understandingly. 'Yes, this is certainly a challenge. But we have to keep the faith; we will take these boys in and we will find others like them – they are only a small group. And you're not alone – other business owners are struggling – do you know Jonathan Cane? Woodbridge Business group?'

Henri shook his head.

'He's a good man to know – they're planning a festival, a carnival to celebrate the town and its businesses. I'll get him to call you.'

Before Livia left, she made Henri promise he'd join her for supper that evening. Michael watched her cross the street and bundle Clochette into the Boxster. 'Take care!' he called out on a strange impulse.

Chapter 21

The Chief was waiting for Kilroy next morning. The night had brought a new lead: it seemed Stephanie Moulin was spotted early on the evening she died. What did Kilroy know about this?

'I know,' answered Kilroy, 'that she was seen with James Court about 6 p.m., in the pub – the Captain Cook.'

'And?' the Chief was tense.

'And that Court is under surveillance – dealing.'

'Exactly. Have you brought him in?'

'No.'

The Chief looked astonished. 'Well, you could have had him last night, surely?'

'I spoke to an informant; we wanted to check out his movements before and after the murder, first.'

'Honestly, Kilroy, why are you always so easily distracted? And why is Collins wasting time on a bag-snatch case?'

'I think there's a connection.'

'Well, here's a connection for you: the Press are expecting a meaningful statement from us tomorrow; let's not spin them a yarn – bring me something concrete.'

'Sir, what's concrete is that we've got her name, we've interviewed her family and we're following several lines of enquiry – that has to be worth something?'

The Chief stood up from his desk and sighed. 'That's not enough, Kilroy. You've had ample time to sort this – and now I find you're sending your team off on red herring chases through the town! It's not what I'd expect from a Senior Detective – in fact, when the dust settles on this, I think you and I need to have a chat about where you see yourself in the next couple of years.' He turned and looked out his window.

Kilroy stood up and headed to the door, but the Chief hadn't quite finished.

'And Kilroy? Hallett is supposed to be undercover – your frequent visits might be putting her in danger. Stay away from her. That's an order.'

Kilroy strode from the room as quickly as he could – he was that *close to punching Gillam in the face. What he hadn't told the Chief was that he'd established the identity of the woman whose bag had been snatched. She was a French national: Josephine Kurtz. She was staying at the George Hotel – with a younger man identified only as Etienne – the concierge believed he was her son, but Kilroy knew he was Stephanie Moulin's brother. His instincts were proving right.*

Chapter 22

Cooking for Frenchmen was a daunting prospect, thought Livia; every Frenchman carried an ideal of dishes based on those once cooked by his mother. She'd learned that from Alex; it had taken her many years to perfect Cotriade, the fish soup much-beloved in Bretagne, and she still felt a little sense of trepidation every time she filled Alex's bowl. She hoped Henri would appreciate the effort.

When he arrived at 7, the soup was simmering slowly, a soft cloud of garlic wafting out into the garden. Henri had obviously got some rest in the afternoon and was now dressed in a casual linen jacket and jeans. Clochette was delighted to greet him, and he patted her warmly, spying the cat who sat on the lounge chair sizing him up.

'Oh, what a lovely cat! Come here, my pretty!'

The tortoiseshell cat stood up sulkily, stretched and meandered over to his outstretched hand.

'Oh, how old is she?'

'I'm not certain,' said Olivia, opening the bottle of red he had handed her. 'She was here when I arrived back from France – no one has any idea where she came from.'

'Oh, she has blessed your house! No wonder it is so charming!'

'Thank you – it's a work in progress. Shall we take our wine outside?'

The garden was washed in a pink glow from the last of the sunlight. They chatted, studiously avoiding the subject of the break-in, until the warm light faded and then made their way indoors to eat.

'Do you know, I don't believe I've ever eaten a Cotriade!' exclaimed Henri, wiping his mouth with his napkin. 'It was wonderful!'

'Not too . . . fishy?'

'Oh, no, not at all! My family lived in Algeria when I was a child – fish was always served.'

'How interesting – what were they doing there?'

'My father was a bank manager – they returned to Nice a couple of years after the war. They never really settled again – they missed L'Algerie. And your parents?'

'My father was in local government – an administrator. And my mother was a housewife. She'd wanted to be 'something' but her family believed all women should marry and raise children, and so...'

'And you have brothers and sisters?'

'Sisters – four.'

'A large family!' He laughed. 'And your husband – I hope I am not being
too forward?'

She smiled and told him about the vineyard, and the years of hard work and, accidentally, the trouble they'd had with the intruder.

'What? And the police did not deal with it? That's terrible!'

She pushed her wine glass away; she had sat on the one glass all evening, but there was a danger she would say too much.

'Oh, it was difficult – it seemed petty, I suppose.'

'What? That they broke in to your home? I now can imagine how that would feel!'

'Yes, it was ... unsettling. The worst thing was that they destroyed our family pictures, our wedding photos and the pictures of my sisters, Alex's parents ...'

Henri paused and frowned. 'Yes, that is unsettling.' He paused again. 'The boy who broke in to my shop? He, too, destroyed my pictures – the ones of my family that I had on the wall. Do you recall? I had one of my parents in Algiers?'

Livia felt a slight chill pass over the room.

Chapter 23

James Court was a 47-year-old petty criminal who'd watched too many of the 'Godfather' films; despite the padded shoulders of his cheap suit, it was clear the body underneath was skinny and unworked. His greasy hair was slicked back and his forehead sported a line of angry, adolescent pimples. When he smiled, he bared cracked, yellowing teeth, a testament to his heavy smoking habit.

Kilroy had not had to deal with him much – that was for the Narcs – but when he had, he'd felt a need to wash his hands. Court was a dangerous kind of villain, in Kilroy's opinion: violent and narcissistic, but stupid. His mistakes were often visited upon the almost innocent, missing the big targets he'd aimed for.

He was seated at his usual table at the Captain Cook when Kilroy arrived, a young girl at his side.

> *'Well, well, well. If it isn't Mr Kilroy.' He pushed the girl's arm. 'Get out of here.'*

> *'A little young to be in a pub, isn't she?'*

> *'Oh, don't you worry, Kilroy, she's got all the paperwork.'*

> *'Good. I'll let my friends in Vice know. But right now, I want to know your connection with another young lady.'*

> *'Oh, there are many young ladies in my life, Kilroy. Where to begin?'*

> *'I don't mean the ones you pimp out; I mean one who ended up in the morgue.'*

> *'I resent the term 'pimp', Kilroy. If anything, I'm a matchmaker. And I certainly don't deal in the dead ones, if that's your penchant.'*

'But you do, see.' He pushed Stephanie's passport picture across the table. 'Stephanie Moulin. You were in here with her last week - don't try and deny it, you piece of shit – you were seen.'

Court looked at the picture, feigning vagueness. 'She does look a little familiar. Is she the one in the papers?'

'She is. And unless you start talking, you'll be in the papers, too, as our main suspect.'

'You can't tie me to that, Kilroy. All I did was talk to her, see.'

'About what?'

'She'd been asking around my girls, wanting to know where she could score. Not for herself – she said she had a few customers who relied on her. Said her source had dried up.'

'And you wanted to help her out?'

'Of course not! What would I know about drugs? One of my girls must have given my name as a joke. I set her straight, and she went along her way.'

'Don't give me that, Court. I reckon you tried to get the name of her dealer from her, but she wouldn't tell you – said she'd only tell the organ-grinder, not the monkey. So, you sent her to him… trying to cadge some good will with the boss.'

'I don't need 'good will', Kilroy. I'm the only Boss in this town.'

Kilroy laughed dismissively and got up.

'You're just a little bitch, yourself, Court. And let me tell you: when I find the guy you sent her to, I won't hesitate to tell him you gave me his name – and, maybe I'll add that you fingered him for the murder.'

Court looked suddenly pale. 'Wait. Wait… '

Kilroy sat back down.

'Rollanson. I sent her to Rollanson. But you can't tell him I spilled…'

'You sent her to Rollanson? You could have guessed what would happen.'

'No, no… I didn't know! I thought he might be interested, you know? She was a cute little thing…French….'

Kilroy's contempt was written all over his face as he got up and left.

Chapter 24

After Henri left, Livia checked and rechecked the doors and flicked the security lights to on. It was probably, undoubtedly, a strange coincidence that Henri's intruder had destroyed his family pictures, but just thinking about it took her straight back to the last time the intruder had visited them at the vineyard…

That evening, she and Alex had secured the house: the main gates were locked and CCTV cameras watched over the outer buildings. The letters had continued, each one more and more bizarre, more threatening; the last one indicated that their emails had been accessed or hacked.

Alex was exhausted; he poured himself another glass of wine and stared at his reflection in the darkened lounge window. Livia and Clochette sat on the lounge, watching the fire.

'Come and sit,' she said gently.

He ignored her. 'I think I'll ask Karl to stay on site from now on – maybe we should hire security?'

She stood up and joined him at the window. 'We've talked about this – we can't afford it. We've got the surveillance – the new alarms…'

'Yes,' he sighed and held her closer.

Several hours later they were asleep, Clochette on the landing outside their room. Livia recalled there was a cold moon, clear stars and sky; the Winter was still very much with them. Clochette's low growl was nearly inaudible; she shifted a little and cocked an ear. Livia sat up, slowly, and strained her ear against the night. Yes: there was a sound – downstairs. She tapped Alex's shoulder. Now, Clochette was on her feet, her barking ferocious. Alex was up instantly. He opened the drawer of the bedside cabinet and, to Livia's surprise, pulled out a gun. Clochette was standing at the top of the stairs looking down into the darkness, her hackles high, she was crouching low, as if to spring.

Alex was already at the door when the first explosion happened: a terrible sound, followed by a rush of acrid smoke up the stairs.

Clochette, stunned, ran back into the room.

>'Call the police!' shouted Alex, as he ran into the smoke.

Livia gave the details to the operator and hurried to the stairs, Clochette behind her, barking wildly.

>'Alex! Alex!' she shouted.

A second explosion rocked the house; Livia lost her grip on the banister and fell back, cracking her head on the marble stairs. She struggled to remain focused and conscious; she became aware of a figure standing over her – a strange, elongated figure that stumbled backwards as Clochette leaped toward it.

She awoke, sometime later, in the lounge room. Alex was speaking to her, through the pounding pain in her temples.

>'No, don't move, Livia… wait!' He moved aside to allow the paramedics access.

>'What the…' she tried to sit up and the young woman helped her.

>'Yes, please, sit slowly… let me see the back of your head. There's a nasty cut…'

Alex was in the corner, speaking with the Detective who made notes on his tablet. The police and the fire engines arrived in good time to save the house, and the forensics team were busily taping off the kitchen.

>'Clochette?' Livia called plaintively. 'Girl?'

'She's fine, Livia!' called Alex, pointing across the room where Clochette was struggling to free herself from a neighbour's protective grip. 'Louis, let her go to Livia...'

The dog limped over and began licking Livia's face.

'Oh, Clochette, bell!' Livia cried. 'What's happened to you?'

Clochette raised a sore-looking paw; it was burned.

Alex was by her side, now. 'She ran out with me, just before the second explosion – then she ran straight back in to find you!'

'Oh,' Livia stroked her head.

'Madame, I think it would be best if you come with us, to the hospital,' said the paramedic.

'No, no, I'll be fine!'

Alex's voice was stern. 'No, you'll go. I want to be sure you're ok...'

'But Alex, really, I'm fine!' she winced as she tried to stand.

'No,' said the paramedic firmly. 'There's a chance of bleeding on the brain. We need to monitor you at the hospital.'

Livia looked around the scene, the air thick with the smell of chemicals and extinguished smoke and fell back onto the sofa, into a deep, dark nothingness.

*****

By the time Livia came home, a week later, a lot of the repairs had been completed, but there was still some cosmetic work to be done. Alex had pieced together the events of that night.

After they'd gone to bed, and the lights were turned out, the intruder had, somehow, disabled the alarm system – not easy and, according to the police, an indication of a professional. They'd then entered the kitchen, via the back door – the lock had been tampered with and the door left wide open.

The first 'incendiary' had, according to the police, been thrown from the lounge into the kitchen. Immediately after the first explosion, Alex had run down the stairs and, seeing the kitchen door open, he'd run out into the night, thinking he was in pursuit of the intruder. The dog had followed him.

At the time Livia had hung up the phone and stepped on to the landing, the intruder was, the police believed, already making his way up the stairs toward her. What he didn't count on was that his incendiary had blasted the gas canisters just outside the kitchen – the second explosion would have surprised him and Clochette's attack had sent him running down the stairs and out into the night.

> 'I saw him, you know,' Livia told the police. 'He was there...leaning over me on the stairs....'

Her description was not useful: a tall, thin figure – like a Giacometti statue, she offered. The police suggested the smoke had obscured her vision and created the illusion of a wasted figure. But Livia was not convinced: her over-riding memory was of long, claw-like fingers reaching for her face.

It was, at this point, that the police suggested the couple leave the house – clearly, this person meant harm to Livia. Alex and Livia would not be driven off their land, their passion of the last ten years. They came up with a plan that would remove Livia from danger – and just might encourage their enemy to boast of his success and, in doing so, reveal himself.

Chapter 25

Kilroy had a hangover. Again. He dropped, heavily, into his chair. His desk was a bombsite of scribbled post-it notes which he screwed up into a ball and threw into the bin.

He looked at the brown box; hand-delivered, the same scrawled writing. John. He smiled: clearly last night's run-in had rattled him. He knew nothing got into the building that hadn't been scanned for explosives, but he shook it tentatively, anyway. He gingerly cut along the manic adhesive tape and peeled back the cardboard flaps, leaning away as he did.

The smell hit him just before he realised what he was looking at; it was a small mound of yellow feathers, bloodied. And then he saw the beak and head. The thing had been crushed.

> *'Jesus Christ!' he coughed a little, tasting last night's whisky.*

There was a letter, too, beneath the bird. He used a pencil to lift it out, onto his desk and unfold it.

> *'I know why birds sing, Kilroy. You think they sing because they're happy! And I suppose, in a way, they are: stupid creatures! Happy in their little cages! And the worst part is they have locked the cage door themselves. They have chosen the cage!*
>
> *That's my mission, Kilroy: to free all the trapped birds – to squeeze the song out of them. You won't stop me.'*
>
> *Kilroy shuddered and called the lab. 'Can you send one of the lads up?'*

He logged in to his computer and pulled the crumpled card, ripped in half, from his pocket: Becky. Good time! and half a phone number were still legible. It was the sort of card you find in phone boxes or in the Gents at seedy pubs – but the area code was not local. He wanted to know where the card had come from because he believed John had dropped it as he chased him down a dark alley at about 1 a.m.

*****

Marie hurried across the street to the café; she was meeting Jess for breakfast. Jess was one of the regular working girls; she had a small room not far from here where she took her clients, but she lived at the edge of town, in one of the poor, terrace houses on the estate. She had two teenaged kids – the oldest already known to the police.

The waitress called over: 'You want to order now?'

'Just a coffee… I'm meeting someone.'

'I bet you are,' smirked the waitress.

'We'll order when SHE gets here,' she said pointedly.

'Takes all sorts, sweetie,' she replied under her breath.

Half an hour later, Marie paid for her two coffees and checked her phone. Jess hadn't called to cancel; she'd call it in and get uniform to check out the house.

Chapter 26

After a fitful sleep, Livia made a decision: she'd go into town and visit Michael at the Police Station. She had to have a look at the CCTV image of the 'lad' who'd smashed Henri's window and torn up his family photos. She'd tell him she'd seen some lads outside the Co-Op a couple of weeks ago, and that she'd realised, maybe, it could be one of them? Of course, she couldn't tell him the real reason she wanted to see it, to reassure herself that the intruder wasn't here, in her town. She shook her head; no, it was a silly coincidence. But she'd check anyway.

As she pulled out of the drive, Matthews' truck was pulling in. She waved cheerily; the boy looked morose, but Matthews smiled and pointed to the corner of the house and the window frame he'd be repairing. She nodded and drove away.

*****

Michael bent down and patted Clochette's head.

> 'Outside the Co-Op? Hmmm. I haven't seen them.'

> 'Yes, I just thought, maybe, if I had a look at the CCTV, I might recognise one…'

> 'It's a lousy picture – very blurred. I reckon we know who it is, but we can't prove it with this pic.'

> 'Oh, sure… you never know, though.'

She was certain Michael was seeing through her charade – she was a terrible liar.

> 'OK, let me just pull up the file …' He tapped away on the keyboard and leaned forward. 'Here you go…'

He turned the screen slightly, so that she could see. She stared at the image: it was blurred, certainly, but there was no mistaking the angular limbs, the elongated shape of it. She was stunned.

'You recognise him? Is he one of the lads you saw?'

'Ummm, no, no…. I … you're right. It's very blurred. Might have been one of them. He's pretty tall, isn't he? For a lad, I mean?' She wiped the sudden sweat from her forehead.

'He is… skinny bugger, too. Are you ok? You look pale…Here, sit down…'

She tried to smile. 'Yeah, I … I didn't sleep well last night.'

'And I bet you haven't had breakfast.'

He told her to wait and he came back with a cup of tea.

'I'm worried about you, Livia.'

'Oh? Why?'

'Well, you're on your own out there – quite off the beaten track. I mean, I assume you're on your own?' He looked at her directly.

She smiled. 'Yes. My husband is in France – we've separated.'

'I'm sorry,' he blushed a little. 'Well, I'll make sure I drop by when I'm out your way – and you've got my mobile number. But you know, these kids won't be going into The Forest - they stick close to town…'

'Yes, thank you Michael. I'd best go… I've got workmen at the house today.'

'Oh? Who's that?'

'Matthews…. he's fixing a leak on an upstairs bedroom.'

'Oh. Does he have his grandson with him?' Michael frowned.

'Arthur? Yes, he's with him… why?'

'Just be careful... he's had a bit of trouble with the law.'

'Yes, Matthews told me – said he got mixed up with the wrong lot?'

'Yeah, well, old man Matthews is always making excuses for the boy, but the truth is, he's mixed up in some stuff. I'd keep an eye on him.'

She wanted to stay and argue in Arthur's defence, but for now, she wanted to be out of the Police station and back at home to gather her thoughts.

Chapter 27

When uniform visited Jess's house, her teenagers had no idea where she was – and they didn't seem particularly perturbed by her absence; she kept weird hours. Six hours later, the call came in: a woman's body had been found at the end of the beach, amongst the rocks.

Kilroy and Collins had to make their way through the crowd of onlookers who had no business being on the beach on such a blustery, cold afternoon.

Jenkins was already there, carefully rolling a cotton bud across the woman's finger tips and under the nails.

> *'She's been strangled. Not much more I can tell you at this stage.'*

Kilroy crouched down to look at the woman's face; once again, the smeared lipstick. Once again, the skirt raised, no evidence of sexual assault... the handbag to one side. Jenkins' sidekick was about to bag it up.

> *'Wait a minute,' and Kilroy reached over for it.*

House keys. A wallet; debit card, taxi card... a library card? 'Jessica Ward'. Condoms. Mints. Make-up bag. And half of a ripped card – the kind you found in phone boxes. Or men's rooms in seedy pubs.

> *'Collins? Run a check on Jessica Ward...'*

> *'No need, sir: Marie called it in earlier – concerns raised. Working woman. Two kids.'*

Kilroy looked away, out to the churning swell of the steel-blue waves. He thought he'd had John on the run that night when he'd seen the figure in the alleyway. Kilroy had been watching the slow, but steady flow of cars cruising the High Street, hoping for something unusual, something that would reveal John. He was just about to call it a night when he saw the slight movement in the shadows. Someone else was watching; waiting. Suddenly, perhaps sensing Kilroy's presence, the figure had hurried away. Kilroy had stepped out of the doorway and given chase. John was quick; he knew his way around the back streets and he slipped away from Kilroy like warm breath on a cold night. Kilroy had found half of the card and smiled at John's sloppiness… but he'd been set up. John had been toying with him.

Chapter 28

Livia and Alex had agreed that they would not make 'normal' contact unless there was an emergency. She wanted to call him now, so desperately, to tell him about the figure on the CCTV, but by the time she was home, the curtains drawn and Clochette curled by her side, she had begun doubting her own judgment: how could the figure who smashed Henri's café be the same creature who'd terrorised them on the vineyard? She was letting her nerves get the better of her.

She sighed and turned another page of the photo album; June 1950. She smiled at the picture of a newly born Alex, cradling in his mother's arms. Jean-Clare Marchal was a beautiful woman: dark, wavy hair framing her pale, heart-shaped face - huge dark eyes beamed proudly on her new-born son. The caption underneath, written in French by Alex's father stated, simply: "*Our boy*".

The album was one of four that had been meticulously curated by Alex's mother, beginning when they married, two years before Alex's birth. Livia had a large chest that contained the albums and the diaries, business and legal documents that covered the vineyard's history from the time the Marchals had purchased it, after the War. She had leafed through it over the years, but now, in light of the intruder, she was drawn to reading it all again – she wondered if the past contained clues. After the explosions of the last attack, Alex had agreed the documents were at risk and that Livia should take them with her to the UK.

Jean-Clare had kept detailed track of their lives – notes on what they'd eaten, who'd visited, the birth of a worker's child, the weather patterns. Livia wondered where she'd found the time, knowing the hours of labour it must have taken to repair the vineyards and the house after the Germans had been through. She imagined Jean-Clare, last thing at night at the kitchen table, her limbs tired and aching for sleep, dutifully recording the day. That same table had been damaged in the blast. She smiled at the picture of Alex's father, Claude, high astride his horse with a young Alex sitting proudly at the front of the saddle.

She felt a small draft of cool air from upstairs and went to check the window that Matthews had been working on; it was on a half-latch, and the night air was slipping in. She locked it firmly, and drew the curtains, closing the door on her way out. The landing was dark, but her bedroom lamp was on and a warm glow filled the space. The cat slipped past her, winding itself about her ankles. Yes, it was late. She went down to double-check the alarm system and called to Clochette. 'Come on, then, let's go up.' She left a small lamp alight in the lounge and took one of the diaries with her to bed.

> ### Mars 18, 1946
>
> *"So, Wednesday is here – the week is half-way through! There is so much more to do before Sunday, and I fear we will not have our day of rest. The vines are being repaired – some need to be replaced – and the team is only employed until the end of the month. They are good men, working hard, but the task may beat them.*
>
> *Today, I have finished our bedroom – the walls are whitewashed and will stay that way until we have paint. But even though Claude does not believe me, I think I prefer them as they are – so clean and bright. I found, in the cellar, a large blanket. It has a pattern of cornflowers against a yellow background. Some of it was ruined by the damp, but I have salvaged enough of it to make a curtain for the window – a splash of the sun – the bed is such a dark wood. As soon as the sunflowers have bloomed, I will fill a jug!"*

Livia sighed and closed her eyes; she could see the fabric – they'd found the curtains folded carefully in Jean-Clare's linen cupboard, its yellow was faded by the sun, but the cornflowers were the same blue. Livia had asked Mme. Fourier to make two large cushion covers from them, and they'd taken pride of place on the sofa ever since. And as she drifted off to sleep, she could feel the whitewashed walls, chalky and cool in the bedroom she'd shared with Alex.

Chapter 29

Kilroy waited in his car until Marie returned to her flat. He checked no one had followed her.

'Drink?' he was already pouring himself a whisky.

'Slow down,' she said, taking the bottle from him. 'Let's start with a glass of wine, eh? And maybe we can eat something....'

Marie changed into her track pants and t-shirt, wiping off the lurid make-up with a wet-wipe.

'So, where are you with Jess?' she asked sadly.

'Strangled – on the beach.'

'DNA?'

'Nothing clear, yet. What have you got from the other girls?'

'Oh, you know, same bunch of weirdos, peccadillos, kinks... She had a couple of regulars, but it's not like her to work on the beach. She felt safer in her room. Did you find anything there?'

'Nothing useful. The only real lead we have is the card – it's from Bradford. Vice are looking into it.'

'Well, if your John had half of it, it's a good bet, you've got your man? What's the Bradford link?'

Kilroy frowned. 'I don't know. The card's a ruse – no reason she'd have it in her bag. He's playing with us... how'd you go with the code? The French girl's diary?'

She smiled, got up and took the book from her bookshelf.

'My code-breaking's not as good as my French, but I pulled out a couple of patterns and I reckon we've *got names, dates and places – she's been watching people.'*

'Anyone we know?'

'Well, James Court, for one,' she pointed to the sketch of a little pig in the margin of the page. 'And a 'Wizard',' she flipped the page to show him the sketch of a malevolent Merlin.

Kilroy gave a low whistle. 'The big boss...'

'A dangerous acquaintance, I reckon. She's got a number scribbled down underneath...'

'Yes, Court gave her Jacob Rollanson's number on that last night.'

'She's also following two other characters. Usually at night – one male, one female. She calls the woman 'Medusa' and the man 'Jumelle'. She watches them – comings and goings. I think they're at the George – the hotel.'

'That'd make sense,' said Kilroy. 'She was following her brother, Etienne – '

'Ahhh – Jumelle means twin. Were they?'

'No, but they look alike, for sure. Medusa's not a very positive character...'

'No – she's crossed that out a couple of pages later. Replaced with the Madonna.'

Kilroy nodded. 'So – she gets to know the woman.'

Marie closed the diary. 'I'd say so.'

'Get those dates and times to Collins, too, can you?'

'Will do.'

Kilroy reached for the whisky, and she placed her hand over his glass.

'No – let's eat something?'

He looked a little irritated. 'Oh, Marie, it's getting late…'

She leaned over and stroked his face. 'What's your rush, Kilroy? You got somewhere you need to be?'

Chapter 30

Arthur Matthews was sitting on a bench by the church. It was 3 p.m. on Saturday and his grandfather had allowed him, for the first time in weeks, to walk in to town on his own – of course, he had to be home before 5 p.m. Now that he'd been allowed his phone again, he'd messaged some kids from school saying he'd be in town and did they want to catch up? A couple replied – one, Melanie, sent him a flirty emoji and a kiss.

The sun hadn't been out for an hour and the clouds were building up – it was going to rain. The wind was picking up, too.

'Oi! Arthur!' Jamie Briggs waved from across the street. 'Coming or what?'

Arthur jumped up and jogged toward him.

'Hey, Jamie!'

'Where've you been? You alright?'

'Yeah, just busy with Granddad.'

'We thought that after… well, you know… the police and all… are you….?'

'I'm ok. Yeah.'

They were walking toward the kebab place on the High Street.

'Trevor's cousin got busted, you know. Cops said he was dealing! They reckon Dev got the stuff from him, nicked it and started selling!'

Arthur looked away, wishing Jamie would drop it, but he went on. 'Yeah, they reckon Trev's cousin got pissed off and shanked him! He's up in court next week!!!'

'Arthur!' Melanie waved from the Kebab Shop door. 'Alright?'

Arthur knew he was blushing bright red, but he didn't care – Melanie's interruption had stopped Jamie in his tracks.

They went inside and ordered kebabs and drinks and settled into the café's curved, plastic seats. Maybe this had been a mistake, meeting up? Arthur tried hard to listen in to Melanie's flirtatious jokes and Jamie's school gossip, but his mind kept turning back to the night Dev had died – something he thought he'd hoped he could leave behind him. The clouds rumbled overhead, and the neon lights grew brighter and more garish. He was glad he'd worn his hoodie; it would be a wet walk home.

*****

Livia heard the first rumbles of thunder as she and Clochette hurried through the wood from Martin's place; his wife and baby were the picture of health. They promised they'd come over for a meal as soon as the baby's sleeping pattern had settled.

As she closed the door and shook off the first spots of rain, Livia heard the phone ringing – let it go to answer phone, she thought, imagining Justin was chasing her for more pages.

Nothing.

About 20 minutes later, it rang again. Same thing – no message, so it definitely wasn't Justin. She tried 1471, caller id: 'the caller withheld their number'.

Outside, the thunder was growing closer and louder, and the rain was a heavy deluge. She watched the spidery lightning cracking through the sky. The phone again. This time, she picked up. There was silence, but the kind of silence you get when someone is listening. She stood, staring at her own fearful reflection in the glass doors. Suddenly, a crack of thunder tore through the sky and exploded into one of the oak trees at the back of the garden.

Chapter 31

As Kilroy left Marie's, he checked and double-checked the street, looking for anything unusual. No, the night was quiet, all curtains drawn.

He drove towards home, but not before he cruised the empty High Street. A few of the working women were braving the cold, despite the police warning that the streets weren't safe. Even Vera Kennedy's gruesome description of the murders in the local paper didn't put them off – but, then, he knew the majority had habits or pimps to feed.

He was about to turn off to home when he saw the car parked on a double-yellow outside the Captain Cook, its hazards flashing. That was nothing unusual, but he was taken aback by the driver who returned, opened the door and bent an almost skeletal frame into the driver's seat – sensing the car behind, the head turned sharply and the gaunt face snapped around to lock eyes with Kilroy.

He sometimes had a feeling – when he looked at people – that he could see inside them, their minds. He sometimes dismissed the feeling, writing it off as 'a moment', down to tiredness or stress. But what he saw usually paid off, and the last time he'd ignored it he'd nearly died – if it hadn't been for Marie…. The gaunt face turned and slid into the car, and as it pulled away, it left Kilroy with a distinct sense of darkness and threat.

A young barmaid ran from the pub, onto the street, looking from left to right. Kilroy stepped out of his car, quickly flashing his badge. 'Everything alright?'

She looked at him and held up a piece of silver jewellery, a necklace? 'Did you see that guy who just left? Did you see which way he went? He left this at his table…'

Kilroy took it from her hand. It was a cheap chain, but it was the pendant that caught his attention: a small, yellow-enamelled bird.

Chapter 32

Arthur lay on the sofa; his Granddad was watching the news. Arthur's phone rang, making them both jump. Unknown number – he saw his Granddad's worried expression.

> 'It's Melanie, Granddad,' he said.

> 'You'd best answer it, then.'

> 'I'll call her later... just saw her, for God's sake.' He switched off the phone's ringer, just before it beeped to notify him of a message.

Later that night, he listened, tensely, to the message. 'We need to talk, Arthur – you know what about. Next time, pick up... or I'll come round to see you and your Granddad.' Arthur felt a sick, punch-like feeling in his stomach: it was Hobbs.

Hobbs was a bloke he'd met through Dev – Dev knew him through Trev and his cousin. Arthur had been to a couple of parties round at the cousin's house – it was always the same. No one talked much, the music was really loud – the neighbours too scared to complain again.

Hobbs was the 'big man' at the parties, always showing off his phone, his trainers – always handing out the drugs, especially to the girls. In the beginning, Arthur hadn't minded; he'd enjoyed the booze and the drugs, always crashing at Trev's place so Granddad didn't know he was wasted. Trev's mother didn't care.

Then, Arthur started noticing that Trev was spending a lot more time with Hobbs, bunking off school, partying. Soon, Dev started joining them and Arthur felt himself on the outside. Trev's cousin had become the town dealer – Friday nights, outside the pub or the kebab shop, he'd hang around, looking edgy, greeting the young men who sidled up to him, close for a moment, maybe a quick fist-pump, and then gone. Soon, Trev was standing with him, acting as a runner between the cars that slowed down and the cousin.

Dev told Arthur that Trev and his cousin were making a killing! Hobbs gave them the stuff at wholesale prices – for every £20 they made for Hobbs, they were making £5 for themselves, and the turnover for a Friday night was anywhere upwards of £500. Dev was envious; he told Hobbs he could help, he could do a stint outside the rec. centre… lots of cars there, late on a Friday night, drinking and smoking. Hobbs put him off; Dev was a small lad, far too keen, far too friendly. But Dev wasn't put off; he talked to Trev one night as he and Arthur made their way home after school.

> 'Come on, Trev. Just tell your cousin to give me a bit of the stuff – I'll go down the Rec., sell it and bring him back the cash – minus my cut…'

> 'Your cut,' laughed Trev. 'Why would we want to give you any of what we're making?'

> 'Because with me doing the rec. you'll make more, see? So many of those guys probably get their stuff out of town – you won't see 'em up there on the High Street, they probably don't know you're there. Come on, man… I really need the money.'

Unlike Trev, Dev really did need the money – not for trainers or phones, but to help his parents feed their large brood of children. Immigrants from Bangladesh, they'd had dreams of starting a restaurant, but the town's economy was already on the turn when they arrived. His mother worked part-time at the Co-Op; his father got the occasional day for the council. Trev promised he'd ask his cousin, but they all knew he wouldn't.

And then, a couple of weeks later, Dev came to the party with new trainers. Everyone noticed and there was a bit of banter; Hobbs was particularly interested, watching from his corner chair, rolling a cigarette. Arthur noticed the hostile attention and had a quiet word with Dev. After that, they avoided the parties.

Chapter 33

Enfin! The sunflowers are out! Claude has left a corner of the fields only for the tournesols! I want to take an armful and fill the house with them! But tomorrow I shall take them to Adeline – her new baby is here! She is such a young mother; Alexandre and I will go to her. Thank goodness her husband has accepted Claude's offer: he will make a fine Foreman, and Alex will have a new playmate: Charles.

There is something so wonderful in a new baby – all the promise, all the chances of such good things! (I must stop: Claude tells I am getting 'broody'!)

Livia took real comfort from Jean-Clare's diaries; she'd read an entire year before she could settle to sleep last night. The lightning had split the tree in half, tearing off one side and all its branches; it was still smouldering. After the shock had worn off, Livia had unplugged the phone and turned off her mobile; she didn't want any more silent calls – even though she'd dismissed the calls as a result of the thunderstorm. She resolved to call Justin and insist he come to see her – he could claim it on expenses, a 'research trip', but she knew he'd love a day spent bitching about the countryside and its privations. And they could talk about the manuscript.

She was quietly pleased with Kilroy and his gruff, Dashiell Hammett attitude; she liked him. She wondered if anyone would recognise Alex in the character? Even though he was probably ten years older than Kilroy, Alex was remarkably, physically strong. Years of physical labour had discreetly maintained his body, where others might have been broken by it. Alex attributed his strength to his parents, particularly his father who could lift oak barrels as if they were plastic. Bretons were like this, Alex had told her. And, like Kilroy, Alex never – or rarely showed his temper – but when he did, it was a truly fearsome thing.

She emailed Justin and settled back into bed with her coffee. The oak tree needed sorting; Matthews had offered to take some of the branches off the other older trees, as a preventative measure – she'd call him.

Chapter 34

In three years, Collins had never seen Kilroy so unsettled; Kilroy could be a lot of things: moody, unreasonable, angry, a brilliant cop – but the driver of that car had really unnerved him. Collins had run the plates, as ordered: it was a hire car, and at 9 a.m., when the rental place opened, they'd have an ID on the driver.

Kilroy was on his phone, rubbing his forehead. Collins signalled 'Coffee?' and Kilroy pushed his mug toward him.

> *'So, when was the last time you reckon she was in Bradford… Right. No forwarding address, I guess?' he laughed. 'Sure. Any chance you could send me through the file on her? Her pimp? Thanks for this; if anything comes up… I don't know… thanks.'*

> *Kilroy put down his phone as Collins handed him his coffee.*

> *'So, do we have the Bradford link, Sir?'*

> *Kilroy had a slug of coffee. 'The girl on the card is known to them – Becky. They haven't seen her for weeks. Assumed she'd moved on.'*

> *'You're not convinced?'*

> *'No. Girls like this don't 'move on' – they're stuck where they are. They're sending down the pimp's file – I'll get you to follow it up. Any word on the hire car?'*

> *'I'm about to phone them.'*

Kilroy turned to his computer. Jenkins had sent through the lab report on Jessica Ward. As they thought, it was strangulation, no sexual assault. But something unusual had shown up: on the woman's right palm there were stray fibres, yellow felt, the kind used by toy makers. And a small yellow feather.

Collins hung up his phone. 'Well, that's interesting,' he said. 'The car was picked up at the train station about a month ago, due back next week.'

'Name? ID?'

'Smith,' said Collins rolling his eyes. 'Tony Smith. London address.'

'Get down there, check out the paper work, put a call in to London. Oh, and while you're about – yellow felt, feathers, used in toys. They found traces on the second vic. Check out the toy shop? Craft places?'

'Might be better to start at the arcade – lots of toys given away as prizes.'

'Good thinking – right by the beach. Give uniform a shout, too – it's a long shot, but get them to check the rocks area again – yellow toy, fabric.'

Collins nodded. 'Where will you be, Sir? In case I need you?'

'George Hotel, interviewing the staff. I need to know more about the couple Stephanie Moulin was stalking.'

Chapter 35

Arthur sat on his bed, staring at the phone, hoping it wouldn't ring. But it did.

'You and I need to meet,' hissed Hobbs. 'You've got something that belongs to me.'

'I, I don't know what you mean, Hobbs.'

'Don't mess with me, kid!' he was shouting, and Arthur worried his grandfather would wake up.

'I'm not messing with you, I promise… I don't want to get involved! I had enough trouble last time…'

'You listen to me, you little punk. You know what I want – Dev had the stuff. You were Dev's mate. So? Where's the stuff?'

'I don't have it! I told you, I don't want to get involved!' Arthur was sweating profusely.

'You are already involved, boy. Now I suggest you go visit Dev's house and you find that stuff. And when I call you next, you had better say you have it. Do you understand?'

'Yes,' said Arthur quietly. 'Yes.'

The line went dead and Arthur fell back on to his bed with an exhausted relief. Hobbs wanted the stuff – Arthur knew where it was. And he'd give it to Hobbs and Hobbs would leave him alone, never knowing that Arthur was the only witness to Dev's death – that he'd been Dev's lookout on the night of the stabbing and he was holding the drugs, in case a customer got greedy. He'd seen Hobbs' car parked in the far corner of the rec. centre, its lights off. He signalled to Dev, but Dev was leaning into a car, exchanging drugs and cash. Arthur had hurried behind some skips and watched the altercation, and the stabbing, in slow-motion.

It seemed that Hobbs had found out Dev was pushing stuff from another supplier – a London guy who'd sent a scout up to check out the market. Dev met him and soon he was bunking school and taking the train down to the city once a month. He was starting to make serious money. He even paid Arthur to be 'his muscle'. Arthur buried his face in his pillow, wracked with guilt at what a pathetic guard he'd turned out to be.

*****

Justin's red Audi pulled up in the drive and Livia hurried out to greet him. He stepped from the car, and peeked over the top of his Tom Ford sunglasses at the vast stretch of heathland that fell slowly down to the cottage. His expression was as if he'd got on the wrong plane and had ended up in someone else's holiday.

> 'Justin!' Livia smiled and hugged him. 'So good to see you! No Clochette! Down! Don't worry, she's had a bath, especially.'

> 'I should hope so!' he said, patting her head with a stiff palm. My God! That track has pot holes the size of bomb-craters! Feel like I've done a round with that big Russian Osteo I told you about!'

> 'Come on in,' she laughed.

The mid-morning sunlight was streaming in through the glass doors and the slate tiles were shining warmly.

> 'God, Livia, it's absolutely lovely! Very quaint! Oh my God! There's a cat, too! Don't tell me you have chickens... that'd be overkill.'

The cat looked bored and made her way out into the garden, her tail flicking.

> 'No chickens, but the ponies wander about...'

'Yes, I saw a few of those on the drive – do they always stand in the middle of the road, or only for me?'

'It's for everyone. Let me show you up to your room… '

The large bed was covered in a soft, grey woven throw and the plain walls were a soft yellow. The wardrobe was antique, an oak wood the same as the floor.

'Very country, my dear!' Justin began unpacking his unfeasibly large suitcase.

'Yes, I suppose it is. Do you want the window shut? It'll get chilly as soon as the sun's down.'

'Please! I don't want bugs in here!' He winked at her and reached out for her hand. 'It really is so good to see you, Liv.'

They hugged. She showed him the bathroom, and said she'd be downstairs when he was ready. 'I told my neighbours I'd bring you over for a quick visit – they're intrigued that I've got friends in London!'

'They're country people? My God… what will I wear?'

She laughed, 'You are fine as you are!' But she knew Martin and Rachel might think the Hunter boots and flat cap a tad affected. 'They've just had a baby,' she called as she went downstairs.

A pause. Then he replied: 'Oh. How joyful. But we've got a lot of work to do, so we best not linger *too* long!'

After supper, Livia and Justin sat down to discuss the book.

'I think it's going well,' frowned Justin, his designer reading glasses perched on his nose. 'I like Kilroy.'

'That's good,' she replied. 'I'm so into making him cool and distant, I was afraid he'd be too icy.'

'No, that's fine... I think you need to make more of him and Marie, though?'

'In what way?'

'I think you're going to have to get a little more *graphic*.'

'Oh, I tend to think of less is more when it comes to sex scenes.'

'Hmmmm. I don't know. I thought you were going to have him fall into bed with the French mother, you know, he'd comfort her ... But don't worry, you just concentrate on the grisly murders and I'll add the sex later.'

They talked late into the night. Justin was seeing a new man – much older than his usual lovers. Certainly, Justin seemed more settled than he had in years.

'So, will you be moving in with him?'

'Oh, God! Far too early days! Besides, he has a contract in Germany – he'll be based there for two months. I'll pop over, of course, but it will be a testing time. I've never been one for long-distance relationships. Anyway, how about you and Alex? What's the latest?'

'Oh, you know... a bit of time and distance is needed.' She hated lying to him, but she felt that anyone she told the truth to would somehow be in danger.

'But you two were so *good* together! I can't believe you won't patch things up! I mean, he's nothing like your old flames!'

'Why are you saying it like that?' she laughed.

'Well, you did have terrible taste in men! Remember that teacher?

The one you worked with in London. What's his name? Dumble?'

She laughed. 'Duncan!'

'Ah, yes, Duncan! What a tosser! Took himself rather seriously, didn't he?'

'He was an environmentalist – comes with the territory.'

'Bloody hell, he made Greta Thunberg look like fun!'

Eventually, they grew too tired from laughing. She wished him a pleasant sleep and checked the doors and alarm before she whispered to Clochette to follow her upstairs. The wind was picking up outside. She turned to Jean-Clare's diaries.

Decembre 1959

The snow has just started... only a brushing, but enough to delight the children! Alexandre and Charles have been playing together,
here in the lounge, by the fire, but they are crying to be let out! I have agreed that when their papas come home, they can run to greet them.

Claude and Armand have spent the day tending the vines, retying the last branches; they will be back before dark – tired, but I know they will delight in seeing their sons! Claude is so content with Armand as his foreman; this has been a very productive four years.

Armand and Adeline have suffered these past years – two of her babies dead at birth – but this has not dampened their attention to Charles. Maybe they give him a little too much, in recompense? He can be difficult at times.

An hour or so later, she woke with a start. She listened: footsteps outside on the gravel drive. She quietly stepped out of bed and tied her dressing gown about her. Out on the landing, there was a soft light from the lounge lamp. She padded downstairs, and switched it off.

She stood still, in the centre of the room, straining her ears. Clochette, close beside her, gave a low growl.

> 'Stay, girl,' Livia whispered, as she parted the lounge curtains a fraction. It was too dark to see anything.

Suddenly the garden was blasted by the movement-sensitive floodlights that were mounted on the barn. She held her breath, watching. At the same time, Clochette moved swiftly from her and crossed the lounge to the front door, her growl growing deeper and more menacing. Whoever it was had moved, with great speed around to the front of the house.

Livia drew back, away from the window and watched the door. The frosted pane of glass was glowing with the front floodlights that had just come on.

She saw the shadow pass the pane and make its way to the kitchen window. The blind was not all the way down, so she fell to the floor, quickly, moving on all fours to a safe vantage point behind the sofa.

The figure hovered there, bending to look in. Clochette, by now, was low to the floor, working her way toward the window, her growl winding up toward a bark.

> 'Hold, girl,' Livia whispered, desperate to see the face.

Within a moment, the figure had moved away, quickly, like a shadow, and the flood lights turned off.

> 'Bloody hell,' she thought, breathing again. 'Clochette, come.'

But Clochette now moved stealthily to the front door, watching the handle as it turned first one way, then the next. Livia crawled forward, imagining that she'd fling the door open and confront whoever it was. She hesitated. Was that a voice?

She listened, her ear nearly touching the heavy wood. Clochette listened too, her ears up in confusion.

'My little belle? Clochette?'

The brick came through the glass pane so quickly, it smashed into Livia's shoulder as she instinctively rolled away. By now the flood lights were in full bloom again and Clochette was barking wildly, madly, scratching at the door.

'What the hell???' Justin stood dazed and confused at the foot of the stairs. 'Livia! What's happening??? Lights? Where's the bloody light switch??'

'No! Don't!' she shouted. 'Get down! On the floor!'

By now, Clochette was running about the loungeroom, looking from kitchen window to door, to the glass doors, agitated at having lost track of the intruder.

Livia stood, unsteadily, wincing at the pain in her shoulder. She went to the kitchen and pulled the blind fully down, and then turned on the lounge lamp. Justin blinked at the scene: the broken pane, the glass shards on the tiles, the brick.

'Who the hell was that?' he said. 'You're hurt, Liv. I'll call an ambulance!'

'No, I'm fine.'

'The cops, then'.

'No, no... I think it was just kids...'

She stroked Clochette's back – the dog was distressed. She couldn't believe this was happening again – and here.

'But you'll have to call the police?'

'I will, but later – it's nearly daylight. We'll be fine.'

Justin argued a little longer, but once the brandy had kicked in, he gave up.

'Dear God! So much for peace in the country!'

Chapter 36

The maid was nervous and Kilroy was doing his best to put her at her ease.

'You're from Spain, eh? You must miss it? Miss home?'

The girl nodded shyly. 'Yes, my mother... I miss...'

'I wanted to ask you a couple of questions...'

The girl looked nervously to the Reception desk where her boss was pretending to look through papers. 'Questions? What for?'

'Oh, no, it's alright – your boss knows I'm interviewing everyone who worked here for the last month.... Isn't that right Mr Burns?'

Mr Burns looked up, as if surprised. 'Oh, yes.... yes, of course. Anything to help the police, but as I've already told you all: we know nothing about the woman or the young man.'

Kilroy winked at the girl. 'Well, then Mr Burns, would it be possible to look at the room we discussed? Number 17, I believe?'

Burns looked like he was going to argue, but Kilroy was already at the desk, staring at him. 'Oh, yes... Cara, take the Detective to Room 17, please. Not that there's anything to see... the room has been thoroughly serviced.'

Upstairs, the girl opened the door. A large room, overlooking the street and on to the Prom. A double room – two singles. En suite.

'Cara, do you remember the lady and the man who were here?' Kilroy pulled back the curtain, as if to take in the view.

'Si. Yes. I remember. Very nice lady – quiet.'

'How long were they here for?'

'Maybe… two weeks, I think.'

'Anything strange about them? Unusual?'

'The woman, she was… how do you say it… nervos…'

'Nervous? What about?'

'I not sure, but she always was having room service and if I knock, she is very quiet in her room. 'Leave it outside, please!'

'And the boy?'

'Oh, him… he was not a boy…' she blushed. Kilroy stared at her, clearly expecting more detail. 'He, he was… fresh. You know, lot of smiling, chatting…. very smooth.'

'Someone said the woman was his …. lover?'

Cara nodded. 'Oh, at first we thought maybe, you know, he likes the old women. But, then – no. Someone said maybe she is the mother.'

'What did you think, Cara?' Kilroy moved closer to her, speaking conspiratorially.

'I… I think he loves the woman who waits outside – over there.'

Kilroy frowned. 'What woman?'

'Young woman – she always there, on that seat,' Cara pointed to a sheltered seat on the Prom. 'I saw him with her one night. They are sitting very close. Talking a lot. He is very nervos. Looking around. They walk together.'

'This man?' He pulled the photo from his coat pocket. 'Is this him?'

Cara took the photo and nodded. 'Yes, that is him.'

'And Cara,' Kilroy pulled a second photo from his pocket. 'Cara, is this the girl?'

'Si! Si! That is her – maybe she and this boy they run away, eh?'

'No, sadly. I'm afraid she's dead.'

Cara looked pale, shocked. 'Oh, mia madre!' she crossed herself. 'Oh! Did he kill her?'

'Why would you think that?' Kilroy was puzzled.

'I see him in the town. He is with those men at the Captain Cook. The bad men with the drugs.'

Kilroy turned to leave, thanking her, but she touched his arm lightly.

'You know this lady – the one that stays here with him? You know she get mugged – on the Prom.'

'Yes, I know – did she tell you?'

'She tells Senor Burns. She tell him she must leave, and she change credit card. She say her bag is stolen with her purse.'

Kilroy went down the stairs two at a time.

'Burns?' He shouted from the desk. 'Burns?'

Burns appeared, flustered.

'Our guest from number 17 – Josephine Kurtz - the one you had no info. on? Seems the lady set up a credit line?'

Burns looked uncomfortable. 'Ummmm…. I don't recall that name….'

Kilroy's temper was rising. 'Listen. Unless you want to be charged with obstruction, I suggest you cut the crap and tell me how her bill was paid. Now.'

Burns was shaking, now. He typed into the hotel computer. Looked at the screen. 'Yes... she called a friend and I had to take payment over the phone.' He reached for a pen and wrote the details on a piece of hotel stationery.

Kilroy snatched it from him: 'I bet they paid a hefty tip? For your 'discretion'?'

The Manager was uncomfortable; he looked around the empty lobby.

'What I received is none of your concern. Clients often show their appreciation...'

Kilroy was thinking fast. 'And I wonder who else has shown their appreciation, since then, Burns? Anyone come looking for her?'

'What do you mean? What are you implying?'

Kilroy sighed, but the colour was rising on his neck. 'Who paid you for information about Josephine Kurtz?'

Burns was shaking now. 'They told me not to tell anyone; to forget about her...'

'And now you're telling me.'

'It wasn't the woman they were interested in! It was the man – Etienne. After she checked out, he never came back to his room, so we had his things stored here.'

'Things? I'm thinking we're not talking his toothbrush?'

'No, no....' he was looking around the lobby and out into the street. ''They were looking for a book, some sort of contacts book, I think. They asked if he'd left it in the room. They took his bag.'

'They?'

103

'If I tell you that, I'll be in a tricky position, Detective.'

'You'll be in a tougher place if you don't tell me.'

Burns wiped his brow with a starched handkerchief, and leaned forward, whispering: 'Rollanson's men.'

'Jacob Rollanson?'

'Shhhh! Yes! Now get out, please. I cannot be seen speaking with you!'

Kilroy smiled sardonically, and headed out into street. So, his instincts had been right: Rollanson was involved up to his neck. Stephanie had called his number on the night she died. And what about the brother, Etienne? Seems he was known to Court and his cohort; and Rollanson was after a note book. He unfolded the piece of paper Burns had given him. 'Edouard Renaud'. And a French phone number. He pulled out his phone and dialled. A gruff voice answered.

'Renaud. Oui?'

'Ah, bonjour Monsieur Renaud. Do you speak English?'

There was a pause. 'It depends. Who is this?'

'My name is Kilroy – Detective Inspector Kilroy. I'm making enquiries regarding a woman – '

'Can I stop you there, please, Inspector. I suggest we speak on a more secure line.'

'I don't understand…'

'I am Edouard Renaud – Inspector Edouard Renaud, Marseille.' Kilroy was surprised into silence, but the Frenchman continued. 'This line – your line – is not secure. I will call you at your office – later today. Au revoir.' And the line went dead.

Chapter 37

Livia made another coffee and waited for Michael to arrive. Justin had insisted she call the police before he left. She'd called Matthews, too and asked if he could come to fix the glass in the door. Clochette was wandering about the garden, sniffing at the ground, growling occasionally. Livia felt physically ill.

She needed to go through her story for Michael. She'd almost called Alex this morning, but she knew he'd be on the first flight out – and that might be what the intruder wanted. What if this was the same intruder? Hadn't he known the dog's name? The thought of the long claw-like fingers at the door made her sick and petrified at the same time.

No, no: it was kids, or opportunistic thieves who'd thought the place was an easy target – the same ones who'd trashed the café. But how did they know the dog's name? Of course! Anyone could have heard her when she called for Clochette on their long walks. Anyone!

Michael knocked at the open door, making her jump.

'Steady,' he smiled gently. 'You look like you've had a fright…' Instinctively, he wrapped a strong arm about her.

She wanted to cry and melt into him, but she gritted her teeth and stepped back. 'Yeah – there's the weapon.'

He looked at the brick on the table. 'From your property?'

'I'd say so – the barn.'

He began taking down notes.

'Around 3 a.m.?'

'Yes, I didn't look at the clock 'til after.'

'And you didn't get a clear view of him?'

'No, not really – it was all shadowy. He had to bend to look in the kitchen window – the blind wasn't all the way down.'

Michael got up and went outside.

'Well, that'd put him at around 5 feet and a bit – that sounds right for your description of the shadow at the door.'

'Yes, I imagine it's those bloody kids – the ones who did the café?'

'Not likely – you're a way out of town and most of those buggers don't drive.'

'Oh…a burglary, then?

'This doesn't sound like a break and enter, Livia. It feels like something else… I mean, they hung around for a while.'

'Yes… I suppose so.'

'They smashed the glass to get to the door lock, I reckon. They knew it wouldn't set off the alarm.'

'Yes, but once the door opened, the alarm would have been tripped.'

'Where's the box?'

They went out to the side of the house and there, to Olivia's horror, she saw the box had been jemmied open, the insides falling out.

'Oh, my God.'

'As I said – there is a lot more going on here than an act of vandalism.' Let's go back in, and he offered a supportive arm to Livia. Once inside, he sat her down at the kitchen table and pushed the hair from one side of her face. They stared at one another.

Clochette barked from the garden; Matthews' truck was in the drive.

'Morning, Michael,' said the old man, reaching out to shake Michael's hand.

'Matthews. Where's that boy of yours today, then?'

Arthur appeared at the door, looking at the floor, Clochette dancing about his legs.

'Hello Arthur,' Michael said in a hard voice.

'Hello.' Arthur's voice was almost inaudible.

'How have you been?'

'Oh, you know…'

'No. I don't. Seen any of the old gang?'

Matthews looked irritated. 'Now look here, Michael. Arthur sees none of that lot anymore! He's keeping his head down.'

Arthur looked upset, like he wanted to run out of the house and into the forest.

'Well, that's the best thing he can do,' said Michael firmly. He turned to Livia. 'OK. Listen – is there someone you can stay with, someone who can stay here?'

'I'll be fine, Michael. Thank you. I'll call my sister.'

'OK. I'll file this – I'll call you later – you'll need a crime ref. number for the insurance. And I'll send a bloke called Johnson out to look at the alarm – he's amazing.' He smiled, put on his hat and left, patting Clochette on the way out. 'Matthews,' he nodded. 'Arthur.'

The police car crushed the gravel as it disappeared. Arthur began sweeping up the glass. 'I'll get on with chopping up that oak when we finish, if that's alright,' said Matthews, looking at her with concern. 'You just relax; you've had a fright. I'll put the kettle on…'

Outside, Arthur started breaking up the smaller branches of the lightning-blasted oak. He felt sick to his stomach remembering his run-in with Hobbs last night. He'd been in town, collecting a few bits and pieces from the Co-Op. As he left the store, Hobbs had appeared and forced him up against the wall.

> 'Hey, Arthur, we need to talk…' And he marched the boy down the side alley, pushing the blade against his back. 'The stuff, I want the stuff.'

> Arthur gripped his shopping bag tightly, as if it might protect him. 'I… I haven't got it….'

> 'Don't give me that! I was going to go to Dev's house myself, when you didn't call back, but I got to thinking… that Arthur, he might be trying to pull a fast one, in fact, I think you are!' And he pushed the blade harder against Arthur's back.

> 'No! No, I'm not trying to pull anything! Swear down! I hid it…'

> 'Hid it where, you wanker? I'm sick of being jerked around by you! At your granddad's, is it? Shall we go round there and find it, eh?'

> 'No! I hid it in the forest!' Arthur was sweating, trying to block out images of Hobbs driving the knife into Dev's back as he pressed him up against the wall of the rec. centre. 'At a house where we were doing a job!'

Hobbs released his grip and Arthur turned slowly to face him.

'So,' sneered Hobbs. 'What's the address? And I tell you boy... you mess me around again and I'll shank you, do you hear?'

Now Arthur realised that Hobbs had not wasted any time; clearly, Hobbs had visited Livia's house last night, trying to get the stuff that Arthur had hidden under the floor board in the guest room. But Hobbs had failed and now he would be furious! He'd come after Arthur. Jesus! He might kill him, just as he'd killed Dev! There was nothing for it; Arthur would have to retrieve the package today and take it to Hobbs tonight. He had to get this guy off his back before it all spun out of control.

****

Of course, Rose had dropped everything when she got Livia's call. She arrived at *Fox Pond* just after 5 p.m. and immediately set about 'sorting' things, despite the calm order of the place. She stirred furiously at the casserole on the hob.

'Rose!' called Livia from the sofa. 'It's fine – it doesn't need so much stirring.'

Rose tapped the spoon against the side of the dish and topped up her wine.

'You?'

Livia raised her glass: 'Yes, please!'

Livia, exhausted, had been half-heartedly reading from Jean-Clare's diary.

Avril 1965

It is too sad to write; today we have buried Armand after a terrible, terrible accident! Mon Dieu! I cannot write more; poor Adeline is so ill – and Charles! The child has collapsed. We have taken food to them and tried to comfort, but only God can help their grief, now. I am holding my family close.

The diary resumed a week later with some notes about the vineyard, but most of Jean-Clare's attention was on Adeline who seemed to be fading away. The doctor had been consulted; his diagnosis was melancholy brought on by her husband's death. Jean-Clare offered to take Charles to give her space to rest, but the boy clung to his mother ferociously when it was suggested. Livia made a mental note to find out about the 'terrible accident' that had killed Armand.

Rose placed the back of her hand on Livia's forehead.

> 'Rose! I don't have a fever! I told you, I'm fine. My shoulder's just a little bruised, that's all.'

> 'I know you said that, but I'm so worried about you! I don't know what I should be doing! Tell me again – everything!'

Livia sighed, but went through the story in less detail than she'd done the first two times.

> 'And the police have no idea?' questioned Rose.

> 'It only just happened!'

> 'But they must have an idea of some likely suspects?'

> 'They're working on it, Rose, please... come sit down.'

Rose shook her head in resignation and flopped down onto the sofa, beside her.

> 'Livia? Why do I get the feeling you're hiding something?'

Livia looked up, surprised.

> 'What do you mean?'

> 'This prowler... you being here on your own. This 'separation'.'

Livia closed the diary and sipped her wine.

'What do you mean, Rose? I've told you…'

'I know you, Liv,' she said softly. 'You haven't told me everything. I know Alex, too. And there's no way on this Earth you two should be living apart.'

Livia bent her head and began to cry quietly.

'You're right, Rose. I miss him so much.'

Rose put her arm around her sister and kissed the top of her head.

'Shhhh, now, shhhh. It's alright, everything is going to be alright.'

Chapter 38

Kilroy waited until he was back at the station to look up Edouard Renaud: yes, he was a Senior Detective in Marseille. And, yes, he'd arranged for Josephine Kurtz's bill to be paid after her bag had been snatched. Kilroy could only surmise she was a French cop, undercover – but a French cop would never have had her bag snatched? And what was she doing shacked up with Etienne, a junkie?

Collins had just come in.

'Any luck?' Kilroy asked him.

'Yes, as a matter of fact – so many toys at   that arcade are made of yellow felt!'

Kilroy sighed. 'Not too lucky, then?'

'Actually,' and Collins dangled a small toy from his index finger. It was a keyring – a little bird with two or three yellow feathers. 'Same as the one we found in Stephanie Moulin's bag. You win them in claw crane – five tries for a pound. Took me ten quid to get this one!'

Kilroy took the bird from his finger, and Collins continued on.

'And we got an address for our hire car driver – Smith. And'… he raised his hand before Kilroy could say it was a fake. 'And it's legit - someone you already know.'

Kilroy was interested now. 'Come on, then, out with it!'

'Same address as Vinnie Roberts. Remember him?'

Kilroy did remember him; a particularly nasty dealer and pimp who'd made a fortune on the backs of girls and drugs. He'd finally gone down for GBH – that's all they could prove. But he'd been out of circulation for a couple of years, retired

– really, his emphysema should have finished him off by now.

> *'I spoke to Vice; seems Vinnie got lazy in his last days, here. Rollanson moved in, screwed Vinnie over – did him out of a fortune. It was ugly.'*

> *'So, what? Vinnie's sent one of his boys up to get his cash back?'*

> *'Now, that's the surprise, you see,' Collins smiled. 'The guy at the hire car place? He showed me the paperwork for the car: Tony Smith...'*

> *'Yes, I know that, Collins...'*

> *'No, no, Sir ... It's Toni with an 'i' – it was a woman who rented the car. And I reckon I've found her – he nodded to a manila file on Kilroy's desk; he was beaming, now, speaking quickly. 'Seems when Vinnie was up here, he got rather close to one of his girls – a junkie, teenager. After he went down, she moved to London – set up house, waiting for him.'*

> *Kilroy opened the file. The young girl's face was hard, pasty from the drugs – like every other teen prostitute.*

> *Collins continued. 'That mug shot's about 10 years old now – she was 16.'*

Kilroy remembered her well; he'd arrested her not long after the mugshot was taken. She was a particularly violent young woman: she'd once beat a client so badly he walked with a cane forever after.

> *'So, Vinnie's sent Toni up here to have a word with Rollanson? Surely not on her own? There's got to be more to it than that.'*

Kilroy thought back to the night he'd seen the car double-parked outside the pub, and he visualised the wasted figure who climbed into the driver's seat. Could that have been a woman? Maybe. Beneath the large coat and hat, there might have been the wasted, skeletal frame of a woman battered by heroin.

'Jesus,' he ran his hand through his hair.

'Yes,' said Collins, proudly, reaching for the file. 'So, your instinct was right - there's clearly something going on with Vinnie and Rollanson. I'll pass all this on to Vice and I'll get back on to the lab to fast track those toys – money's on them both coming from the same machine.'

'No,' said Kilroy placing his hand on the file. 'Let's keep it with us, for now. I want to take a closer look at the girl.'

Collins look confused, but he was used to Kilroy's ways and he was in awe of Kilroy's nose for trouble. He wondered, sometimes, if Kilroy wasn't psychic.

Chapter 39

Livia found Armand's death certificate online – one of the ancestry sites. April 3rd, 1963. He was crushed by a truck – on the vineyard. The coroner's report was not available, but the archivist she'd contacted had found several references in the French national newspaper archives. That was surprising, considering this was a local, parochial, accident. However, when she read the reports, she understood the interest.

Monsieur Armand Justas was killed in an unusual accident yesterday, 3rd April. Witnesses say that M. Justas had been out late, tending to his duties as foreman of Marchal's Vineyards, as was not unusual. When he did not return home, his wife raised the alarm.

A party of searchers set off around midnight and came upon the terrible sight of M. Justas crushed beneath the rear wheels of his truck. Efforts to revive the poor man were pointless. The tragedy was declared a 'terrible accident'.

However, Officer Pierre Gentry has issued a statement that the official report will not be concluded until further investigations have been undertaken. These 'investigations' involve transporting the body to Paris for further examination. When pressed for further details, Officer Gentry refused to comment.

We have spoken to sources who wish to remain anonymous and we have been told that several days ago, a group of travellers were run off the land by M. Justas. One was heard to vow vengeance.

Livia emailed the French archivist again, and asked for any further reports regarding the death. Next time she spoke with Alex, she would ask if he remembered anything about that time. She sighed; she was so tired. Matthews and Arthur were just packing up.

Arthur appeared at the door with a delighted Clochette at his heels.

'Excuse me, Mrs Marchal,' he looked up at her from under his long fringe. 'Is it ok if I use your toilet?'

'Of course! Would you like a cold drink when you come down?'

'Oh, no, I'm fine, thanks. Granddad wants to be getting back.'

She went outside to admire the neat pile of logs that were now stacked in the barn.

'That's fantastic,' she smiled at Matthews. 'That'll get me through until next November, I reckon.'

'Well, I see you've got an old apple tree over there – it's on its last leg – they don't do more than 30 years. I could come out and cut that one up before it falls, if you like. That'll cover December!'

'That's a great idea. Thank you, Matthews.'

Arthur came from the house, pulling his jacket about him.

'You all set then, son? Goodbye Mrs Marchal – I'll give you a call and we can arrange a day to do the apple tree. And don't forget: call anytime if you need us.' He climbed into his truck.

Arthur hesitated at the passenger door and turned back to Olivia: 'I'm sorry about your door, Mrs Marchal.'

She smiled. 'It's not your fault, Arthur. Thank you for fixing it.'

They drove away and Arthur watched Clochette running alongside the truck as it headed to the drive. It *was* his fault, and it could have been so much worse. Tonight, he'd give Hobbs the stuff he'd retrieved from under the floorboards; it would all be over.

Chapter 40

Another package had been delivered to Kilroy. He didn't fancy opening it, but his curiosity was running wild. The small package was wrapped in meters of sticky tape, almost an inch thick. 'Bloody lunatic wrapping,' he thought.

He held it at arm's length as he peeled back the adhesive flap. Some synthetic, thank God, feathers fell out onto the desk. There was a note and a key with a huge fob – a hotel key. No name. He read the note.

> *The hotel, dear Inspector, is the place the harlots take their clients. That's where you'll find me – well where you'll find my handiwork. The beautiful Marie... I've saved her for last. You really are a stupid bastard, Kilroy. You've had so many opportunities to find me... I bet you thought you had me the other night, in the alley? Sleep well tonight, Inspector. You have a busy week ahead.*

Kilroy gritted his teeth.

> *'Collins? Did you manage to get anymore from Bradford? The girl on the card?'*

> *Collins looked uncomfortable: 'I'm sorry – I haven't followed up. I'll do it now.'*

> *Kilroy felt his temper rising and forced it back down. The case was getting too big for just the two of them. 'We need help – anyone from uniform you can grab? Maybe get them to do some of the plodding? Have them check this out.' He passed him the hotel key and the note.*

> *Collins nodded and picked up his phone.*

> *Kilroy leaned back in his seat: it wasn't like John to express his anger so directly. Things were escalating. He felt a small wave of panic, wondering where Marie was right now. He called her – answer phone.*

'Marie? We need to meet – tonight? Why don't you come out to mine? And Marie? Be careful. Please?'

Chapter 41

Livia waved goodbye to Martin, at the edge of the wood; she'd been to visit Rachel's baby and Clochette was keen to get home for her supper. As they approached the cottage, she could see the cat pacing back and forth in the kitchen window.

That morning, Michael's friend Johnson had come to look at the alarm.

> 'Hmmmm, they've made a good job of it, that's for sure. I'll call the company – get them to send us a new unit. This one's beyond repair.'

She felt a little vulnerable without it, but there was not much she could do. She tried not to dwell on it. Tomorrow, she had books to collect from the library, and she would lunch at Café Italia. Her phone buzzed; a missed call? She hadn't heard it. She looked at the number, but it had been withheld. 'Dammit!' she wanted to cry. 'Damn you, you bastard!'

She went around the house, checking each door and window was locked, and drew the curtains, even though it was only just getting dark. She would get back to Kilroy – his drama was a distraction to her own.

****

Arthur pressed himself against the wall of the church, looking down the row of gravestones for Hobbs. He'd arranged to meet him at 6, so Arthur wanted to be there first – as if that gave him more power, the upper hand.

Just before 6, Hobbs appeared, walking quickly and silently, flicking his cigarette out across the graves.

> 'Well, where is it?'

Arthur passed him the bag and turned to leave.

'Where the hell do you think you're going? You and me have business to discuss.' He spun Arthur around.

'No, we don't,' said Arthur, surprisingly firmly. 'We're finished. I don't want to see you again.' And he turned away.

Before he knew what was happening, Hobbs had him pressed against the wall, the knife, once again pushing against his back.

'We're finished when I say we are, boy. You're going to do a little job for me, see. You're going to call Dev's friends in London and you're going to tell them you want to get in on the action, like.'

'No!' Arthur shouted and turned quickly, pushing hard at Hobbs.

'You little shit!' Hobbs brought down a heavy punch into Arthur's face, sending the boy flying on to the lawn that edged the path.

Hobbs was already on top of him; he hit him again. Arthur's mind was spinning, his hands clutching at the grass, trying to get some leverage to pull himself up. Another punch, and he was losing consciousness.

Someone shouted, and suddenly Hobbs was off him, Arthur scurried away and turned to see his grandfather wrestling the knife from Hobbs. He'd used the element of surprise to his advantage, landing one or two good hits before Hobbs had lunged forward with the knife.

'No, granddad!' Arthur shouted and ran forward, punching Hobbs' temple, sending him reeling to the church wall, and sliding to the ground. 'Granddad! Just leave it!'

'I'll not bloody leave it! I'll have no one lay a hand on my boy! Get to your feet, you scum!' he shouted, kicking the knife across the path.

At that moment, Michael was running toward them, followed by two other officers.

'Stand down, Matthews! We've got him!'

The officers quickly cuffed Hobbs and searched him.

'Well, well. What's this, then, Hobbs? There's enough here to get you 20 years!'

'It's not mine! It's his... little shit tried to sell it to me!'

Matthews lunged forward and swung a punch at him.

Michael held him back. 'Hey, hey! Matthews, stop!' And he turned to Arthur. 'Looks like you've got some explaining to do...'

'He didn't do anything!' shouted Matthews, but Michael was already cuffing Arthur. 'We'll talk about it at the station.'

One of the officers had picked up the knife and was slipping it into a plastic evidence bag.

Chapter 42

Edouard Renaud did not like England. There was no logic in his contempt – he believed it was something deep within his bones, something maybe he'd inherited from his father. He particularly hated these northern towns and their tawdry Promenades. He knew their underbellies, the disgusting things that went on behind the façade of arcades and cheap hotels. Of course, the same things went on in Marseilles, but not with the same gaping openness displayed here. He hoped this meeting with Kilroy and his team would be over quickly – he would simply ascertain just how much Kilroy knew about Josephine's activities, satisfy himself that Kilroy would not cause issues, and then he would take the last flight home. 'Home,' he thought. It should have been a warm word.

Kilroy met him at the airport. The Frenchman wore a tailored suit and wheeled a pert travel suitcase; he also had a battered, old briefcase. An odd juxtaposition; Kilroy wondered if it was conscious. Kilroy's suit hung loose on his lean frame, but what it lacked in tailoring it made up for in the weight of its fabric – a Scottish tweed.

> 'Hello!' Kilroy reached out and shook Renaud's hand. 'Nice to meet you. My car's out front.'

In the car, there was no small talk, no niceties.

> 'So, the woman's one of yours, I assume?'

> Renaud nodded, trying to hide his annoyance. 'Yes, Josephine Kurtz – Vice.'

> 'She's back with you? In Marseilles?

> 'Non – no. She's in Paris, now. I need to know what she was doing out here – what she was looking for in my neighbourhood.

> 'Her investigation was quite complex, Kilroy…'

Kilroy swung the car into the station car park. 'Looks like there's a lot we need to catch up on, then …'

Renaud turned in his seat. 'Yes, a lot. But we'll need to do it quickly and, Kilroy, it'll be on a 'need to know' basis. I've worked too long on this case – too many people have been hurt – for me to risk it blowing up.'

Kilroy stared at him: 'Nothing will blow up on my watch, Renaud.'

The two men nodded and stepped out of the car.

Collins watched from the window upstairs.

'Bloody hell,' he thought. 'Hard to tell who's the most pissed off.'

Chapter 43

Livia had enjoyed the walk almost as much as Clochette. The days were growing warmer, but the evenings still held a crisp chill and now a heavy rain was falling. She closed the curtains, and sat down to re-read the email from the French archivist; she had found several more references to Armand's death, and she'd found references on his wife's death soon after. This didn't surprise Livia as she'd read it in Jean-Clare's diary:

> *Juliet 7 1969*
>
> *Today, we have buried sweet Adeline; her heart was broken. Poor Charles found here there – she had used Armand's shotgun. That poor child. He has not spoken since. He is staying with us – he was in Alex's room, but his fits of rage make it impossible for poor Alex to sleep. Dr Camille will come tomorrow: the boy is in such pain. I wish we could do more for him; poor Alex is so distressed*
> *to see his friend like this. What a terrible time – one hardly notices the Spring.*

She downloaded the files and sent them to print. She refreshed her inbox; still nothing from Alex. If she hadn't heard from him tomorrow, she was going to call – she didn't give a damn.

She stopped – was that a car on the gravel? She jumped up and switched off the lights, closed the lid of her laptop. Clochette was already up, growling as she hurried to the door.

Livia's heart was racing. Wait! She listened again. Nothing. But Clochette was now creeping to the glass patio doors. There was a tapping, like a timid knock – Clochette exploded into fury, pushing her way through the curtains. Livia saw the shadow, a tall figure standing still, unmoving. Livia had had enough.

She grabbed the large branch she'd brought in and gripped it firmly. She quietly drew back the lock on the front door, while Clochette clawed at the glass, bouncing about, barking loudly. She slipped out.

She made her way down the side of the house, pushing herself against the wall to avoid the floodlight sensor. At the corner, she stopped, took a deep breath, squeezed the branch and stepped out – the floodlight illuminated her and the whole back garden.

'What the hell do you think you're doing!' she cried, raising the branch up aggressively. The rain fell in white sheets that separated her from the figure like panes of glass. 'Who are you?'

The figure turned and took a step forward.

'Livia? It's me! Alex!'

Livia stood frozen, like a sculpture, arm still raised. 'Alex?'

He moved forward quickly and folded his arms around her. 'Darling! Come, we must go inside!' Gently, he took the branch from her and guided her back around to the front of the house. Once inside, he turned on the lights and greeted Clochette who had rushed at him, teeth bared, skidding to a halt when he spoke to her.

'Clochette! Rest! Bonne chienne! Bonne!'

Chapter 44

Kilroy gathered his team around the large table in the conference room.

> 'This is Inspector Edouard Renaud. He's come over from Marseilles to support us in our investigation into the murder of Stephanie Moulin.' He gestured to the photographs on the whiteboard. 'Detective Collins, please review the case for the Inspector.'

Collins stood up and went to the whiteboard.

> 'Stephanie Moulin. French national. Found murdered in Compton Way. Cause of death….'

Renaud listened half-heartedly to the young police officer. He looked around the table: most of the team were uniforms, juniors, but it was still larger than his own team. (He wondered if Kilroy had stacked the numbers to impress him.) Back in Marseilles, he had one officer working with him – a junior detective – Jules Blanchon. And, of course, he had Josephine Kurtz – a retired detective who had a personal stake in the case and worked behind the scenes, without authorisation.

When he was young, Renaud had imagined that now, at 58, he'd be a Chief Inspector in a regional city like Lille. He'd be settling down, ready for retirement. Married. Kids about to fly the nest… He sighed.

Collins was finishing up.

> 'To-date, we have no further information on Josephine Kurtz or her connection to the victim.'

Kilroy motioned for him to sit down.

> 'Perhaps, Inspector, you can bring us up to speed?'

Renaud did not stand up, and he didn't open the manilla folder he'd taken from his brief case. 'We start at the beginning, non? Always a good idea…' He smiled at the *team, and Kilroy realised that several of his female officers were blushing demurely. 'Jesus,' he thought. 'The allure of the French accent!'*

Chapter 45

Alex poured them both a glass of red.

> 'I'm sorry, cherie – I couldn't call – you know why.'

> 'Yes, yes... but why, why are you *here*? I thought we agreed?'

> 'We did,' he sighed. He sunk down into the sofa beside her. 'But the insurance people emailed me about your claim – the broken window in the door – I knew you were in trouble!'

> 'Oh, of course! I didn't want to worry you, darling!'

> 'I know, but this is beyond our agreement. I'm here now... let me look at you.'

She smiled as he held her face in his hands. She loved this man. She studied the lines of his face – the frown lines had deepened. Alex was not young, but there was nothing frail about him. He was a tall man, still over 6 foot. He was heavy with muscle, and he moved quickly, purposefully. His thick dark hair was threaded through with mercury silver strands, and his eyes were a warm, dark chocolate. He wasn't handsome in the modern sense – there was nothing smooth or shaped about his face. Instead, there was a ruggedness that came from years outside, in sun or snow.

He, modestly, referred to himself as a 'farmer', but his bookshelves housed history and art books, classic literature – in three languages. His parents had instilled a passion for learning in their only child, along with a fiery sense of social justice.

Livia brought down his hands and kissed them.

> 'You don't know how much I've missed you, Alex...'

> 'I do, I do – as much as I have missed you.' He kissed her passionately.

'I wanted to. But what if it was him, Alex? What if he's followed me here? I didn't want you anywhere near …'

Alex flushed, angrily. 'You are not entitled to make that decision, my love! If that … bastard is here, he'll have me to contend with, now!'

'But Alex, what about the vineyard?'

'I've hired a security firm – they're looking after the place. Jean-Marc is overseeing the vines.'

She took his glass and went to the kitchen to refill it. The cat had already decided that this big man was good for sitting on, and Clochette was beside herself, whimpering, sidling up to Alex and rolling onto her back for a belly rub.

Alex continued: 'So, have the police offered any explanations? Do they have suspects?'

Livia sat down beside him, handing him his wine. 'Well, yes, but I'm not sure … Michael, the police officer, called me today. He thinks a local boy is responsible – a young lad who's been coming here with his grandfather – fixing the barn and things. But I'm not convinced – Arthur is a good kid. I can tell.'

'But that's good, isn't it? If this boy is to blame, then ….'

'Then our own intruder isn't here? I don't think it's that easy, Alex. The boy is good – and I can't see him wanting to scare me. No. Whoever it was, they wanted to scare the life out of me. And they did. Anyway, I'll hear more tomorrow.'

'Hmmm.'

'And the phone calls have started again, here. Has there been any trouble on the vineyard? In the last few weeks?'

Alex frowned. 'No. I don't think so.'

'Maybe that's because he's here,' she said sadly.

'Well, if he is....' Alex was lost for words.

'If he is, we'll have to be careful. He can't know you're here.'

'That's one of the reasons I've crept in so late.' He kissed her again. 'I'm so tired, my love. Come, come… let me sleep beside my wife. I have missed you so much.'

Together they checked the locks, re-drew the curtains and made their way upstairs.

Chapter 46

Marie was shivering; the wind was brutal tonight, but Kilroy's warning was ringing in her ears as she hurried down the alleyway behind the pub. 'He's after you, Marie. He knows you. You have to come in – drop your cover.' She would drive out to see him and calm him down. Marie would have loved to come in, but she felt a protective loyalty to the women who worked the street. It wasn't enough that they had to sell themselves cheaply to support drug habits, pimps and families – now they had to contend with a Jack the Ripper.

She felt someone watching her from the shadows, about 20 minutes ago as she hugged Danielle goodnight. She walked a little way along the High Street, waiting for him to follow – and he did. Her car was parked at the back of the shops, so she walked in the opposite direction, stopping in a doorway to look behind. Nothing. She gently cursed Kilroy for spooking her. She stepped out and turned into a back street to double back to her car.

The pub had closed an hour before, and the lights from the fridges chilled the windows with a neon-blue glow. She pulled her coat about her more tightly; maybe Kilroy was right. It would be nice to wear flat shoes again.

Her phone buzzed in her pocket, making her jump.

Chapter 47

Matthews pulled the truck into the driveway and turned off the ignition. Arthur looked tired. And scared. They'd said nothing all the way home. Once inside, Matthews put the kettle on and began setting up the tea things.

'A bit of toast, boy?'

'No. Thanks, granddad.'

'You need it. What did they feed you in there – you look rough.'

'Food was ok. I just wasn't hungry. Couldn't sleep. So bloody noisy.'

Matthews set the teapot on the table and let it brew.

'Arthur. We have to talk. That solicitor bloke is coming round later. He said you need to tell the truth, now. This is serious.'

'I've told you granddad – it was Hobb's stuff. I don't know anything…'

Matthews sighed and poured the tea.

'Do you remember, Arthur, when your mum and me took you to the beach?'

Arthur winced; he didn't like remembering his mother - it was too painful. Matthews continued:

'Remember? It was so hot – your mum packed us lunch, a real picnic! You were so excited! Couldn't shut you up! Well, we got there and you ran off – just slipped away from her and off you went, into the crowd and she lost you! She just lost you!'

Arthur sipped his tea; he knew the story well.

'So, I ran into the crowd, calling out "Arthur! Arthur!"
So loud, shouting out over all the kiddies and the
noise. "Arthur!"'

'I know the story granddad,' Arthur said, a sad edge
to his voice.

'And we looked for you for a good hour! Your mum
had got the lifeguards and they'd got the police...
and then we saw you! You were sat down the end of
the sand, on the rocks, just sitting there. Quietly.
You were crying. Do you remember?'

'I do.' Arthur wanted to cry now. 'I'd run off and
when I turned around, you were both gone. I walked
and walked... couldn't see you. I thought I'd lost
you!'

'Yes. And what did your mum say? Eh?'

Arthur bent his face lower, unable to answer.

'She said, "Arthur? This is a good lesson: we will
ALWAYS come looking for you, see? Doesn't matter
where you are, or why you've gone – we will come
for you."'

Arthur let a silent tear roll down his cheek. He only had
vague memories of his mother, but they were of hugs and a
soft voice, and the pink scent of roses. Matthews reached
over and put his hand over the boy's.

'I've come for you, Arthur. Your mum's gone, but
here I am – and I don't care what you've done. It's
time to settle this.'

Now, Arthur was sobbing, and he leaned forward on his
arms on the table. Granddad was right: it was time to say it
all. Maybe then he could stop the sick feeling in his stomach
that had stayed with him every night and every day since
Hobbs had killed Dev.

'That's it, son,' said Matthews quietly. 'You let it all out.'

****

Livia woke and saw the sun was already up; downstairs, the radio was on – BBC4 – and she could hear Alex making the coffee and chatting to Clochette. Her heart filled with love.

She pulled on her jeans and sweatshirt and went down to him, wrapping her arms around his waist and nuzzling into his broad back. 'Good morning, darling.' He turned and kissed her, folding her in his arms.

'Cherie,' he sighed into her hair.

Clochette barked merrily in the garden and a New Forest Pony appeared at the kitchen window. They laughed.

'Quite a menagerie!' Alex laughed.

Over breakfast, she mentioned the research she'd been doing on Alex's mother's diaries.

'The last newspaper report I have is the police trying to track down the travellers… the ones who'd allegedly threatened Armand.'

He sipped his coffee. 'I don't remember Armand at all. I remember the funeral – the church was full of people. Father and some of the other men carried the casket… Adeline was so ill.'

'Did your parents ever discuss it? The death, I mean?'

'Oh, sure, but much later. After Adeline passed away, their energies were all for Charles!'

'Really?'

'Oh, God, yes. That poor boy! He was so traumatised. At first, I think the plan was for him to live with us, but he had strange 'fits', if that is the right word.'

'Fits?'

'At night. All day he would say nothing – he was in a state of shock, I imagine, finding his mother like that. But at night, it was as if all the anger, the rage, came up inside him like a volcano! He would shout out and smash things about! It was awful. They were afraid he might hurt himself – or me. The doctors thought it was better he stay in hospital for a time... a specialist hospital.'

'And what happened to him? Charles.'

Alex breathed deeply and sighed. 'He did not get well. He grew more and more unbalanced as he grew older.'

'Poor boy.'

'Yes. He became a … what's the English term – 'pupille de l'etat'?'

'Ward of the state. And after he was released?'

'Well,' Alex shrugged. 'We don't know – at 18, he is an adult in France and it seemed he wanted no connection to us anymore. Not surprising, considering the memories he must have had of the vineyard.'

'No. Quite.' She stood up. 'OK. I'm going to have a shower – I'm seeing Michael this morning – we'll see what he has to say about Arthur. I was thinking, Alex, I might tell him about what happened to us – in France. I mean, it does seem that he's hell-bent on blaming Arthur – if he thinks there's someone else, maybe he'll change his mind?'

'Maybe… but what if he contacts the police in France? What if word gets out that you're here, or that I'm here…?'

'Yes… but I'll play it down. Say we had some trouble with a prowler in France and maybe he's followed us. She stopped, aware of how unconvincing her story would sound. 'No, you're right. Best not.'

'I don't think anyone should know I'm here, Livia. Not for the moment – not until we know who tried to break in. If it was this Arthur, then maybe we can believe that our plan is working – that the intruder believes you have left me and that our marriage is over. Perhaps, then, he will leave you alone.'

Livia felt a rush of adrenalin. 'But what about you?' She stepped forward, took his hands and looked up at him. 'How do we protect you?'

He held her tightly, glad that he hadn't told her about the latest incident. He had returned to the house, a month ago, having been with the vines until late in the evening. He'd waved goodnight to the men and gone in to the house.

Upstairs, in their bedroom, he turned on the light. Astonishingly, the bed was covered in rose petals, much like it had been the first night of their honeymoon. But now, the bed was also covered in photographs of Livia. Livia in the vineyard, Livia getting into the truck, Livia coming home with shopping, Livia and Clochette playing in the garden. The intruder had been watching her the whole time! And in the middle of her pillow, there was a black-bordered envelope with his name written on it in elaborate copper-plate. He opened it and his knees felt a little weak.

Dear Alex, I watched you, today, in the market.
You were alone. Alone. How does it feel? Your father
is gone, may his soul rot in Hell. And L'Anglaise?
Where is your wife, now? How does it feel to lose,
Alex? But this is nothing; soon you will know my

pain, dear Alex. And I will come to you and you will know why I have come to you. Yes! That's it: I am the pain, and I will show myself to you. A bientot, Alex.

Chapter 48

Renaud was winding up his summary of Josephine Kurtz's investigations. 'So, I would suggest that the murder of Stephanie Moulin is, perhaps, linked to organised crime... certainly, Josephine Kurtz was investigating the activity of a cartel operating out of Marseilles, but I cannot see an obvious link between them.'

Collins raised his hand. 'Inspector, can you tell us more about this cartel? Do they have any operations here?' Renaud looked doubtful, and Collins continued. 'After all, why did you send an operative here, if not? Is your interest in Etienne Moulin?'

Renaud raised his chin. 'Etienne Moulin was helping us with some of our enquiries, so, yes perhaps Kurtz was looking at ....'

''Yes, and Etienne Moulin was connected with Vice here, too, Sir, which indicates a link between activities in Marseilles and activities here?'

Renaud sounded dangerously patient. 'Organised crime looks the same everywhere, I'm afraid. Etienne Moulin is an addict – it is not surprising he has made contact with some of your local mafia.' Several female police officers giggled at the joke. 'For you, Sergeant Collins, I think you are busy looking at this serial killer, non? The fact that my agent was here at the time of these killings is happenstance.'

'Wouldn't you like to know more about our 'mafia', Inspector, on the off chance there might be a connection? Doesn't it pique your interest?'

'My interest?' Renaud smiled condescendingly. 'My interest is often piqued, Sergeant. But my experience guides me to the areas where that interest will be most usefully deployed.'

Collins looked to Kilroy for support, but Kilroy simply stared back at him. Collins would make a good enough cop one day – when he'd learned to read people. Kilroy could see that Renaud was only here to ascertain just how much they knew about Kurtz and how much he had to cover up back in Marseilles.

'OK, folks,' said Kilroy, as he stood up. 'Inspector Renaud has a flight to catch; it's getting late.' Collins looked like he might ask another question, but Kilroy's warning expression shut him up. The team filed out.

'Thank you,' said Renaud. 'I'm sorry I could not be of more assistance...'

'So, the Marseille cartel,' said Kilroy. 'How active are they over here? The real story, please.'

Renaud was putting the file into his brief case. 'The Marseille group is actually a group from Paris – a sub-group.'

'And it's Paris you're after?'

'Oh, no, Kilroy – I'm only looking at Marseilles.'

'So why send Kurtz here? Do your colleagues in Paris know about her work? He paused. 'Do they know you're here?'

Renaud looked up quickly, surprised at how deftly Kilroy had figured him out. 'No. And I'd prefer they didn't.'

Suddenly, Collins flung open the door. 'Sir! You've got to come quickly! They've found another woman – at The Cloisters – that's where the key was from – the one John sent. It's Marie...'

Kilroy felt the blood drain from his face as he stood up. Renaud noticed: 'I'll come with you...'

Chapter 49

Michael took Livia through to the interview room. 'It's a little quieter in here...'

'Thanks. So, you think Arthur is my prowler?'

'I do.'

'I can't believe it, Michael. He's just not that sort of kid.'

Michael shook his head. 'I arrested him, two days ago: dealing.'

'Oh my God! I can't believe that!'

'Yep. Caught him red-handed, by the church. He was with a toe-rag called Hobbs – the guy's got a long record.'

'Oh, no. Poor Matthews.'

'Yes. I feel for the old man – he's done his best... we've known Arthur was involved in the local scene for a few months now. He was a mate of the lad who was stabbed - Dev...'

'Yes, Matthews told me. But he said it was a case of wrong place, wrong time. Do you have any idea who the murderer is?'

Michael sat back in his chair. 'We don't. I reckon they're long gone – back to London. Dev was selling in the Rec Centre the night he was killed. When they found him, he had no drugs on him – but he had a wad of cash in his jacket.'

'How do you know he was selling?'

'A couple of witnesses came forward... said he was their supplier. We were surprised.'

'Because he was a kid?'

'That, but also because he wasn't working with our local 'drug lords'. There's one gang down here who are responsible for supply and distribution. We know who they are. They get busted occasionally, someone else steps up, they get out of jail and re-join the network... small time, but manageable for law enforcement.'

'So, who was Dev working for?'

'We reckon it was a London-based gang – they're pretty adept at getting kids like Dev involved.'

'Do you think Arthur's doing the same thing?'

'I do. The stuff we caught him with isn't local. And the knife we found – Hobbs says it's Arthur's – it's the knife that killed Dev.'

'But this other guy – Hobbs – he seems a more likely candidate?'

'At the moment, they're blaming each other. Either way, I reckon Arthur's involved up to his neck.'

'That's awful. But what's that got to do with *Fox Pond* – why would he have wanted to break in to my house?'

'We're thinking that maybe he owed some people money... hard to tell at this stage. The Met are sending some of their people down.'

'No, that doesn't make sense – he had ample opportunity to rob my place – he's been alone there, working with his grandfather.'

'I know you want to give him the benefit of the doubt, Livia, but he's got a lot going on in his life, I'm afraid... '

Leaving the police station, Livia was so glad that Alex was at home waiting for her; she was so depressed by Michael's information. But she was certain Arthur was not her prowler. She stopped by to see Henri.

'Ah! Livia! Ca va?' he cried, hugging her.

'I'm fine. Wow! The redecoration looks fabulous!"

'Well, why stop at replacing a window, hey? And I've been so busy - people are loving my food!'

'So they should! That's why I'm here, actually. Do you have any lasagne to go?'

'Oh yes, of course! For your cousin?'

'Hmmmm?' Livia looked confused.

'Your cousin. He dropped by yesterday – said you had recommended he try my gateaux!'

Livia felt ill; she instinctively turned to look out on the street.

'Mon Dieu! Livia? What on earth is the matter? You are very pale!'

'Henri – this man. Did he give you a name?'

'Yes. Monsieur… ummmm…. I forget! But Olivia, this is not your cousin?'

Chapter 50

Kilroy skidded to a halt at the front of The Cloisters; uniform was there, flashing lights turned the dark sky blue, and the steps up to reception were taped off. Renaud followed close behind him.

'Sir!' the young officer lifted the tape.

As Kilroy entered the hotel in long, strong strides, two paramedics were pushing the stretcher through the lobby.

'Marie!' Kilroy shouted.

Marie was a bloody mess, her face brutally beaten and a savage red bruise at her throat.

'Stand back, please,' said one of the paramedics, as she raised the bag of fluid a little higher.

'Marie!' Kilroy's voice broke as he reached forward for her hand.

'She's unconscious, Sir, let us get her to hospital!'

As they wheeled her away, Kilroy felt bereft, set adrift.

'Come on, Kilroy,' Renaud's voice was low and firm, as he guided him to the stairs. 'Let's go see what we can find.'

Jenkins was swabbing a side table.

'Kilroy,' she looked worried for him.

'This is Renaud, he's over from Marseilles. What've you got?

Jenkins nodded. 'She took a chunk out of him – swabbed her nails before they took her. We've swept the bed, but this place is fluid filthy – we might find something... And, here...'

Kilroy took the plastic sample bag from her; the same soft yellow feathers.

'Anything else?'

'Just the letter…' Jenkins nodded toward the dresser. John was gloating, revelling in his handiwork, lamenting Marie's passing. He clearly hadn't counted on her fighting back. Kilroy prayed silently that she kept fighting.

Collins appeared at the door and Kilroy looked over to him.

'Any witnesses?'

'No, sir. The room was booked earlier in the evening – in Marie's name.'

Kilroy shook his head. 'No way. She wouldn't have risked it.'

Collins nodded in agreement. 'No CCTV – cameras don't work. But there might be something….'

'What?'

'This room: 206. James Court books it often – for his 'best' girls – he runs a tab with the hotel.'

'Collins, I want a guard outside Marie's room at the hospital – make it two. We've got to tie this whole bloody mess up – all of it! Now. Call London. Ask them to pay Vinnie a visit – I want his woman – Toni. I want to know where she is – right now. Maybe she's brought some boys down with her.'

'But how does that make any sense? This John character, he's a bloody psychopath! How does he fit…'

'Just do it Collins!' shouted Kilroy.

Jennings looked up, surprised at the edge in Kilroy's voice. Renaud saw her concern. Kilroy ran a hand through his hair – there was so much blood on the bed!

Renaud cleared his throat. 'Kilroy, let's get some air...'

They walked out of the hotel, under the tape and back to the car.

> *'I think you've missed your flight...'*

> *'Yes.'*

> *'I'm trying to think of a decent hotel ...'*

They got in the car.

> *'Well,' said Renaud. 'I doubt either of us will sleep soon – there's obviously a lot we need to share...'*

> *'Yes,' Kilroy said. 'Come back to mine – I could use a drink.'*

Chapter 51

Michael greeted Matthews and nodded to Arthur. An older man in a suit stepped forward and introduced himself.

'Good morning, officer. I am Daniel Gibbons, from Gibbons & Threwall. My client is here, on a voluntary basis, to share information pertaining to the murder of Dev Anand…'

'Yes,' Michael interrupted. 'I know. My colleagues from London are keen to hear from him. This way, please…'

'London?' the lawyer looked irritated. 'We weren't informed that…'

'Well, I've just informed you. We have reason to believe the murder is linked to a County Lines set-up – and to be honest, the Met is more experienced when it comes to drug-related killings.'

Michael opened the door of the conference room; Arthur felt sick.

'Matthews, you'll have to wait outside…'

'I will not!' said Matthews angrily.

Michael sighed. 'You'll have to – this is a formal interview…'

The lawyer interrupted. 'I don't believe it is, Officer. As I said, my client has come forward, voluntarily, to share vital information…'

A woman's voice called from the room.

'It's ok, Officer Cummings. Let the grandfather come in.' She stood to greet them. 'Hello, Arthur. I'm Detective Sergeant Felice. This is Detective Sergeant Hollins…' The young detective smiled kindly.

Arthur nodded and sat down in the seat Felice indicated. Gibbons sat down, clicked open his briefcase and pulled out his yellow legal pad. 'Daniel Gibbons, Gibbons & Threwall. My client is here to...'

Felice interrupted. 'To help us find the bastard who killed his friend Dev. Isn't that right, Arthur?'

Arthur looked up at the older woman's face; it was serious, but the eyes were kind. He nodded.

Matthews clapped the boy's knee with his hand. 'He's a good kid. He's not done nothing wrong!'

Felice smiled. 'Great. So, Arthur – if I asked you to start from the beginning?'

Arthur sighed. Where was the beginning? Was it the parties at Hobbs' place? Getting trashed and forgetting all the sadness? Was it school, where he was never happy, never understood what the teachers wanted him to learn? Was it the memory of his mother, the smell of pink roses? The only thing he knew for sure was that Dev was dead and he had a duty – some sort of obligation - to tell them all how it happened. He looked up at Felice who waited patiently for him to speak.

****

Alex was waiting for Livia to return from town; he was leafing through his mother's diaries, old account books and photo albums. He'd never really looked at them before. After she'd died, his father had locked them in the cellar with some of her paintings – his grief had been deep. It was Livia who'd 'discovered' them when she first started clearing the place, after Alex's father had died. She said she wanted to get to know Alex's mother, but there had not been time, not with the demands of the vineyard.

His mother's warm, decorative hand writing made him smile; he flicked through the months, catching glimpses of notes about the weather, about the crops. He poured himself another coffee and set an album down on the table. There was the house – a fading sepia-coloured print. His parents' wedding pictures! How happy they looked! The workmen all toasting with the vineyard's own wines. He turned the page. Who was that? He looked closely – confused. The woman held a child close to her and beamed at the camera. Was it Adeline? Yes, perhaps it was. He turned the page – ah, yes, and there she was again, now with a boy of maybe six. Charles. Yes, that was him. He smiled at their happy faces.

More pictures: he recognised his own young self – maybe about 10? Standing side-by-side with Charles – both dressed in sailor suits, beaming at the camera. He thought back to the last sad days before Charles went to the hospital; the boy's grief was raw and violent. Destructive.

There were no more photos from this time; but at the back of the album there was an envelope that was becoming brittle and yellowed with age. He carefully opened it and saw there were several letters. He brought them out on to the table and unfolded them gently.

The first letter was dated February, 1970. From De Guisy Hospital, near Nantes. The writing was young, consciously formed – the pen pressed hard onto the page. He turned the page to the signature – Charles! He settled back into the chair to read.

Chapter 52

Kilroy lived about 20 minutes out of town. As the car pulled into the drive, the headlights swept across the yard, capturing the large, rough-looking outline of Digger who, when he heard Kilroy's voice, dropped his tense shoulders and shuffled over to greet him.

Once inside, Kilroy lit the old iron cooker and the log burner in the lounge, and motioned to Renaud to sit at the heavy oak table. He pulled a bottle of whisky from the shelf and poured two glasses.

'Hungry?' he asked absent-mindedly.

'A little,' admitted Renaud.

'Omelette ok?'

As Kilroy busied himself in the kitchen, Renaud looked around him. It was a plain, open-plan space; the original stone floor was worn into a comforting sheen. A large leather sofa stretched along one wall of the lounge, opposite the log burner. There was a modest library of, what looked like, the English classics. Kilroy's laptop was plugged in on a small desk in the corner.

The dog sat patiently, observing Kilroy.

'Hello, boy,' smiled Renaud. The dog continued to stare at Kilroy.

'What's his name,' he asked Kilroy.

'Digger. He'll be more responsive if you can open this…' Kilroy passed him a large tin of dog food. The dog watched the exchange and turned his focus to Renaud, seamlessly.

Kilroy served up the omelette. 'Wine?'

'Merci,' said Renaud, tentatively.

'Don't worry, it's French,' smiled Kilroy. He pulled open a small cupboard door to reveal two or three bottles of wine. 'A Cabernet, I reckon?' And he passed the bottle to Renaud.

'Well, yes please!' smiled Renaud approvingly.

They ate slowly, thoughtfully.

'So, this Marie… I gather she's more than just a colleague?'

Kilroy shifted uncomfortably. 'We go back a long way. Nearly 20 years.'

'Ah, I see,' nodded Renaud.

Kilroy took another sip of his wine. 'I don't understand how she let herself get to that hotel…'

'Do you think she was meeting someone?'

'No – at least not there. She wouldn't have let herself be cornered.'

'So, she was tricked…'

'Yeah. Maybe one of the girls set her up ….' Kilroy felt a tightness in his chest thinking of Marie in the hospital. He cleared the plates and topped up the whisky. They moved into the lounge; Digger stretched out on the worn stones.

Renaud smiled at the domestic nature of the scene – so different to the character Kilroy had presented in the office.

'How long have you lived here?'

'Oh, about 10 years – bought it for my wife – ex-wife – just after we married.'

'Ah, ex-wives… they seem to be part of a detective's job description, non?'

'Yes,' Kilroy smiled ironically. 'You, too, hey?'

Renaud nodded. 'She grew tired of my job – the hours, the dangers... they were too much for her.'

'I can understand that...'

'Well, perhaps I could, too, if she wasn't now married to another cop!'

Kilroy laughed. 'Oh, sorry...'

'Eh, well. What about you – did the job ruin your marriage?'

'No, not really – but it didn't help. Kirstin is an alcoholic – she chose drink.'

Renaud nodded sadly. 'I'm sorry.'

'So,' said Kilroy after a moment. 'How about you fill me in on this case of yours – and this time,' he met Renaud's eyes, 'the whole story.'

Renaud smiled. 'Yes. You're right – our cases overlap a lot more than I have said. Let me start with Josephine, Josephine Kurtz. She is, as you know, back in France now. She came out here about two months ago –'

'On the trail of your drug investigation.'

'Yes... and, no. She was more on the trail of one man – your Jacob Rollanson.'

'Mr Big.'

'Yes – also 'big' in Marseille.'

'Really?'

'He and his cousin have made a very lucrative alliance: Rollanson runs the English side of things, Marcel Daubre the French. Their mothers were sisters.'

'Narcotics? Girls as well, I imagine.'

'Indeed. A lot of girls from Eastern Europe – some very young. Josephine, my agent, lost her daughter to Daubre.'

'What do you mean?'

'Her daughter, Amelie, got in with the wrong people – she started using, she got caught up in the whole scene. She ran away about three years ago. She was only 16. Kurtz did everything she could to find her – used all the police resources we had. But there was nothing, no trace – only a link to Daubre and talk of him shipping the girl to the UK.'

'And Kurtz set out to bust him.'

'Yes. She became quite crazy, really, obsessed. But I understand.'

'Is that why she left the force?'

Renaud shifted a little on the sofa. 'There was a shooting; one of Daubre's men – a pimp. Kurtz was cleared of any wrong-doing – he'd drawn first, according to her – but it was clear she'd have to step down.'

'But she didn't drop it, right?'

'No. And unknown to my superiors, neither did I. She found Daubre's contacts in London, and, then, she tracked down Rollanson, here.'

'So, she's here looking for Rollanson – how does Stephanie Moulin fit in with it all?'

'Yes, that's our point of intersection, Kilroy,' he replied, crossing his hands to illustrate the point. 'Stephanie was here because she, too, was tracking someone – her brother Etienne.'

'We're aware of him – he's disappeared.'

Renaud sighed. 'He is a sad case; he really did want to help us…'

'Ah, so he was working with Kurtz, was he?'

Renaud nodded. 'Etienne was a user, a junkie in Marseilles. Kurtz got to know him when she was searching for her daughter. He was the one who led her to the pimp and his associates. She got him help, he got clean for a while, and he offered to help her find Amelie.'

'That's why he lost contact with his family – '

'Yes, he didn't want his mother or his sister involved or connected in any way.'

'So, he and Kurtz are shacked up in a hotel together. Why?'

'Etienne spent a few months getting close to Daubre's inner circle in Marseille – proved himself. Soon, they had him running errands to London – he was a messenger. Then they had him coming up here to meet with your Rollanson. Rollanson liked him and asked him to stay. Kurtz came over to join him once he'd established himself.'

'That was risky? Rollanson's men would have been all over it, surely?'

'Have you met Rollanson, Kilroy?'

'Of course – we've had a run-in or two.'

'Yes. Well, English criminals – I don't want to offend you – but Rollanson is not as astute as his French cousin.'

Kilroy smiled. 'I would agree that Rollanson is not the brightest… and, yes, his people are even less 'astute'.'

'So,' Renaud continued, 'they were discreet and they were working to bring Rollanson down. Etienne was using again – sucked back into the game. He was making Kurtz nervous. And then –'

'His sister turned up.'

'Yes. Stephanie was doing her own investigations – desperate to find her brother and save him from the drugs. She found him – he told her to go home, he told her the danger she was in. He hoped she'd return to France. But she realised he was still using; she wanted to disconnect him from his dealer. And then you found her murdered.'

Kilroy topped up their whisky and went through the sequence of events.

'So, Stephanie talks to some of the working women, or the junkies. Maybe she pretends she wants to score. They send her to Court – we know she met him on the night she died. She tells him her supplier has let her down – indicates she's working with a rival in town. Court sends her to Rollanson...we have her phone records – she called him. Did Kurtz mention her bag being snatched? That's the same day that Stephanie was killed.'

Renaud nodded. 'Yes. It wasn't a mugging. Kurtz said that in the evening, the night Stephanie died, Etienne had received a call from Rollanson. He told Etienne that there was a young French woman in town, a new supplier was muscling in … Rollanson was not happy. Etienne realised it was Stephanie. He met up with her, outside the hotel, and warned her off again. She promised she'd leave, if he promised to follow.'

Kilroy sighed. 'The killer got to her first?'

'Etienne got another call that night – Rollanson wanted him to go to London – check out a lead on this imagined rival. It was urgent. Etienne left straight away – it was the perfect cover. He called Stephanie and left a message for her to join him in London.'

'So, as far as Kurtz was concerned, Etienne and Stephanie were on their way to safety in London?'

'Yes – until she got a call from a man who said he worked for Daubre. He told her he had Stephanie with him, and that the girl would come to harm unless Kurtz had the money to buy her back.'

'So, Daubre had sent his own people over …'

'Yes; it seems he doesn't have faith in Rollanson's abilities…'

'So,' said Kilroy impatiently. 'Kurtz got the money? Agreed to meet on the sea front?'

'No. Kurtz didn't get the money – she had no intention of paying. She was armed.'

'So how did he calmly take her bag and walk away? I've seen the CCTV…'

'He took the bag to make it look like a mugging.'

Kilroy frowned, and Renaud explained.

'When she met the man on the seafront, she was surprised by how well-dressed he was. How calm. He knew her name. He knew she was a cop. She demanded to see Stephanie, to know that she was ok. And, then, the story grew darker. He told Kurtz that unless she left the UK that night, unless she forgot this 'little holiday' not only Stephanie, but Amelie, Kurtz's daughter would be dead.'

'What? Amelie – she was here?' Kilroy was wild-eyed.

'No, I don't think so.'

155

'My God! So, this bloke takes the bag and walks away?'

'Yes. He told her he would call the hotel later, and let her know how to find Amelie. The bag had her purse, her phone. Of course, Kurtz, hearing her daughter was alive, was overcome. She called me straight away.'

'From the café...'

'She was distraught. I insisted she leave town immediately. She was reluctant, of course. Then, this man phoned the hotel and left a message: it said she would find Amelie in London, at an address in King's Cross. Kurtz left immediately.'

'Did she find her?'

Renaud shook his head sadly. 'No. They were bluffing. Kurtz returned to France, to regroup.'

They were quiet for a few minutes. Renaud arched his aching back. Kilroy listened to the storm blowing up outside; his thoughts turned to Marie, but he struggled to keep his thoughts with Daubre and Rollanson.

'I can't imagine,' he said, 'that Rollanson hasn't been brought up to speed, by now. Daubre can't have been happy that a French cop was watching the UK side of his operations.'

'I suppose – perhaps we should meet with him together? And if he is involved in the killing –'

'Yes, we'll meet Rollanson – but for now, I think we need to get some sleep.'

Renaud did not disagree.

Chapter 53

Alex turned to the next letter:

> 'Dear Aunt, I am writing again to ask, no, to beg:
> may I please come home? I know that I was
> unpleasant to Alex, but after my rest, I am a happy
> boy again! I so long to be with you all, my family,
> and not here. I am lonely. Please, please dear Aunt,
> when will you come to see me, again?'

'Aunt'? Alex was confused – he never recalled Charles calling
Jean-Clare 'Aunt'. But he was young, perhaps he had
forgotten. He felt a pang of sadness for the boy's obvious
distress; how awful to lose one's parents at such an age.
Alex shook his head sadly. He flipped through the other
pages – more letters from Charles, but also some
correspondence written on a typewriter – from De Guisy
Hospital, according to the imposing letterhead.

> 'Chere Madame,
>
> I received your letter and, while I am sad to hear
> that you are concerned, I must insist that Charles
> Justas does not receive visitors in the coming weeks.
> We have, finally, calmed him thanks to our regimen
> of exercise and diet and a new pharmaceutical
> intervention. However, his depression continues to
> express itself in violent outbursts. As such this makes
> it impossible for him to receive visitors. Please trust
> me, Madame, that, like you, we have only the boy's
> welfare at heart.'

And then, another, months later:

> 'Chere Madame,
>
> It was helpful to meet with you and your husband
> last month. As discussed, Charles' therapy with Dr
> Lange has concluded that Charles' difficulties stem
> not from his grief, but from a pre-existing condition,
> most likely Schizophrenia....'

The letter went on to explain the condition in the old-fashioned terms of 'split-personality', and it suggested that Charles would never leave the hospital. Enclosed was an invoice for the past six months of accommodation and treatment – Alex had never realised how much Charles' institutionalisation had cost his parents and he was filled with love for their generosity.

But he was confused; why had his parents never shared this with him? The only news he had of Charles was when Alex was about 18. They told him that Charles had 'left the hospital' and had decided to move to the south, where he had a distant relative – a cousin of his mother's who had grown frail. This had saddened Alex, as he would have liked to have seen his friend again. But shortly after, he stopped thinking about Charles. Now, he wondered what had happened to him; he hoped his life had been happy.

Clochette nuzzled her nose under his hand.

'Oh, petite! You want to walk? Eh? Maybe you can show me around this forest of yours?'

The dog barked delightedly, and Alex pulled on his coat. He left a note on the kitchen table, telling Livia he'd back shortly.

****

Detective Sergeant Felice smiled kindly at Arthur. His grandfather had stepped out to use the bathroom while the lawyer went to check his messages. Hollins went to get them coffee.

'Are you sure you don't want a drink, Arthur?'

'Nah, I'm fine. Thank you.' The boy looked exhausted.

She smiled. 'I know this is tough, Arthur, but once we've put Hobbs away, you'll be able to sleep a lot more solidly.'

Arthur looked dubious. 'Sure. But what about all his mates in London, eh?'

Felice looked up from her phone. 'Hobbs is nothing but a petty crook, Arthur – he's hit the big time with murder, though; forensics have confirmed the knife found by the church is the same knife that killed Dev. His 'associates' in London won't give a damn about him going down – his type are a dime a dozen.'

Arthur looked, for a moment, relieved.

'What about Dev's family? They're gonna hate me.'

'Why? For speaking up and getting their son's murderer sent down? Doubt it; they have enough to deal with – Dev chose to get involved in this business – no one forced him.'

'I suppose…'

The door opened and Hollins put down the coffees. Matthews touched Arthur's shoulder; the boy looked tired. 'How much longer do you think we'll be, Detective?'

'Oh, not long now, Mr Matthews. We just need Arthur to look through some of these mugshots – to see if any of this lot were at the parties. I doubt it, but we need to be sure.'

'OK. But I'd like to get him home. He needs his sleep.'

Chapter 54

It was only a couple of hours, but Kilroy felt as if he'd been asleep for days. His brain was fogged; he needed coffee. Renaud was already awake, walking the garden while Digger watched from the doorway.

'I hope the spare bed was comfortable?' asked Kilroy as the coffee was brewing.

'Oh, fine, thank you – but, you know, I think I could have slept anywhere. So, we will meet Mr Rollanson today? We can establish his involvement with Stephanie's murder. He might be able to shed some light on Daubre's man being in town.'

Kilroy nodded. 'If you don't mind, I want to swing by the office first - I want to run something by you.'

After coffee, they drove to the station. Kilroy pulled out John's file and slid it across the conference table to Renaud.

The Detective flipped through the pages. 'Crazy, for sure, eh? Increasingly angry. You think he's your man?'

'I do,' said Kilroy. 'But I think he might be your man, too.'

Renaud frowned.

'I don't think Rollanson had Stephanie killed. Nor Daubre.'

'Oh?'

'Oh, I don't doubt Rollanson or Daubre panicked – the whole set-up of sending Etienne to London, of setting up Kurtz to believe her daughter was alive or in danger... that's all on them. But Stephanie's murder – that's not Rollanson's style at all.'

'You think this crazy – John – you think he might have killed her?'

'I do.'

Renaud was quiet, thoughtful, waiting to hear more of Kilroy's plan.

'I think, we can help each other: we can put pressure on Rollanson – we know the girl called him. We'll pressure Rollason and he'll implicate Daubre – trust me, no loyalty among this scum. Don't forget we have quite a load to dump on Rollanson – there are two murders – and the attempted murder of a police officer – Marie.'

Renaud nodded. 'Yes, yes. But what about your man? John?'

'When Marie comes to – if she comes to,' Kilroy swallowed hard, 'we might have a description of the guy we're looking for.'

Collins arrived; he looked like he'd slept badly.

'Sir, good morning, Sir,' he nodded at Renaud. 'Any word on Marie?'

Kilroy shook his head.

Collins looked sad. 'We've had a call from the Met – they've been to see Vinnie – about Toni Smith. He reckons he hasn't seen her in months. Said she was visiting family – in Bradford.'

Kilroy turned to him sharply: 'Bradford?'

'Yes, the card.'

'Becky,' murmured Kilroy, running the facts through his mind. Becky a well-known prostitute from Bradford; Becky's card in Jessica Ward's purse; Jessica Ward murdered by the same person who killed Stephanie – at least that's what it looked like; Toni Smith, the prostitute girlfriend of Vinnie Roberts; Vinnie Roberts once getting screwed out of a lot of money by Rollanson; Toni Smith visiting family in Bradford; Toni Smith here in town.

Collins continued on: 'I called your contact in Vice, in Bradford – he said we must be psychic. Becky's turned up.'

'Does she have any idea why her card was found here, in a dead woman's purse?'

'None,' said Collins. 'Becky turned up dead. Strangled. And you'll never guess whose number they found on her phone…'

'Vinnie's.'

Collins look astonished and crest-fallen at the same time.

Kilroy continued. 'Any joy at finding Toni Smith?'

'Doing our best, Sir. If she's still in town, she's without a car – the rental turned up last night. Burned out on the Industrial Estate.'

'Get forensics over there – '

'But, Sir, it's a complete burn out…'

'Do it Collins. I want anything they can find. And bring in Rollanson.'

'On what charge?'

'Tell him he'll be helping us in our enquiries into the murder of Stephanie Moulin.'

Chapter 55

Clochette led the way into the dark forest – she seemed to know where she wanted to go. Alex checked his phone, to see if Livia had called – no signal. Oh well, he'd left Livia a note.

The path was made of wide, pale yellow gravel and there was the scent of damp bracken in the air. Alex thought again of the letters from Charles – his pleading. Schizophrenia? Something stirred in his memory – a hot afternoon. He and Charles were alone, playing in the front room of the small cottage that was assigned to Armand when he became Foreman on the vineyard. They were playing with figurines – soldiers maybe. The shutters were closed against the afternoon sun and there was a fly floating heavily in the air.

Charles was talking excitedly about the game – lining up his soldiers in neat rows, instructing Alex to move his back, behind the sofa leg, and to put some under the table, too. The boy was flushed, his voice rose higher and higher as he imposed his strategy on Alex.

'You know your men will be killed, non?'

'No!' cried Alex. 'I don't want my men to be killed! I will arrange them over here and then you won't be able to get them!'

'Why not?' said Charles angrily.

'Because there is a river here,' laughed Alex, drawing an imaginary line in front of his men.

'There is no river!' said Charles, and his voice dropped suddenly to a deep, monotone. 'There is no river unless Daniel tells us there is a river.'

'Who is Daniel?' asked Alex in bewilderment, looking about the room.

Charles smiled strangely. 'He is the angel who protects me, Alexandre, and he is here now and he says there is no river.'

Alex looked around the room again. 'There is no one here! I say there is a river and, so, there is a river!'

Charles stared at him and began speaking in some kind of meaningless, strange language. Alex was afraid. Charles' chanting grew louder and louder, repeating the strange phrases over and over again, faster and faster.

Adeline, who had been hanging laundry on the line, came running in the door. 'Charles!'

He ignored her; by now he was rocking to and fro.

'Charles! Stop it, my darling, shhhhh! Calm yourself!'

Charles threw her off and let out a guttural, primal scream that seemed to echo out of the room and across the vineyard.

The sound stopped suddenly. Charles smiled at his terrified mother. 'Mama? Are you alright?'

'Yes, my darling,' she began.

'No, maman. You are not alright. Daniel is not happy with us...'

Now Adeline looked even more terrified. 'Alex, will you go and fetch Charles' father? Please tell him he must come...'

Alex was frozen to the spot.

'Now, Alex!' And he ran from the room into the blinding sunlight.

Alex snapped out of his daydream and saw Clochette ahead on the path. The letters had, clearly, brought back some lost memories. Now, he could see Charles' possessed face again, and it frightened him.

He heard the snapping of the twig from the deep wood to his right. He stopped and listened, as did Clochette; they stood still. Another footfall – soft, but heading toward them. Alex strained his eyes, trying to see through the shadows of the tree trunks. A movement: a slender figure flitted between trees – it was moving quickly, lithely, zig-zagging closer.

> 'Hello?' Alex called.

Nothing.

Then, a soft laugh and a voice came from behind him.

> 'Did I frighten you, Alexandre?'

Alex turned. The gaunt-faced, thin figure was standing about six feet from him. Clochette had returned, and she stood close to Alex's leg – silent, but her tail wasn't moving. The hackles were rising slightly.

Alex felt the beginnings of an adrenalin rush.

> 'A little, yes,' he frowned.

> 'Oh, good! We like a surprise...'

> 'I don't believe I've had the pleasure....'

The figure let out a screech-like cough of laughter.

> 'Come, come Alexandre! We do not need to stand on formalities!' He stepped forward a little. 'Alexandre! It's me! Charles!'

Alex felt a little giddy.

> 'But how.... why?'

> Another laugh. 'But you are confused! How? How did I know where you were? Oh, Alexandre, did you really think that sending Olivia away would fool me?'

The mention of Livia's name increased Alex's adrenalin; he needed to get home, to protect her.

The yellow face seemed to shine in the darkened woods. He was wearing a hooded top – a very thick fleece, too much for the crisp air. A little of his hair poked out from under it: a faded ginger, greasy and clinging to the stretched skin of the smooth forehead. His eyes were a honey colour, empty, but with a brightness that looked feverish.

'And 'why'? That's a much more interesting question. Surely you know why, Alexandre?'

Clochette growled, low and deep. Alex stepped back a little, reaching down for her collar. 'Easy, girl.'

'Why, oh why! Where do I begin, Alexandre, my brother?'

'Well, perhaps we can go back to the house, have a glass of wine and talk about it, Charles?'

'Wine? Oh, yes, the answer to everything for you and your father, non? A glass of wine, a good crop this year!' He sang the last phrases in a tuneless, high-pitched voice. 'Oh, Alexandre… I waited. I waited. But no one came to see me….'

'My mother – I saw her letters – she went to see you. She was so sad after you'd gone, Charles! Come home with me, I will show you her letters!'

Charles seemed to leap forward with no physical effort.

'Sad? She was sad? My God, Daniel warned me about you people - "Don't get close to them," he said. "They will destroy you, break your heart!" But I did not believe him – I couldn't! Why would these people hurt me?' He seemed to be asking himself the question, staring beyond Alex into the trees.

'No one wanted to hurt you, Charles.'

Charles re-focused. 'Oh, yes you did, Alexandre. But yes, you did. You left me there, in that damned hospital to ROT!' His voice had changed from a simpering whine to a booming baritone.

Clochette jumped, then regained her composure and barked a warning.

'Ahhh, little belle! You know me... no need to be angry.

Alex had had enough. 'Charles, I'm going home – you are welcome to join us – we can discuss the past, we can...'

'Shut up!' Before Alex knew what happened, he was on the ground; Charles had the strength of a wild creature. He sat astride him; a long, thin blade pushed to Alex's throat. 'Do you really believe we can simply 'discuss' what you people did to me? Do you think you can fix things with words? You people took my family from me! And then you locked me away, far, far away!'

Alex was breathing rapidly. 'Charles, your father's death was an accident, your mother's...'

'Accident?' Again, the screeching laughter. 'Accident? No, no my dear Alexandre. As soon as we knew that my father had succumbed to your family's charm, as soon as we knew that he, too, wanted Daniel and I to be banished – how did your father convince him, eh? What LIES did he tell?'

Alex was sweating, the smell of Charles' rancid breath was making him nauseous.

Charles continued. 'So, I stopped my father's plans, you know. Oh yes, you look surprised... have I surprised you, Alexandre? We do love surprises!' And he smiled; his teeth were small, like baby teeth. 'Oh, yes. That night, after mama had sent me to my bed (she was already looking at me like Papa did), I crept out. I ran across the hill, to the gate where I knew papa would be parked. It is remarkable how strong a child can be – but Daniel helped me. My Daniel, my protector, brought down the rock so hard. Once we had Papa on the ground, the car was easy to roll over him....'

Alex felt the knife dig a little deeper into his flesh. 'My God,' he whispered. 'You killed him!' He searched the strange face for any trace of remorse – but then he saw the darkness in the eyes and gasped. 'And you killed your mother....'

'Ah! You have spoiled my surprise, Alex! Yes, she was in on the plot – Daniel told me. Do you know, I think she knew I'd killed Papa – she was a stupid whore. The shotgun blew away that worried frown of hers...'

Alex braced himself and grabbed at the knife, cutting his hand, just as Clochette flew through the air and tore at Charles' other arm, ripping the fleece. Charles let out a screech and swung the knife wildly at the dog – she yelped in pain.

Alex was now crouching, nearly on his feet. Charles' wrist was bleeding; Clochette had left her mark. Charles jumped back and then ran forward at a great and sickening speed. Clochette rushed at his leg and sunk her teeth in, deep, and Charles shouted out in real pain.

'Damn you!' He rushed at Alex again, this time plunging the knife into his chest. 'Damn you!'

A shout came from the woods. 'Hey! What's going on?' And Martin came running along the path. 'What the hell? Clochette?'

The dog barked hysterically and limped slowly toward Martin, as Charles ran crookedly into the shadows.

Chapter 56

Kilroy and Renaud had spent the past hour quizzing Jacob Rollanson. He was 64, short, grown plump on his illicit earnings. He had a ridiculous coif of white, glossy hair and a network of purple, broken veins across his cheeks.

'I've already told you: she called me. That's it.'

Rollanson's lawyer, Belling, smiled nastily. 'Lots of people call my client ...
lots of young ladies.'

'I'm sure,' smiled Renaud. 'But not many French nationals, I imagine. I assume they all call Monsieur Daubre? Monsieur Rollanson's cousin...'

'We've no idea what you're getting at,' said Belling.

'Oh?' Kilroy said. 'I'm sure you're aware of Rollanson's links to Marseille, Belling. Inspector Renaud is very keen to clean up his town – he's hoping Rollanson will help him.'

Belling laughed, but not convincingly. 'Well, it doesn't sound like you have much of a reason to hold Mr Rollanson...' He stood up to leave.

'Ah, but we have something that might make a case,' said Renaud, bluffing. 'I believe you know a young French man, Etienne Moulin? He is being very helpful.'

Belling looked from Renaud to Kilroy. Rollanson leaned over to whisper. Belling sighed. 'What do you want, Kilroy?'

'I want to find who killed two women and nearly killed one of my officers, Belling. And if I have to tear apart Rollanson's UK drug operation in the process, I will. And if that happens, his French connection will take a lot of heat, too.' Renaud nodded.

'Come off it, Kilroy. You know that's not Rollanson's style – no way he's involved in those murders.'

'Sure. I know. But I'm willing to smash Rollanson's world into pieces if it means I get closer to the killer. Rollanson knows something – he'd best share it.'

Rollanson was looking more and more uncomfortable. 'I had nothing to do with the murders.'

Kilroy stared at him. 'I want Daubre's man – the one who met with Josephine Kurtz.'

Rollanson swallowed. 'I didn't have anything to do with that. Didn't know Daubre had any of his men over here – not until later.'

'Later?'

'After he was already back in Marseilles. Daubre called me. Said he'd sent Alain Vincent over to deal with 'my mess'.'

'When did he call? We'll check your phone records...'

Rollanson sneered. 'Of course you will... next morning. About 5 am. Vincent was already back in Marseilles – he'd filled Daubre in on the French boy.'

'The French boy?'

'Etienne. He was a plant. Working with your lot,' and he nodded at Renaud. 'So, I really don't know how I might be of any more assistance, Inspector.'

Kilroy's voice dropped a little. 'Let's come at it from a different direction, then. Vinnie Roberts.'

Rollanson glanced at his lawyer.

'I'm not sure that this has any bearing on the current issue, Kilroy,' said Belling briskly. 'My client has come in to...'

'Roberts,' repeated Kilroy, ignoring him. 'You pissed him off a few years back, didn't you Rollanson?'

Rollanson smiled. 'Pissed off a lot of people.'

'Roberts reckoned you took him for millions ...'

Rollanson laughed. 'As if that nonce could gather up that much cash!'

'But he did, didn't he? Why else would you have wanted the territory? You and your cousin moved in just after Roberts went down....'

Belling smiled. 'Inspector, I really don't know what you want Mr Rollanson to say! You bring him in regarding a Stephanie Moulin, then you quiz him about criminal activity in Marseilles, now we're discussing an old lag from London! I think we'd best be leaving, Jacob....'

The men stood up.

'One last question,' said Kilroy as he stood up. 'Toni Smith.'

Rollanson stopped in his tracks. 'Yes?'

'I believe you've seen her lately?'

Rollanson turned to face him. 'I have. Bloody mad bitch.'

'What did she want?'

'Oh, you know... these junkies need a lot of support.'

'And were you 'supportive'?'

Rollanson laughed. 'I told her never to come back. Seriously, Kilroy, she's completely crazy. Dangerous.'

'Was she after Vinnie's missing millions?'

'I don't know what she wanted, but it took three of my blokes to throw her out. Raving, she was. Bloody mad! Prophesies, old Bible, sinners in Hell and all that...'

After Belling and Rollanson had left, Renaud turned to Kilroy.

'So, it's likely Daubre's man left shortly after he met with Kurtz? No chance of him killing Stephanie?'

'No.'

'And this Toni Smith? How does she fit in?'

Kilroy smiled. 'Gut feeling.'

'Well, I would like to stay and help with your case, Kilroy, but I must be back in my office – I am eager to catch up with this Alain Vincent.'

'You've got leverage with him for sure...'

'Yes. I will be bringing him in on suspicion of murder – until Etienne turns up, we must suppose that Daubre's men have removed him.'

The men shook hands warmly and Kilroy went back to his desk to see if Jenkins had left a message; the forensics on the burned-out car were back.

She was sitting, impatiently, in his seat.

'Honestly, Kilroy, I'm a highly-skilled pathologist! Burned-out bloody cars!' She feigned annoyance.

'Sorry to offend. What'd you find? You wouldn't have come in person if it wasn't good.'

She smiled proudly: 'Well. You wondered if this 'Toni Smith' was driving the car? She was.'

'DNA?'

'Not yet... that's underway – any minute now.'

'So how do you know it's her?'

Jenkins passed him a large black and white photograph. 'We found this – it's a letter... a note. Digitally enhanced.'

Kilroy looked impressed. It was a note to Vinnie Roberts, the envelope was clear – telling him how she missed him, and how she was coming home soon. She said the old problem had come back. The rest of the letter was indecipherable. Clearly, she'd decided not to send it.

Kilroy frowned. 'The old problem...? Rollanson? Or was there something else?'

Chapter 57

Livia rushed into the house; the drive home had been torturously long – Alex wasn't picking up. The intruder was here, here in the Forest. She was sure. The front door was smashed open – she hesitated; where was Alex?

'Clochette?!' Nothing.

The house looked like a tornado had ripped through it. Broken glass littered the floor, and Alex's mother's letters were screwed up, ripped, thrown across the room. Shaking, she dialled 999.

She heard a sound at the kitchen door and looked around for a weapon – a knife maybe.

Clochette whimpered as she fell on to the stone floor.

'Oh my God!' cried Livia as she saw the blood on the dog's fur. 'Clochette! Where's Alex? Oh my God!'

Martin's car pulled up outside the house. 'Livia!' he shouted. 'Livia! Oh, thank God Clochette's here – she was with a man in the wood – and then some nutter – he had a knife!'

'Martin! What happened? The man with Clochette – that's Alex – my husband! Where is he?'

'They've taken him to hospital – it was really bad, Liv. What the hell happened here?'

'Oh, no! Alex!'

Outside, sirens as the police cars skidded into the drive.

The next hour was a blur of police questions, Michael telling her to sit for a moment, officers photographing, dusting for prints, Martin comforting Clochette, wrapping her leg, waiting for the vet, a call from the hospital to say Alex had lost a lot of blood/surgery she should come right away.

'I'll drive you – where are your car keys?' asked Michael. 'Where's your coat? Martin, will you be ok looking after the dog?'

On the drive to the hospital, Livia told Michael the whole story – about the intruder, about the problems with the vineyard and how they'd thought it best that Livia 'hide' here, in the Forest.

'And you've no idea who it is? Who would want to hurt Alex?'

'No one would want to!' she answered fiercely. 'We thought it was me they were after! But seeing how they've destroyed Alex's mother's albums and letters...'

'Well, we've got an alert on all ports – he'll probably try and get back to France, if he thinks he's killed Alex...'

Livia felt the nausea rising. 'Maybe he has.'

At the hospital, the nurse told her that Alex was in surgery. She should take a seat – it would be a long wait. Michael wanted to stay, but she told him she'd rather he go back to work and find the bastard.

'OK. I'll call the station for a lift. Call me when you hear anything – anything.'

Chapter 58

Marie Hallet opened her eyes to a grey, dull light. A machine beeped in time with her heart beat and her mouth was dry. As her eyes focused, she looked around and realised she was in hospital. She felt a dull ache all over her body; she imagined the needle in her arm was morphine. That might explain the dreams she'd had. She set about remembering what had happened, how she'd got here – it was all so blurred.

She'd been in the alley – on her way back to the car. Yes. It was cold. There was someone behind her, someone following her. Then she was in her car. The phone rang. Who was it? She swallowed, and her throat hurt.

The phone rang – yes. It was a woman, the woman she'd met on the street. A small woman, addict. She'd been on the street for years. She was crying – someone had beaten her up. 'No, don't call the cops... just come here. Help me, please?' The hotel, The Cloisters. 'Help me, please?' 206. The fire escape at the back was open – she slipped in. 206.

Marie heard the heart monitor beep faster.

She knocked at the door, gently. No answer. She tried the handle – the door opened. Darkness. The light didn't work.

Out of nowhere, a swoosh of dark fabric, a coat? was around her head, pulled tight and she was thrown down onto the bed. A punch, another punch, cracking her cheekbone. Teeth were loose, her nose was smashed.

She kicked out with her legs, she drove her nails into flesh, she cried out. Another punch.

And then the hands had her neck, pushing down with a ferocious force, she couldn't breathe, she struggled to pull the coat from her face, she was losing consciousness, fast. Her legs were no longer working, she was dizzy.

The coat slipped to one side and she looked up into the face of the woman she'd come to save. The dirty hair was pulled back into a short pony tail, the skin was pasty. The mouth was twisted into a skewered grimace and the eyes were insanely focused on Marie's face.

> *'This is for Kilroy, Marie!'*

The heart monitor was now shrieking loudly and the door opened, nurses, the light brighter, someone was calling to her:

> *'Marie! Marie! It's ok, you're safe. You're in the hospital. I'm a doctor – you've been in a coma.'*

She tried to speak, to answer, but her throat did not work. She had to warn Kilroy, she had to protect him! The heart monitor stopped it's shrieking and gave way to a monotonous flat line.

Chapter 59

Alex was out of surgery; it was 1 a.m. and Livia sat by his bed, holding his hand.

'My God, Alex, if I'd lost you....'

A grey-haired doctor stood at the door. 'You won't lose him, Mrs Marchal. It was touch and go, but he's stable now.'

'Thank you, doctor. When will he wake up?'

'Not for a day or two – it's best we keep him sedated for the moment. His   body needs a chance to repair. And his mind – the shock must have been   terrible.'

'Yes. Thank you so much for saving him.' She began to cry quietly.

'And I think you need time to rest, too. Why not go home and get some sleep?'

'Oh, I can't leave him alone ...'

'It's ok; they've got an officer outside – they'll keep an eye on him.'

'Yes.' She kissed Alex's hand. 'Darling. I've got to go – check on Clochette. I'll be here when you wake up, my love.'

Martin was waiting for her when she got home. Clochette was fast asleep on the sofa.

'The vet gave her something – she's out cold, bless her. A couple of stitches. Matthews came out to fix the door – he's put a dead-bolt on. He says he'll come by today, sometime, and check on you.'

After a lot of argument, Martin agreed to go home and check on her first thing in the morning.

'The police reckon he'll try and make it to France,' she said. 'Yes, I'll call if I need you.' She hugged him warmly.

She looked around at the chaos – there was no way she could sleep. She poured herself a brandy and sat down beside Clochette. It was only then that she began to sob and the pain in her chest seemed to burst open. Soon she fell asleep, exhausted.

****

Arthur looked at his bedside clock; 1.30 a.m. He and his grandfather had gone out to Livia Marchal's place just after 8 p.m., to replace the door lock. God, the place was a mess! He was so happy Livia hadn't been hurt – but a man, her husband the cops said – had been stabbed!

Memories of Dev twisting in pain, then laying very still, flooded his mind. And he saw Hobbs' face – the smile he had, like something from an animated horror film. Arthur couldn't shake the feeling that, somehow, the stabbing of Livia's husband was connected to Hobbs. Of course, Hobbs was in jail – he wouldn't come out for years. And Felice had told him that the London mob didn't give a damn about Hobbs and his kind – they'd simply send another bloke down to maintain their business. Still – what if Hobbs knew that he'd stashed the stuff at Livia's? Of course, it was gone now, but what if Hobbs had told one of his London mates and they thought there might be more to retrieve? And what if Livia's husband had confronted them, and …. Jesus. What if they went back to search again? He sat up; he had to do something, had to shake this feeling.

He dressed quietly, crept downstairs, took the truck keys from the sideboard and headed out to *Fox Pond*.

Chapter 60

Kilroy looked around the office; he was the last one there. The hospital said Marie was still out – whatever she'd gone through had stressed her heart she'd woken for a minute, only to suffer a minor heart attack. They were keeping her sedated. There'd been no further contact from John after Marie's attack – he thought he'd killed her. But just in case, there was a guard outside her room 24/7.

Kilroy sighed; he wanted to reacquaint himself with Toni Smith – and figure out her connection to Rollanson. His gut was shouting to him, now, that he needed to check this out. She was born here – father unknown, mother a hopeless drunk. In and out of care when she was a kid – inside for drugs and prostitution when she was 13 and 14. Left the system at 16. Kilroy remembered the last time he'd busted her: he leaned back in his chair and tried to recall the interview.

She'd been picked up in the Captain Cook – underage, soliciting. The Landlord there usually turned a blind eye, but she'd taken a knife to a bloke who'd rejected her proposition and ridiculed her in front of his mates. She was a small-framed, bony young woman – but she moved like a lightweight boxer, with a quick, sharp energy. Her naturally dark hair was bleached into a yellow blonde – canary yellow – her skin was acne-scarred and caked with make-up. Cheeks and lips were a purple bruise. She was wearing a very short, denim skirt. Her low-cut top revealed no bosom, but a bony chest. Nail varnish chipped; a sweet, cloying perfume covered the smell of perspiration and cigarettes.

The interview was not straight-forward – she kept veering off-topic, asking Kilroy about his mother, ranting about the many abuses she suffered, and whispering, confidentially, about people who followed her, lived in the shadows, in side-streets and alleyways. Her eyes were bright, the sort of bright heroin induces, but hers had the added shine of madness.

Kilroy had asked her who her pimp was, but she insisted she was an independent.

Kilroy had scoffed. 'Sure,' he laughed.

'I am!' she insisted.

'Well, you're certainly going solo tonight, Toni, all the way to the cells. Unless you have something to trade – pimp? Dealer?'

She snarled, like an animal. 'I am not trading anything. Do you really think you can cage me? I am free! My soul is free!'

'Bullshit,' he'd said testily. 'You're a strung-out junkie... you've already started shaking. Imagine what it'll feel like in an hour or two.' And he got up to leave.

'Do you really believe that I am enslaved to their poisons, Officer Kilroy?'

His hand on the door handle, he'd turned in surprise at the sudden drop of her voice.

'It is only this body that is ensnared by the poison – my soul flies free.'

And he saw, with genuine shock, that she'd stopped shaking, her hands resting placidly on the table. Even the perspiration on her brow seemed to have evaporated. She smiled into space.

'Well, I wish your soul a good flight.' And he left the interview room.

She was done for GBH and put away for two years. He leafed through her Parole Officer's reports; not much except for the standard times/dates of statutory, perfunctory meetings. But, on one page, a report? Detailed notes from a psych at Young Offenders: 'Psychotic episodes/sexual abuse as a child/depersonalisation – schizophrenic tendencies...'

All the standard diagnoses that accompanied all the junkies who ended up in the system.

Finally, she was shacked up with Vinnie Roberts, in London, and between the two of them maybe they'd imagined a campaign of vengeance against Rollanson – the man who'd taken their treasure. Who knew?

Kilroy picked up the folder and decided he needed to go home and get some space. Maybe take Digger out along the dunes. Fresh air to think.

Chapter 61

Livia woke, surprised to find herself on the sofa, Clochette sleeping peacefully beside her. Outside, it was still not light, but there was a small, timid chorus of birdsong. Of course, the previous day's events came flooding back. She sat up and reached for her phone on the table; no messages from the hospital. She'd call them. Clochette was beginning to stir, but happy to drop back in to her deep sleep.

As she dialled the hospital's number, she heard a faint movement – from upstairs. Hyper-alert, she began shivering on a rush of adrenalin. There it was again. Outside, it was windy, maybe light rain. She wondered if she hadn't left a window open upstairs? She unstretched her legs and stood up quietly, softly padding across the room and to the stairs. The bedroom lamp was on, pooling a light on to the landing. She must have left it on when she'd come home.

She pushed open the bedroom door gently. The bedclothes were folded back, as if a hotel maid had prepared the room. The lamps were on and – a rose? – on her pillow. Had Alex set this up before he went for his walk?

The movement was swift – from behind the door, Charles had his arm around her neck, squeezing it tightly. She struggled, but he pulled tighter, until she felt she might lose consciousness. He wound a piece of fencing wire around her wrists, behind her back, and pushed her onto the bed. A six-inch strip of silver packaging tape was stuck to his coat and he removed it deliberately before slapping it across her mouth.

> 'Ahhh, Olivia! That's better, isn't it? Now we can get to know each other, non? Oh, but of course, we have not been formally introduced! I am Charles... Alexandre must have mentioned me?'

Olivia was wide-eyed with terror, her heart pounding. She nodded, hoping not to antagonise him.

'So,' he said, sitting on the chair, legs crossed coyly. 'Alexandre and I talked yesterday! Yes! It was lovely to catch up, to talk over the old days! What memories we have, Olivia! Oh, yes, such memories....'

He looked at her, but his eyes seemed to glaze over and lose focus. 'Such memories...'

Livia moved her wrists a little, but the wire was tight and it cut into the skin. Here was the intruder. She understood why she'd always seen him as sharp and angular: he was emaciated, his cheekbones almost tearing through the skin.

Charles' voice changed as he resumed, moving low into a deep baritone.

'But not all the memories are good, I'm afraid. I don't imagine Alexandre told you what his parents did to me? Non, of course not. Well, if it had not been for Daniel...' He reached over to the dresser for the glass vase and threw it, with full force and rage, at the mirror.

'Those people!' His voice was deep, booming over the ringing sound of the vase and the mirror shattering. 'They promised us so much, Olivia! She said, Aunt Jean-Clare, she told me: 'Charles, you are like a brother to Alexandre!' A brother! Even as my parents turned on me – and they did, Olivia! Oh, the evil thoughts they had toward us – I knew – Daniel told me – that Jean-Clare and Claude loved me. They would be my parents now....'

He pulled a long knife from an inside coat pocket.

'But then, then... we realised that Alexandre was putting stories into their heads! He was turning them against me with his crying and his lies! He turned them against us and so they sent us away... to that dreadful place.'

He was now leaning over Livia; she tried to rise up, to make a quick jump for the door, but he cracked her face with the back of his hand. Blood spurted from her nose.

> 'A dreadful place! And all because Alexandre did not want to share what he had. Are you aware how *selfish* your husband is, Olivia? I could have killed him yesterday – oh, he makes me sick! But, no: Daniel says there is a better way… Your husband has taken so much from me! My father, my mother – victims of his stories! You see? Even before they died, Alexandre wanted to be certain that he was the only boy! That he was the only one!' This last phrase he shouted out in a high-pitched screech.

Downstairs, she heard Clochette move from the lounge, then up the stairs. Slowly. Perhaps she could use the distraction…

> 'The only one! That's what he says to you at night, isn't it, Olivia? When he holds you close in your bed? Well, now, he will find you here, dead and he will be – truly – the only one!' He giggled hysterically, covering his mouth for a moment. 'He will know what it feels like to be alone. To have no one…' He raised the knife, with both hands, high above his head, ready to plunge it down into her breast.

At that moment, someone flew at him, at full force, and tackled him to the ground. Charles shrieked and slashed at the air furiously, blindly, with the blade. Arthur kicked hard at his ribs and the knife dropped to the floor. Livia was on her feet and kicked the knife away, out of Charles' reach. Arthur kicked again and again until Charles stopped moving and whimpered on the floor, gasping for air. Arthur stood up and took the tape from Livia's mouth, then he untwisted the wire. 'Are you ok?'

Before she could answer, and with lightning speed, Charles was up. He grabbed at a thick piece of the vase's base, a sharp shard, and lunged at Arthur, plunging it deep into his shoulder blade.

Livia screamed, and, on a sort of auto-pilot, she bent down to the knife, rose up just as Charles lunged forward. They were face to face, his rancid breath and yellowing baby teeth bared, he raised his arm just as Livia drove the knife into his chest. For a moment, he froze staring into her eyes with pure hatred, then he crumpled down, concertina-like, to the ground.

> 'Arthur? Arthur?' The boy was groaning, reaching for the chair to help himself up. She helped him up and onto the landing, glancing back at the body on the floor. 'I'll call an ambulance!'

Chapter 62

The dunes at night felt 'silent', even though the crashing waves and the high wind offered a constant white wall of noise. Kilroy stared out across the black water, aware of Digger running along the shoreline.

The image of Toni Smith had stayed with him, since he left the station. Her intensity, he remembered, had unsettled him for a moment back then and he'd dismissed her as a crazy junkie. Now, he recalled it and felt sorry for the child she'd been: what chance had she had, really?

He looked down the beach, to where Digger had been. 'Digger?' he shouted into the wind. 'Come!' Nothing. He walked on; the dog tended to take itself home some nights. When he got back to the house, he saw he was right.

Inside, he poured a whisky and poked at the logs in the wood stove; his phone buzzed – a message. It was Collins – Marie had woken up and he wouldn't believe what she'd told them! He pressed call-back, but stopped when he heard the creaking of floorboards above him. The hairs on the back of his neck lifted in warning. Someone was upstairs.

Chapter 63

Livia looped her arm through Alex's as they walked up the stairs to the small, independent cinema, as photographers and interviewers held microphones scanning the arrivals for 'Someone'. Livia and Alex walked past without anyone noticing.

Inside, there was no press, just people chatting and laughing, their cheeks flushed with the cheap wine. It had been over a year since Livia and Alex had been out, apart from small dinners with Tony or Martin and his wife. And, of course, Arthur; she worried about him living alone, since Matthews had died. Alex was walking again, and soon he wouldn't need a stick for support.

Justin was in full flow, talking to Hamish Gabriel, the actor who played Kilroy in the mini-series that was premiering tonight. He caught sight of Livia and hurried over to her, dragging Hamish behind him.

> 'Livia! Livia! Big kisses!' and he air-kissed each of her cheeks. 'Hamish, this is Livia! The Writer – your creator, really!'

> Livia smiled. 'Yes, I know Hamish – we met when I visited the set.' 'Hamish, this is my husband, Alex Marchal.'

The men shook hands.

> Justin had the uncanny ability to talk to one while surveying the whole room. 'Did the press rush you on the way in, Liv?'

> 'No, we were unmolested.'

> 'That's terrible!' exclaimed Justin. 'We need to get some pictures of you! TV is out there, I think – can you pop back out and have a chat? I'll come with you...'

'No! No way,' said Livia. 'That's part of the deal, remember: I don't do press. You've already got me in the *Radio Times*.'

'And that's all! Honestly, Liv, people are so interested in your story,' he lowered his voice. 'People want to know about what happened to you. And Alex.' He smiled apologetically to Alex.

'People found out enough from the papers at the time. I'm not comfortable bearing my soul.'

Justin rolled his eyes. 'OK. I hear you. Oh my God!' He raised his arms, ready to embrace, and ran across the room to greet Rosie George, the actress playing Toni Smith in the series. She was lean with sharp cheekbones and elbows; her shoulder blades seemed to be always pressing against the skin.

Alex put his arm around her shoulders. 'Are you alright, darling? A bit cold? You shivered.'

She smiled. 'I'm fine. I'm more concerned about you; this is *so* not your scene.'

'Darling,' he kissed the top of her head. 'My scene is wherever you are.'

Someone coughed, awkwardly, behind her. There was Arthur, in trendy jacket and jeans, he could have passed for a young production assistant.

'Hey, Arthur!' she leaned forward and hugged him. 'You look great!'

'Bonjour, Arthur,' smiled Alex, clapping his shoulder.

'Well,' said Arthur blushing, 'thanks for inviting me. It feels a bit weird, though – I hate leaving the vineyard...'

She smiled. 'Jack's there. He and Clochette will keep an eye on things.'

After they'd sold Marchal wines – at a much higher price than they'd imagined – a vineyard had come up for sale on the western edge of The New Forest and they were now close to launching Noveau Forêt Wines. After Matthews' death, Alex had taken Arthur on to help out around the place; he was a good handyman, but he was starting to show that he was also adept with the vines.

Arthur screwed up his nose at the wine he was holding. 'Oh, dear,' he placed the glass back on to the table.

A bell sounded and Justin hoisted himself up onto one of the tables.

> 'Ladies and Gentleman! Thank you all so much for coming this evening! As you know, 'Kilroy' airs on ITV next month as a three-part mini-series. It has been a labour of love and much toil to bring this baby to the screen,' he wiped his brow dramatically. 'And I know you are going to love it. There is talk of a spin-off series for France – 'Renaud' – and Olivia Bowman-Marchal,' he pointed to Livia, 'is in discussions about a sequel!' Seeing Livia's warning frown, Justin quickly shushed down the applause. 'As I say, we're only at the discussion stage…'

He introduced the lead actors, and soon Livia and Alex were settling down in the darkened cinema. He held her hand tightly as the film opened on a scene of a young girl's body in a cold and grey alleyway. She sighed; it seemed like such a long time ago. Now, she sunk back into the plush seat and watched the story unwind to its final chapter.

Chapter 64

Kilroy lifted the heavy poker and tightened his grip. Another sound – almost lost to the rising wind. The roof above him creaked a little as the intruder made their way along the short hallway.

Just as he decided to go up and face them head on, he saw the skinny jeans making their way casually down the stairs.

> 'Hello Kilroy,' she said, waving her gun. 'You've no need of that... put it down.'

> He stood the poker beside the stove. 'What do you want?'

> She laughed, humourlessly. 'You don't remember me, do you?'

He looked more closely. The woman was thin, brittle-looking. Her hair was greasy, yellow. Above the skinny jeans, she wore a black, turtle-neck jumper. She wore little make-up, only a light touch of lip gloss. Then he noticed the eyes: hard and polished, like stones.

> 'Toni,' he nodded. 'You're looking well... off the shit, are you?'

> She ignored the question. 'I am well, thank you Kilroy. But I'll be better, shortly, when we've finished our meeting.'

> 'Meeting? You've just broken into my home... that's an offence, you know. Join me in a drink?'

> 'Sure.' She smiled coquettishly.

He took the bottle and looked around for a second glass. He pointed to the kitchen cabinet above the sink, and she nodded OK. He took a glass from the second shelf and reassured himself that his loaded gun was there, on the bottom shelf. He poured the whisky and returned the bottle to the cabinet – just by the gun.

He motioned for her to sit down opposite him, in the armchair; she did so, all the time pointing the gun at him.

'Do you remember the last time we talked, Kilroy?'

'I do. In fact, I was just remembering it tonight...'

'While you walked on the dunes? I thought you might be thinking of me.'

'Well, I was thinking of a lot of things...'

'Like what?' she sipped her whisky.

'Oh, you know... Vinnie – how's he doing, by the way? – and Rollanson, and some thugs operating out of Marseille.'

'You've no need to mention Vinnie,' she said angrily. 'And don't you dare mention him in the same breath as Rollanson.'

'Yeah, I forgot – you and Rollanson know each other, right? He had a lot to say about you – said you'd done him a few 'favours'.'

'Shut your fuckin' mouth!' She held the gun a little higher. 'I never worked for that scum!'

'Right – you were Vinnie's girl, right? Always and forever,' he smiled and sipped on his whisky.

'Vinnie's been a rock....'

'Yeah, I'm sure. You probably feel like you owe him a lot... is that why you decided to come back to town? To sort Rollanson out for Vinnie?'

Toni looked confused. 'If I'd wanted to sort Rollanson out, he'd be dead by now.'

Kilroy went on. 'Right, right. So, why'd you go to see him?'

She tugged at the neck of her sweater, as if trying to remember. 'I ... I... just catching up, I suppose....'

Kilroy thought he'd play on her confusion. 'How's the family, by the way – you went up to Bradford to see them?'

She stopped pulling at her sweater. 'Bradford?'

Kilroy took a gamble. 'Yeah, how is Becky?'

A white, cold anger seemed to peep out above her jumper and rise up into her sunken cheeks. 'She called me. She wanted me to visit her.'

He was beginning to see it all.

'You're old mates, right? She was inside at the same time... in the secure unit?'

Toni was looking around, as if chasing her line of thought. 'Yeah, yeah. She called me...'

'Oh, so it wasn't you chasing her?'

'No! She called me, said she needed to see me...'

'She reckons you called her – day and night, like some love-sick teenager.'

'Shut up!' She shouted and stood up. Kilroy's legs tensed, ready to leap out of her line of fire. 'She's lying!'

'Calm down, I'm just telling you what she said!'

Toni stared and then broke into a wild laugh. 'Well, she won't be telling it any more, will she?'

'No. You killed her, didn't you Toni?'

'No, no, I didn't!' She looked confused, as if she were trying to remember something.

'You did. We got the forensics back – '

'You and your fucking forensics,' she hissed, shooting him in the left thigh.

He winced. Digger appeared in the kitchen, a terrible growl coming from him as he saw her gun; she spun toward him. 'Out!' said Kilroy quietly, and the dog stepped backwards into the kitchen without taking his eyes off the woman. Kilroy pushed his hand down onto the wound.

She was up, now, and he watched as she paced back and forth, slowly. She was mumbling, words running together. When she turned back to him, her face had changed its expression so much that she seemed like another person. She was suddenly harder, her voice dropping lower.

> 'You just never know when to shut up, do you Kilroy? Isn't it enough that you've lost Marie? Sweet, lovely Marie... I warned you: I told you I'd take her.'

Kilroy held back; he didn't want to antagonise her with the news that Marie was alive.

> 'Bitch put up a fight – I'll give her that. Look at this,' and she pulled up her sleeve to reveal the deep furrows made by Marie's nails.

> 'And the others? Stephanie and Jessica? They didn't fight back, did they?'

> She threw back her head, laughing. 'Not a bit. Too easy...'

> 'You like a bit more challenge, do you... John?'

> She looked up at him and smiled. 'You've got me, Kilroy! Bravo! But all that means is that the game is almost over. Shame, really, I was enjoying it!'

> 'Tell me about the game, John. What was the point? It can't be all about me.'

> She laughed a deep, cold sound. 'It was only a little about you, Kilroy. You're part of the problem – part.'

The pain in his leg was increasing, the sofa cushion now wet with blood. 'The problem of Harlots?'

She nodded. 'Harlots, the poor sad Harlots. They're their own worst enemies, Kilroy. Weak spirits – they get sucked right into it by those bastards.'

'Bastards like Rollanson?'

'He's nothing, really, but, yeah, even he can suck them in.'

'Like Jessica Ward?'

She nodded. 'Pathetic.'

'She had two kids, you know… she had to work. A good mother…'

She seemed shocked. 'Two?'

'Yeah – they'll probably end up in care…'

She let out a guttural groan. 'And you think that's my fault? You really are clueless. It's the SYSTEM! The SYSTEM! She could have chosen another way to feed her kids, but the system, every bloke cruising the High Street, the pimps and the drugs – it's all out there to tempt the weak… and I despise these women and their lack of backbone… Really, I have freed them….'

'And Toni? Do you despise her?' He was desperately trying to buy time.

'I do. I hate her with every fibre of my being. The things she's done, just to satisfy her need for poison.'

'I feel sorry for her… she was only a kid…'

She stepped forward and swung the gun down hard onto the side of his head. 'We don't need your pity! I could see it in your eyes the night you busted me!'

He sat up again, desperately trying to stay focused.

She had fallen back into her seat; she looked tired, distracted. 'I couldn't stand the way you pitied me… her.' She began to cry, without blinking, mumbling in strange phrases.

'Do you mind if I get another whisky? Would you like one? I want you to tell me more about this system ….'

He stood up, painfully, and limped over to the kitchen, reaching up for the bottle. He deftly pushed the gun into his belt and pulled his shirt out over it.

She shouted out. 'She didn't deserve your pity, Kilroy. She was pathetic. Weak.'

He sat back down, a little forward and passed her the whisky bottle. She ignored it.

'If only she'd been stronger, stood up for herself…. but it's you, people like you who made her weak. You offered her a way out, but you gave her false promises – they all offered her a way out – but in the end, she was enslaved.'

She was sneering, now, years of rage bubbling up from inside. She aimed the gun at his face. 'She didn't stand a chance! You killed her! And now justice will be served and I will be free – I will fly from the cage she has built for me.'

Kilroy's gun was already in his hand; he pulled the trigger and moved to the side as her bullet grazed the side of his face.

He heard the sirens as Collins and his team raced toward his house. Digger crept in, looking over the scene. 'Come here, boy,' he said, as he stood up, finished his whisky, and stepped over the crumpled, lifeless body on the flagstones. He opened the front door and stared out across the dunes, Digger dutifully by his side.

Printed in Great Britain
by Amazon